CRYING WIND

MY SEARCHING
HEART

by Crying Wind

Sequoyah

CRYING WIND

MY SEARCHING HEART

by Crying Wind
Published by Sequoyah Editions
an imprint of Indian Life Books
A Division of Intertribal Christian Communications
P.O. Box 3765 RPO Redwood Centre
Winnipeg, Manitoba R2W 3R6

ISBN 0-920379-21-4

An autobiographical novel first published as separate books,
CRYING WIND and MY SEARCHING HEART by Harvest House, 1980.

First published as combined edition, November 2001
by Sequoyah Editions

Printed and bound in Canada.

Visit Indian Life Ministries' website at www.indianlife.org

Visit Crying Wind's website at www.cryingwind.com

CRYING WIND

by Crying Wind

Dedicated with love to
Joanie Orlando Herkovits,
My Forever Friend,
who hurts when I lose, cheers when I win,
and loves me even when I'm wrong.

CHAPTER ONE

Moccasined feet moved quietly down the dry arroyo. The only sound was that of leather fringe flapping against bronze skin.

Thunder growled in the distance, and a few flashes of lightning outlined the ragged, purple clouds as I began slowly to work my way up the sharp rocks of the cliff. My hands were already scratched and skinned from clutching at rocks in the darkness. I tried not to think about what would happen if I grabbed a loose rock or lost my balance. I knew only too well it would be a long and painful slide down the steep, granite hill with yucca spikes slashing at my legs.

Straining my eyes, I tried to see the narrow, almost invisible path that led to the secret circle on top of this sacred hill. I wondered if there had ever been such a dark night. A flash of lightning lit the hillside long enough for me to see the large rocks ahead. I was nearly at the top.

I felt dizzy, and my hands began to shake from hunger. I hadn't had anything to eat or drink all day. I had fasted to prove myself worthy to speak to my god.

In a few more minutes I would be talking to my god, Niyol, the great and mighty wind god of the Indians.

At last I reached the crest of the hill, and I hurried over to a flat stone buried in the earth. I knew that hundreds of other Indians had stood on this same stone in the distant past to call to their gods for help.

I carefully removed the feathers and stick from my leather pouch and tied them together with strips of rawhide. Then I drew our clan sign in the dust and stood to face the wind.

"Oh, strong and fearful wind, most powerful of all the gods, hear my words—"

I finished my prayer and threw my prayer stick into the wind and quickly turned my back, because to see your prayer stick fall to earth meant your prayer would not be answered. I hoped the wind would catch my prayer stick and blow it up into the sky.

The thunder warned me one last time to come down off the mountain before he let loose his storm horses. I quickly ran my hands through the dust to wipe out all traces of the drawing. Even as I did so the sky began to cry, and large, heavy drops of rain hit the tops of my hands and turned the dust on my fingers to mud.

I hurried across the open space to the large boulders that marked the path leading back down the hill. The drops of rain were bigger, and they stung when they hit my face. A loud clap of thunder crashed all around me and made me jump with fright.

My buckskin dress was already becoming wet and heavy, and it clung to me, making it even harder to inch my way down the narrow path. I wondered if lightning would strike me as I clung to the side of the hill and if I would be found dead tomorrow.

My heart raced faster. I couldn't tell if I shivered from the cold rain or from fear or if I just trembled from hunger. I was nearly at the bottom when the gravel, loosened by the downpour, gave way under my feet. I slid the rest of the way down the hill. When I was sure I hadn't been hurt, I picked myself up and brushed off the mud and thanked Niyol for sparing my life. After all, he could have told the lightning to strike me, or he could have killed me from the fall. Wasn't the fact that he spared me a good sign? Didn't it prove I was in his favor? Perhaps it even meant he had heard my prayer.

After I got home I hung up my dress to dry out. It was heavy and sagging from the water it had soaked up. The elk-skin dress weighed sixteen pounds when it was dry, but now that it was wet it must weigh twice that much. Some of the beads on the right sleeve were missing. They would have to be replaced before I could wear it again. My moccasins would have to be cleaned tonight. If I left the mud on, they would be too stiff to wear by morning.

My body ached as I finally crawled into bed. My hands burned where they had been scratched raw. I was still hungry, but I couldn't eat until morning.

"Oh well, it was all worth it if the wind heard my

prayer—if—if—" I tried to ignore the uneasy feeling in the pit of my stomach and tell myself it was only hunger. I would eat a big breakfast tomorrow morning, and the empty feeling would go away.

The last thing I remembered before I fell into an exhausted sleep was, "If he heard my prayer, if—if—"

I was glad I believed in the wind god. He was the most powerful of all the Indian gods. The bear god was strong, but he slept all winter. I didn't want a god who was asleep half the year. The snake and horned toad were ugly gods. I didn't like them. The wolf and eagle were beautiful and clever, but they could both be killed, and you could see their bones turning white in the sun. The sun god was mighty, but you couldn't call on him at night, and during the day, clouds could cover his face. No, the wind god was the best. He could be everywhere. He couldn't be caught or killed. He could blow your house down. He could tear at you until you couldn't stand up against him. He could be so cold he could freeze you to death or so hot that you would faint from his hot breath. Of course, the wind was a fickle god; he could be good or evil; he could answer your call or not as he chose. But a god can't be everything. A god can't be perfect, and I was satisfied with this one.

It was Grandmother who had taught me all about the Indian gods and legends. I had been with her ever since I could remember, ever since my mother had abandoned me.

I was never really sure why she took me in when my mother

left me behind. Grandmother had seven sons and four daughters, and certainly didn't need another mouth to feed. I knew she was disappointed I was a girl. In our culture sons meant everything, and a daughter was practically worthless. Whenever a girl was born, people would shake their heads sadly and say, "Don't feel bad, maybe the next time you will be lucky and have a son."

After a few years had passed, I was big enough to help with the cooking and cleaning and any other work that was considered too lowly for my uncles to do. I learned to do "woman's work"—chopping wood, skinning the animals my uncles killed for meat, gardening, and feeding the livestock. I was too skinny to be very much help, and many times I failed to do things because I wasn't strong enough. My grandmother would shake her head, throw her hands up in the air, and say, "You are lazy! You are lazy!" Then she would scratch my arms with her fingernails until they bled to let the lazy blood out of my body so I could work harder.

Grandfather had died when I was small, and gradually my aunts had married and left home. My uncles had drifted away, one by one, until there was only Grandmother and me left in the little house.

Grandmother's face had a thousand wrinkles and looked like old leather. Her eyes were black and sharp as an eagle's beneath her hooded eyelids. Her hair was white as snow, and she wore it in two braids. When she was a young woman, she had been beautiful. Her hair had been black and shiny and had hung past her hips. When Grandfather had died, she had cut off her hair to show she was in mourning. She had taken a knife and cut the palms of her hands to show her grief. In the old days Indian women often cut off their fingers when they lost their husbands.

Now her hands were wrinkled and scarred and her left thumb had been injured so that the thumbnail was always split down the middle, but her fingers were nimble for a woman her age and she could do finer beadwork than any other woman in the valley.

Grandmother. *Shima Sani*—"Little Grandmother," we called her. She looked a hundred years old. She wasn't sure, but she though she must be in her eighties. Of course, even if she had known exactly how old she was, she wouldn't have said so, because there was always the danger that the Spirit Horse would hear her and say, "I did not know you had lived so long. It is past time for you to die." And he would take her away. Most of the older Indians would say, "I am 104 years old." That seemed to be a favorite number to say, but it was unlikely that any of them were much over 90.

Shima Sani was orphaned when she was a small child and had worked in other people's cornfields to earn enough money to keep herself and her two sisters from starving. When she was about fourteen, a laughing young Navajo man came riding by on the most beautiful black horse she had ever seen. He didn't even speak to her, but a month later he came carrying a shawl for her and cigar box half full of nickels for her sisters. She married him a week later and followed him to his small farm in Colorado, where he, too, raised corn. There they had eleven children.

I couldn't remember Grandfather very well since he had died when I was still small. I could only remember his dark, tough skin and his loud, happy laugh and his whiskey smell. He was walking home from town one night, after spending his entire week's wages on liquor, and he passed out. The next morning his son Cloud found him frozen to death in a cornfield less than a quarter of a mile from our house.

I knew none of my uncles grieved for their father. He had beaten them too many times in his drunken rages and had nearly killed some of them. Once he had broken Pascal's arm.

Although Cloud was the youngest of my uncles, he was the tallest and the strongest. When he walked through the door of our house, he seemed to block the whole doorway. His head would touch the top of the door entrance, and his shoulders would almost touch each side.

No one was as big or as important in my life as Cloud. It was always an event when he came to the house. I looked forward to seeing him because he always livened things up with a story. Somehow he could take the most common, ordinary happening and tell it in such a way that would make it seem like an adventure. He was my idol. I thought no one in the world could be as strong or as handsome as Cloud. He could follow animal tracks no one else could find and tell you within an hour when the animal had passed through. No wonder he was the best hunter and trapper around.

My Uncle Flint was as tall as Cloud, but he was thin and didn't have the weight or strength that Cloud had. He was quiet and moody and never joked or laughed the way his brothers did. I wanted to feel close to Flint, but he always withdrew whenever I tried to be friendly, until I finally gave up and accepted the fact that Flint and I would never be close. We would always be strangers.

Pascal was several years older than Cloud and Flint. He had a sad face with deep lines around his mouth and a crooked wrist that hadn't been set right after Grandfather had broken his arm years ago. He was a quiet man—too quiet. You could never tell what he was thinking.

Once Shima Sani had tried sending me to the school in town but it was a disaster. The other children in my class were all non-Indians and had made fun of my name, Crying Wind. They called me "Bawlin' Breeze." There are few things more precious to an Indian than his name, and their jokes hurt me deeply. They had called me a wild savage and laughed at the beads I wore in my braided hair.

"Indians eat dog meat," they would call after me. "Hide your dog, or Bawlin' Breeze will eat it for supper—eat it raw!"

A few times I tried to tell them that if a person were starving to death he would eat anything to survive. Besides, Indian dogs weren't pets. They weren't the pampered, useless, spoiled things dogs are now. They carried small travois loaded with clay pots and blankets. They were watchdogs for the camp. When there was no game to hunt or when there were blizzards and the snow was too deep for the men to go hunting for meat, the dogs were already there in the camp and could easily be caught. Dog stew saved many people from starving in hard winters. Perhaps, when all was said and done, the Indians thought more highly of the dog than the white man, because the Indian's life often depended on his dogs.

I tried to tell them we weren't savages. It was the Indians who taught the white settlers about foods like jerky, popcorn, maple syrup, peanuts, corn, potatoes, rice, fruits, berries and nuts. The Indians even had chewing gum hundreds of years ago. Most of the food the early settlers had was a result of the Indians' teaching them how to hunt, what to plant, and how to prepare what they caught and grew. But they never listened to me. They didn't care about history or facts; they only cared about having someone to laugh at.

I ran home in tears day after day while the other kids chased me, throwing rocks at me and calling me names. Finally, one day I decided I wouldn't take anymore. Instead of running, I stood my ground and put up a fight. It was a short one because one of the larger boys picked up a long stick and hit me across the mouth.

Blood gushed out and I was sure he'd knocked out every tooth I owned. The sight of blood sent panic through the small mob and they turned and ran, leaving me alone in the schoolyard with a swollen mouth and blood dripping off my chin, onto my only dress.

I ran all the way home. Grandmother had seen me coming and was waiting at the door for me.

I told her what had happened as she wiped away the blood and changed my clothes.

I was relieved to learn I only had a split lip and cut gums and that none of my teeth had been knocked out. My mouth was so sore and swollen I couldn't eat or talk for a couple of days. I enjoyed being petted and pampered by Grandmother and my uncles, who were furious at the way I'd been treated and called my attackers a pack of yellow dogs.

Cloud had been so angry he'd gone to the schoolhouse to talk to the teacher, but she wasn't interested in our problems. She said her job was to instruct the children in the classroom from 9:00 a.m. to 4:00 p.m., and anything that happened to a pupil after 4:00 on the way home was none of her business.

Cloud had come home with his temper blazing. "White man's schools!" he spat. "Let them be for the white man's children. Cry will not return!"

Grandmother nodded in agreement.

I could have shouted for joy. I would never have to return to that daily torture they called school. No more being taunted or chased or beaten up! No more angry looks from teachers. No more pointing fingers and laughter from the children.

True to my uncle's words, I never returned to school. Grandmother received several letters from the school demanding that I return, but she just threw them into the fire and never bothered to answer any of them. Once some people came out in a big fancy car, but Grandmother met them in the yard and spoke to them while I hid inside the house. I don't know what she said to them, but they never returned, and the subject of school never came up again.

Grandmother gave me the proper education for a girl of my age. I was taught how to skin animals and tan their hides, how to do beadwork, and how to make medicine from plants. During these long days of tedious chores she would tell and retell the stories of the glorious days when the Kickapoo were the "Lords of the Plains."

"In the old days—" she would begin, and I would listen carefully, anxious not to miss a single word of the exciting accounts of our tribe's past history.

Over and over she would say, "Kickapoo is a name to be proud of. Our real name is *Kiwigapawa*. It means 'He moves about,' because our people were always restless, always looking for a home and never finding one. We were always searching."

I would feel a pang of anger as I remembered how the people made fun of the word *Kickapoo* as if it were some kind of joke. They would say "Kickapoo" and laugh. They knew nothing about the honor or meaning of our tribal name.

Grandmother's voice would go on, "Our people fought everyone. There was not a tribe anywhere that did not fear the name Kickapoo. They were no better warriors than ours. We fought the Sioux, the Iroquois, the Fox, Chickasaw, Creek, the Osage, the Cherokee—we fought all those tribes and we always won. The Fox and Illinois Indians." She would laugh, "We wiped them from the face of the earth. Our people fought the French, the British, and the Spanish and drove the traders from our lands. We killed the missionaries and burned their churches." Her eyes would snap with fierce pride. "There was no one who could win over the Kickapoo. Our warriors didn't think the odds were fair unless they were six to one against us. People's hearts stopped with fear when our name was spoken. From Maine to Mexico, our warriors left a bloody path."

She told me some of the stories about the great battles dozens of times, but I never grew tired of hearing them. Perhaps other children went to bed with stories or nursery rhymes, but I went to bed hearing about blood-chilling raids of the Kickapoo warriors. My heart would pound with pride at the stories of our past victories against our enemies and burn with anger at the stories of the lies and broken treaties thrown at us from the government.

Grandmother loved telling stories about Kennekuk, who was called "the prophet." Kennekuk had started a new religion among the Kickapoo in 1830. Although it wasn't the old Indian religion, neither was it Christianity; but it was enough of both to keep the "new white man's religion" from getting started in the tribe.

Kennekuk died from smallpox about 1850. Before he died he promised he would rise from the dead and come back to life in three days. His body was buried in a dry well, and a large group of his followers waited beside his grave for his last prophecy to come true. At the end of the three days many left, but some stayed on a few more days. More left each day until finally everyone was gone, and the body of the prophet remained at the bottom of the old, dry well on the dusty Kansas plains. Grandmother would always add, "But who knows, the prophet may return some day."

She told me about the battle of Bad Axe and the Black Hawk War and the battles of Dove Creek and Rush Springs. She told me about Chief Keotuk, Chief Kapioma, Chief Ockquanocasey, Chief Quaquapoqua and Chief Wahnahkethahah. Names like Whirling Thunder, Little Deer, White Horse, and Big Elk would echo in my head as I pictured them swooping down on their enemies, killing them and galloping away with enemy scalps and stolen horses.

Time seemed to stand still on the reservation. One day was so much like the next we didn't bother to keep track of the months, only the seasons. I knew before I got out of bed that each day was the same, yesterday, today, tomorrow, always the same. Only a birth or death in the family would change the monotony.

When one of my aunts became pregnant, everyone was overjoyed that there would be new blood in the family—but the happiness turned to tragedy when twins were born. It was a bad omen to have twins, because everyone knew that a woman was to have only one child, and the second child was an evil spirit that was following the first from the darkness before birth. The second baby lived only a few days. It became weaker and weaker, and then it died. The first baby thrived and grew strong and fat. My aunt told everyone that she just hadn't had enough milk for the second baby. I had never seen a set of twins on the reservation. Something always happened to the second baby, but no one spoke about it. Some things were better left unsaid. People on the reservation understood how things must be and the Indian agent and other authorities couldn't be bothered—so another Indian lost one of her newborn babies—who cares?

I knew that there must be dark, shadowy things, bad things that Grandmother and my uncles talked about when I was supposed to be asleep, but I didn't know what they were. Even though I was curious, I wasn't sure I really wanted to know everything that went on around the reservation.

I was about ten years old when one of the dark facts burst into my life and left its shadow on me for years to come.

Grandmother and I had been asleep for hours when suddenly there was a wild, frantic pounding on our door. Grandmother got up to open it while I snuggled farther down into the blankets, too sleepy to care what was happening. Then I heard loud, excited talking. I could tell by the way Grandmother spoke that she was upset. I got out of bed, sneaked over, hid behind her, and I peeked around her long flowing nightgown. I was shocked at what I saw.

There in the darkness stood a young man, naked except for a loincloth of coyote skin. He was covered with mud and so terrified, he was shaking from head to foot.

He was begging grandmother for help. He said he had just gotten married and moved into the far end of the valley. He had been married only one month when his new bride died of pneumonia. He was grief-stricken and went to the medicine man for help. The medicine man had told him he could raise the young girl from her grave and make her live again. The young man had followed the medicine man's instructions to the last detail. He had stripped and covered himself with mud, and the full moon had risen, he had gone to his wife's grave and covered it with the skin of a coyote. He had sat there for an hour, for two hours, and nothing happened. In the third hour the grave began to shake, the ground began to tremble, and he knew something evil was happening. This thing that was coming from the grave couldn't be his beautiful, sweet wife; it had to be something so terrifying that his mind couldn't grasp it. He jumped up from the grave, and clutching the coyote skin around his naked loins, started running screaming through the night.

He was afraid to stop, afraid to look back. I don't know how many houses he stopped at before he reached ours that night. He had been running a long way, because his body was streaked with sweat, and he was gasping for every breath. Suddenly he started screaming and turned around and ran off into the darkness.

"What's happening, Shima Sani?" I whispered as I watched the man disappear.

"He shouldn't have done that," she said quietly and shut and bolted the door.

I wasn't sure what she meant and what he shouldn't have done, but I didn't think I wanted to know any more about it, so I followed her back to bed without saying anymore.

I felt cold and I started to put my arm around her to keep warmer but as soon as I barely touched her she jerked away quickly and asked, "What's that?"

"It's me, Grandmother. I am cold."

She tucked the blankets around me.

"What did you think it was?" I asked.

She waited a long time before she answered. "Maybe I thought it was a bug."

I laughed, knowing she couldn't have thought it was a bug. I was too young to understand the depths of her fear.

The next day the story was all over the countryside. The young man had gone to my uncle's house.

"He said he felt something coming out of the grave—he said he didn't know what it was, but he felt something and the ground was moving." The story was repeated over and over. Could it have been his wife? Maybe it had been evil spirits? Could the medicine man really raise people from the dead? What had happened to the young man? No one knew. Many people had seen him running through the night with the coyote skin flapping behind him, but no one knew where he had gone.

We never saw him again; he never returned to our valley. No one ever moved into his house, and no one ever quite forgot the story. Maybe a year or more would go by without hearing it. Then a group of people would discuss something they didn't understand or something they feared, and someone would begin, "I remember this one time—" and the story would be told again. The people would nod their heads. Some of the women would shiver and some would say it wasn't the earth he had felt tremble, it was himself, because he was so afraid. Others would say that maybe the medicine man really could raise a person from the dead.

Nothing was ever solved. No one ever knew what happened to the young man, and after discussing it awhile, everyone would shrug his shoulders and shake his head, and it would be forgotten again. For a while.

CHAPTER TWO

Summers turned into winters and winters back into summers again. It was late August, and already the leaves on the trees spoke in dry whispers, warning of an early autumn. The wild asters made the valley deep purple, and the last of the loco weed was fading away. The songs of grass-hoppers filled the air all day long as if they were trying to warn each other that summer was nearly over; perhaps even tomorrow the first frost could come.

I gathered more wood and stacked it beside a large tree. Later I would carry it back to the house, but right now I needed to catch my breath. I was hot and tired and needed a drink of water. I'd been gathering wood since early morning. I knew we would need it this winter, but right now, on this hot summer day, winter fires seemed far away.

I sank to the ground and lay flat against the earth with the grass tickling my face. I could feel my strength returning slowly, but I wasn't anxious to pick up any more wood, so I just rolled over on my back and watched the white clouds float across the turquoise sky.

The wind cooled me with his breath, and it felt good to be alive. It was late afternoon when I walked back toward the house.

When the house came into view I was surprised to see an old, blue pickup truck drive into the yard. Two women and a man got out of it and walked toward the house. One of the women had her face buried in her hands, and I could tell she was crying. Grandmother hurried outside to meet them and put her hand on the shoulder of the crying woman.

I was too far away to hear what they said, but I felt it must be something very important, because Grandmother looked very serious. The man had a dark look on his face, and the other woman began to cry.

I walked slowly up beside the house. My curiosity was gnawing at me, but I knew better than to interrupt, so I stood there motionless and waited.

After they had talked a few more minutes, Grandmother turned back up the path and went inside the house. A moment later she came back carrying an old quilt in her arms. She handed it to the man, who took it to the truck and wrapped it around something in the back. When he had finished he climbed into the truck and started the engine. The two women, still crying, got back into the truck with him.

I walked over and stood beside Grandmother but didn't take my eyes off the truck.

"Who are they? What did they want?" I asked, knowing they couldn't hear me over all the noise their old truck was making.

"They are Navajo. They live down on the flats. They used to know your grandfather," she said.

"Why did you give them a quilt?" I urged her on.

"They had a death in the family. They needed a quilt to wrap him in," she said.

Just then the truck backed up and pulled away and, for an instant, I saw the small bundle in the back of the truck.

"Is that—is that the body?" I already knew the answer, and added, "It's terrible for a little child to die."

"It wasn't a child. It was a very old man," Grandmother said, squinting to see the truck which was now nearly out of sight.

"But the body—it looked so small—"

"Yes, it was old Twice Blind, their medicine man. He died angry and cursing, and his family was afraid he would walk back from the grave and haunt them. So they cut off his legs and buried them separately. Now they will bury his body far from home. They will make sure he cannot walk back from the grave."

The truck was gone, but Grandmother still squinted at the distance as if she could still see far beyond the horizon. "Old Twice Blind was a bad medicine man. He was always putting a curse on someone and making them pay him many sheep to remove the curse. Maybe now they will have a good medicine man."

I finished my work and went to bed, but that night I didn't sleep well. I had bad dreams about a small bundle in a quilt on the back of an old truck and about an old medicine man crawling around on his hands looking for his missing legs. That dream came back many nights, and I would wake up trembling and terrified. I wondered if it was really possible for Twice Blind to come back from the grave. I hadn't thought much about death before, but now I spent a lot of time thinking about old Twice Blind.

No one ever talked about dying; it was bad luck. Talking about dying would make you weak and sick.

Many times I wanted to ask Grandmother questions about death, but I was always afraid to bring up the subject. Then, one day while we were sitting together and quietly making beaded necklaces, I gathered all my courage and spoke so suddenly that I startled her. "Grandmother, what happens to us when we die?"

She looked up from her beadwork, and her hooded eyes looked like two pieces of black flint. "When you die, you die," she said simply and went back to her beads.

"No, Grandmother. I mean, what happens to us after we die?"

This time she did not bother to look up. "After you die, you are buried, and your body rots."

I swallowed hard. Was I pushing her too far? Would she become angry if I asked one more time?

"If your body rots, what happens to—" I didn't know the right word to use, "What happens to the rest of you—I mean your spirit?"

She looked up again, but she looked beyond me to somewhere in the past.

"I used to think there was a place the Great Spirit made just for Indians. It was a beautiful place where all the red people were always happy, and there was always plenty of food for everyone, and no one grew tired or old. Lodge fires never went out, and it was always summer." She was silent a long time, but I knew she wasn't finished. I waited.

At last she spoke again. "I used to ask the same questions you are asking now. I would say, 'How do we get to this place?' but no one ever told me. No one seemed to know. They would say 'Ask the old ones.' I would ask them, but they would shake their heads and say, 'Our people used to know before the white man came, but we have forgotten and no one knows the way any more.' Now I am old, and you ask me. I must say 'I do not know.' I am too old to live any more, and I am tired. I will be glad to die." And she added bitterly, "And to rot."

She looked again at her beadwork, but I caught a glimpse of something in her eyes. I knew I had to be wrong. It had looked like fear, but I knew my Grandmother was never afraid of anything. She would not be afraid to die when it was her time.

We finished the rest of our work in silence, and I was glad when I was allowed to go outside and be alone. I didn't like the answer she had given me.

So, I thought gloomily as I leaned on the corral fence, *so there is no place for the red man to go when we die. We rot.*

I watched an ant crawl along the top pole of the fence. "Are you and I the same? Am I not any better than a bug?" I took my fingers and brushed him to the ground. He landed unhurt and hurried along his way, but I didn't see him because my eyes were burning with tears. I remembered the look in Grandmother's eyes. I knew she was afraid, and that made me afraid. If death was something she couldn't face, then I knew I couldn't face it either. I felt as if the dark shadow had moved into my life again, and I wished I could move time backward to the days before I started to learn about life and death.

On hot, still, summer nights I could sometimes hear Cloud playing Indian songs on his wooden flute. The soft music would float down the valley to us like mist and then fade away. Not many of the young men knew how to play the ancient flute anymore, but Cloud did. He could play it better than anyone. In fact, he could do almost anything better than anyone I knew. I smiled as I wondered how many young girls wished Cloud would come to their homes and court them by playing his flute for them, but he never did. Many of the young girls had tried to catch him, but it was beginning to look as if he would never be caught. Sometimes he would laugh and tease about the girls who would try to get his attention by leaving food on his doorstep or by just happening to be out riding their horses on the road when he was going to the trading post. He always made everyone laugh with his stories, but when he thought no one was looking, his smiling face became sober.

His eyes had a lonely, far-away look. I wondered if he really didn't want to settle down, but he wanted someone besides one of the silly, young girls around here.

Sometimes Cloud would talk to me when we were alone, really talk to me as a friend and not just his niece or as a child. I always felt so special when he spoke to me, like we'd shared a secret of some kind and that we were really alike in many ways. Sometimes his music sounded so sad, I wondered if he felt dark shadows in his life, too. Someday I would ask him.

Autumn came late, but when she did come, she made up for it by being more beautiful than anyone could remember. Never had the leaves been such brilliant golds and reds. I spent hours just looking at the aspen trees on the hills around us. When I rode my horse, Thunder Hooves, through the piles of crunchy dry leaves and watched them scatter beneath us, I felt strong and beautiful and wise, all the things I wasn't. The trees would drop their leaves down on me as I rode past as if to say "you are part of us, part of the trees and the earth and the wind." It was a good feeling, but it came to a sudden end.

An early snow came. It was a heavy, wet snow that piled up on the trees that hadn't yet shed their leaves, and it tore their limbs off. The golden leaves turned brown and black. The autumn beauty was gone forever, because there would never be another autumn as beautiful as that one was.

The snow came early and stayed and stayed. Months passed and the bare ground wasn't seen.

It seemed as if January would never end. Cold, gray clouds hung low over the mountains, and each day more snow fell from the sky. The wind was angry and slapped our faces and stung our hands whenever we had to go outside for more wood for the fire or to pump another bucket of water.

Grandmother complained of the cold and said her bones ached. She spent most of the time in her bed wrapped up in as many quilts as she could find.

"Don't worry, Grandmother," I would say as I piled more wood on the fire. "Spring will be here soon, and the sun will shine warm on us, and the snow and ice will melt, and the Mother Earth will breathe again. This spring I am going to get some seed from the store and plant bachelor's button flowers. I saw some in a woman's yard last summer, and they were bright blue and some were red. You'll like them, and they will make the yard look nice." I rubbed my raw, red hands together over the stove. "Spring will be here soon," I repeated.

"It had better hurry. I am old, and the winter makes me hurt. I get stiff, and it's hard to move," came her muffled voice from behind the pile of quilts.

"Would you like me to heat up the rabbit stew again? It might warm you up a little," I offered.

"Yes, I might like that," she said. She sat up for the first time since breakfast.

I carried the iron kettle over and put it on the heating stove. There wasn't much left so I added a little water to stretch it. I would have to walk down to Uncle Cloud's house and tell him we needed more food for tomorrow. I hoped he would have something besides rabbit. I was sick of rabbit stew. We had eaten it every meal for five days now.

Grandmother didn't seem to mind having it again, because she ate a large bowl of it and seemed to feel stronger afterwards. She got up and walked around the room and looked out the windows at the snow piling up everywhere.

"Maybe spring won't come this year," she said as the wind made the windows rattle and blew more snow in through the cracks around the door.

"Spring always comes," I said.

"But maybe it won't come for me this year." She kept her back turned toward me.

"You'll see many springs come and go. This summer we'll fix the house up. We'll put in a better door, and your sons can patch the cracks in the walls to keep the cold out. Remember how much warmer it was last winter when we had the tar paper on the outside of the house before the wind tore it all off during the bad storm?"

She turned around and laughed, "The wind was jealous of our warm house, and when we didn't invite him inside, he grabbed the tar paper and tore if off and blew it away. Everyone was outside running around in the storm, trying to catch the pieces of tarpaper, but they were torn into such tiny pieces they couldn't be used again."

She was getting in a better mood, and I wanted to keep her cheered up. "Well, this time we will nail it onto the house better, and wind won't be able to take it away from us, no matter how hard he tries," I said boldly, hoping he wasn't listening and wouldn't punish me for defying him.

"It would cost twenty or maybe even thirty dollars to buy enough tar paper for our house. Where would we get that much money?" she shook her head.

"We can sell our beadwork at the trading post. If we start making things now, we might have enough by summer to buy what we need."

"Maybe," she agreed. "But when it's cold like this, my fingers are too stiff to do good work." She looked at her hands.

"My fingers aren't stiff. I can make lots of things while it's snowing, and when spring comes and it's warm again, you can sit in the sun and make bead necklaces. We could do it," I encouraged her.

It was getting dark. I would have to hurry if I was going to give hay to the horses and still have time to walk down to my uncle's house.

"I have to go do chores now," I told Grandmother. "I'll bring more wood in when I get back, so don't go outside yourself." I didn't have to worry. She was already climbing back under her quilts.

I pulled on my short, leather coat and tied a woolen scarf around my head. I could only find one glove, so I put it on and stuffed my other hand in my coat pocket. If I took time to look for the glove now I would be too late in getting to Cloud's house.

When I stepped outside the door a blast of cold air took my breath away and hurt my chest. My eyes stung from the freezing temperature, and I had to blink back tears as I hurried through the snow and toward the corral.

The sky was a pale pink in the west, and the snow looked pink where the sunset was reflected.

The horses saw me coming down the hill and lined up against the pole fence and whinnied at me. I pushed them aside as they crowded against me. Steam was rising from their backs. I could feel their body heat as I walked between them.

There was always a warm, horsy smell in the barn, and the air always seemed to be filled with dust and the scent of hay. The horses followed me inside, one by one. I knew War Cloud was the last one in, because he never picked up his left hind foot high enough to clear the board in the doorway, and he always kicked it.

They stirred around eagerly, and Thunder Hooves nipped War Cloud to make him move over and give her more room at the trough. I threw some hay over to them and stood there, watching them greedily munching. Thunder Hooves stopped chewing for a second and looked at me and then went back to her dinner. I decided to give them each a scoop of grain, even though there wasn't much left, and we had been saving it in case we ran out of hay. When they heard the oats being poured in their buckets, the horses nickered and stamped their feet. It wasn't often we had grain for them. They knew it was a special treat. I stroked Thunder Hooves' nose and patted her neck and reluctantly headed out of the barn, leaving the horses well fed and warm.

Thunder Hooves—was there ever a horse so beautiful? Her coat shone like morning sunshine, and her mane and tail were like white clouds. My Uncle Cloud had given Thunder Hooves to me when she was a foal. I could never be poor or alone as long as I owned such a fine horse.

First dust, months and months of hot dry dust, and then rain and mud, everything was mud, and now snow, so much snow.

Snow. I had almost missed it. I stuck my hand out and let the clean white flakes rest on my fingers. I looked at the tiny flakes. I had never really seen snow before, not so close. I'd never really paid any attention to it. Each flake, complex and perfect and beautiful. They say there are no two flakes alike. I reached out again and caught more snowflakes. They were so much like people, each one beautiful in its own design, each one different. Then the flakes began to melt and, in an instant, they were gone forever.

Again, like people, here for an instant and then gone forever. Gone forever? Was that true? It was hard to imagine not existing somewhere, in some form. Perhaps people came back to live again as something else. Perhaps they even came back as snowflakes. If that were true, they would only come back for a short time and then be gone again. Was that what life was? Living and dying and then coming back to live and die again? The snow no longer looked beautiful. I stuffed my hands into my pockets and ignored the snowflakes falling on my coat. I didn't want to look at them again. I didn't want to see how beautiful they were and watch that beauty disappear.

I walked down the valley and across the creek to my uncle's house. He was outside chopping wood. When he saw me, he put down his ax and came forward to meet me.

"Is anything wrong?" he asked.

"No, but I came to see if you have any food to spare. The rabbit you gave us will be gone by morning."

"I could get you a couple of chickens," he offered.

"That would be good for a change," I said. My mouth watered at the thought of fried chicken. "How's the trapping, Cloud?"

He shook his head. "No good. Snow's too deep, so I gave up and brought my trap lines in yesterday. This is not a good winter. I don't like it. Lots of bad luck. Yesterday I broke my knife. An Indian is no good without a knife. One of my traps fell into the stream and froze in the ice. I was trying to chip it out and broke the blade. That was a good knife. I've had it a long time. It will cost a lot to get another one that good; three, maybe four fox pelts. I'm going to the trading post tomorrow. Do you need anything?"

"Sugar, flour, and coffee," I said, "and some thread. I'm going to do some beadwork."

"The trader will be glad to hear that. He asked me last time I was in when you and Shima Sani would be doing more. He said he could sell a lot this summer." He looked at the sky. "You'd better leave now, you won't get home before dark." He disappeared into his hen house. A few minutes later he came back with two chickens and tied their feet together so I could carry them back.

They were heavy and I stopped to change hands. This meant laying the chickens in the snow, taking the glove off one hand, putting it on the other, picking up the chickens, and starting off again. I had to do that three times before I reached home.

I shut the chickens up in the woodshed. They would be all right there until morning. Then I took the hatchet and broke the ice on the water barrel and took a bucket of water inside. I made two more trips outside for wood. It was pitch black outside when I shut the door for the last time that night.

I had wanted to tell Grandmother we were having chicken tomorrow, but she was already asleep, so I lit a kerosene lamp and started a bead necklace. We wouldn't have to be cold next winter. We would have tar paper on our house to keep out the snow and wind.

I looked around me at the place we lived in and called home. It was only one room. One corner of the room was our "kitchen." A bucket of drinking water sat on the floor with a clean cloth spread over the top of the bucket to keep dust and bugs out. Some rough board shelves were our cupboards. The opposite corner of the room was our "bedroom," a lumpy, old double bed piled high with quilts and blankets. In the center of the room was a large, round table and five non-matching chairs of wood, our "living room." Our clothes hung on wooden pegs near the bed, and an old wooden chest at the foot of the bed held a few personal belongings.

I was hungry, so I opened a can of evaporated milk, poured it over some bread, and added sugar. I wished I had remembered to put the can outside in the snow so it would have been cold. I liked cold milk, but since we didn't have a refrigerator or electricity, we couldn't have any foods that spoiled easily.

I watched Grandmother sleep and wished that somehow tomorrow could be different from the hundreds of other days. Maybe I was restless because my fifteenth birthday was coming soon and something seemed to be missing from my life.

Several times lately Grandmother had reminded me that by the time she was fifteen, she had been married a year and had a child. Most of the other Indian girls my age were married, but I had never even had a date. The only men I ever saw or talked to were my seven uncles, who lived in the valley. Maybe when I was fifteen things would be different.

I put away my beadwork for the night. It was good to have something to do for a change. All my life I had had almost complete freedom to do anything I wanted to do, but it hadn't taken long to learn that freedom meant nothing to do, no place to go, no one to care. Soon things would change, because I would be fifteen. I would be a woman!

CHAPTER THREE

I quietly slipped out of bed and into my clothes and hurried outside to meet the morning. It was going to be a wonderful day, because today I was fifteen years old. I was no longer a child; I was a woman. I would have new status in everyone's eyes. I heard some birds start their morning songs in the trees on the hill.

"Sing a happy song for me, little bird!" I said, and suddenly my joy of the morning was lost. Why had I said "little bird?" That was my mother's name, Little Bird. I didn't want to think about her, but sometimes she crept into my thoughts like a shadow across the sun. She had been silent nearly all the time she had been with me. She had never forgiven me for being born. She couldn't look at me without remembering how much she hated my father. Her name was Little Bird, but after I was born she had insisted that everyone call her "Little Dead Bird," because she said now she was dead. She had never touched me. When I was an infant, she had refused to feed me. My grandmother had saved me from starving to death by pouring canned milk and coffee and bacon grease down my throat.

Then one day my mother left, and I never saw her again. No one knew where she had gone. I didn't care that she had left, because now there was no one to give me long, hard stares out of cold, dark eyes. Now I didn't have to feel guilty about being born. The family spoke about her less and less and finally, not at all.

I wondered if my mother remembered that fifteen years ago today she had brought a life into the world. Did she ever think of me? Was she even alive? Was my father alive?

No, I wouldn't think sad thoughts today. Today was going to be happy.

I heard Grandmother stirring around inside the house and turned my back on the rising sun and went inside. I hoped she would remember it was my birthday.

"Good morning, Grandmother." I smiled and searched her face for some sort of sign that she knew this was a special day.

"You forgot to make coffee," she said. She added some water to yesterday's coffee grounds and put the pot on the stove.

"I'm sorry," I said reaching for a skillet to fry some eggs and squaw bread.

"An old woman likes her coffee in the morning," Grandmother complained and blinked her sleepy eyes.

I patted out the fry bread and dropped it into the hot grease, watched it turn brown and then flipped it over and took it out. Grandmother stood beside me waiting for the coffee to boil.

I broke some eggs into the skillet. Grandmother reached across the skillet to get the coffeepot. The eggs popped some hot grease on her arm. She jerked her arm back, dropping the hot coffeepot on her right foot. The scalding hot coffee and grounds spilled over her bare feet, and she cried out and stepped backwards.

I stooped down and started to brush the hot grounds off her feet but she slapped me across the face. I jerked back.

"Get away!" she snapped. She finished wiping off her feet. She shuffled over to the bucket of water and poured several dippers of cool water over her feet and legs.

I stood there helpless, my cheek blazing where she had slapped me. Tears blurred my eyes. I turned my back on her and looked at the spoiled breakfast. The eggs had turned black, the fry bread was soaked with spilled coffee, and the floor was covered with coffee grounds. I started to clean up the mess, glancing over at Grandmother. I hoped she would say something, but I already knew what was coming next—the familiar silent treatment. She used it on me every time I did anything to make her angry. It seemed to happen more and more often lately. She would go for days, or sometimes even a week at a time, without saying one word to me. She ignored me completely. Sometimes I could hold out for a day or two, pretending I didn't care whether she spoke to me, but eventually the silence would wear me down. I would apologize to her and ask her forgiveness so she would speak to me again.

Today, of all days, I didn't want to get the silent treatment. I decided the sooner I apologized, the sooner it would be over with.

"I'm sorry, Grandmother. If I had made the coffee when I got out of bed you wouldn't have had to make it, and you wouldn't have gotten burned. Does it hurt?" *Well, at least that much was over with*, I thought as I swept the floor.

No answer. She was mad and was going to sulk awhile. How I hated the silence and being treated as if I didn't even exist! It was only a small dose of one of the worst punishments the Indians used. In the old days, when someone had brought such shame to his family or tribe that it could never be forgiven, that person was declared dead by the family. A death chant was sung, and often a grave was dug and the person's belongings buried in it. That person no longer existed. The family never mentioned him again. It was the worst shame that could be placed on a person. It was hardly ever used anymore, but sometimes Grandmother would give me a little dose of it just to remind me that she was still the head of the family.

Even though all eleven of her children had left home now and some of them were married, she was still in control, and if she snapped the reins, her family obeyed.

I knew her feet hurt and that she blamed me for it. She had forgotten my birthday, and now there was no point in mentioning it. The day was spoiled.

I went outside and sat on a tree stump. Then I saw the

horses coming up the draw toward the barn. I jumped up and started down the hill to meet them. I would go for a ride. That always made me feel better.

I grabbed a bridle out of the barn and caught Thunder Hooves. I put the reins around her neck to hold her while I slipped the bit into her mouth.

She wasn't happy about going for a ride; she had become fat and lazy and spoiled. I glanced over my shoulder at the house. I didn't see Grandmother, but I decided not to take time to saddle Thunder Hooves. If Grandmother saw me, she might think of some work for me to do, and I wouldn't be able to go riding.

I swung onto Thunder Hooves' back and urged her toward the timber. I was in a hurry to get out of sight of the house and away from Grandmother's anger.

Thunder Hooves broke into a full run. The pounding hooves seemed to catch the rhythm of my own heartbeat. The cold wind whipped around me and bit through my threadbare shirt.

Gray clouds moved across the sky as if they were following us, trying to darken our winding path across the valley. My palomino pony raced with her head low and outstretched, her mane and tail flowing in the wind. I bent low over her neck, and her mane slapped me in the face. I held onto the reins with one hand and tangled my fingers into her mane for a better grip. My knees dug into her sides. I hung on as she seemed to fly over the rough ground.

I could feel her heart pounding between my legs. She was getting hot, and foam was appearing on her neck. She didn't start to slow down until we had reached the top of the highest hill around. Then I jerked her to a sliding stop and spun her around to look back in the direction we had just come.

I leaned down and felt the sweaty neck that was quivering from the run. I slid off her back and felt my own legs shake as they hit the ground.

"We're both out of shape, old girl," I said and patted her nose. I turned her loose to graze, and I walked a few feet and sat down on a pile of large rocks. I'd start riding more often. I used to ride every day, but lately Grandmother always found work for me to do.

I took a deep breath. The air was clear and fresh and smelled like pine. I felt better. I was glad I had come for a ride. I heard Thunder Hooves snorting behind me and chomping grass. She was a good horse. She was spoiled and hard to manage sometimes, and she wasn't the fastest or the smartest. But she was the beautiful color of liquid sunshine, and she was mine. She wasn't just a horse—she was the best friend I had. It bothered me that she wasn't young anymore. My uncles kept telling me to trade her off and get a colt, but they only thought of her as a horse. They didn't understand she was my friend, and I didn't want to trade off a friend.

I sat there until time didn't exist. I dreamed impossible things. I thought about the past and worried about the future.

It wasn't until I noticed how silent it was that I was forced back to the present. I jumped to my feet and looked around. Thunder Hooves wasn't anywhere in sight. I had let her wander off while I was daydreaming.

"Oh, please don't let her have gone home!" I said, not knowing to whom I thought I was talking. I didn't want to walk three miles back home, not today—especially not today.

I ran over the far edge of the hill searching everywhere for her. There! There she was in a small stand of aspen trees. I hurried to her and grabbed her loose reins. I surely wasn't going to take a chance of losing her now! I jumped on her back and pulled her head up. She stomped her feet while I tried to make up my mind where to go. I didn't want to go back to the house yet. I wanted to ride over the ridge and down the other side, but that would take at least another hour. I looked at the sky. It was getting late. I still hesitated. If I didn't get back in time to cook dinner I would be in trouble, and I was already in enough trouble today. Thunder Hooves shook her head up and down and snorted impatiently that she was ready to go.

"All right, you win." I headed her toward home but held her down to a walk. I wasn't in a hurry to get back. I felt as if this ride had been special. I didn't want it to end, because I felt like there would never be another ride quite like this one.

"Hey, Thunder Hooves," I said. "Today is my birthday." Her head jerked up and down as if she understood.

We were both tired by the time we reached the barn. I slid

off her back and took off her bridle. She sank to her knees and rolled over on her back, kicking all four feet into the air, and wiggled until she had rolled all the way over. Then she stood up and shook the dust off.

"You are worth ten dollars, because you only rolled over once," I told her. I went into the barn and poured out a small can of oats for her. She was chewing the first mouthful before I stepped out the door.

I made my way up to the house. It was already getting dark, and Grandmother had lighted the kerosene lamps.

As soon as I stepped inside I smelled dinner cooking, and my heart sank. She was sure to be angry because I had stayed out so long.

I washed my hands in cold water and dried them on my shirttail. "What do you want me to do?" I asked, and then added, "I went for a ride. I'm sorry I'm late." This seemed to be my day for apologizing.

"Food's ready," she said and spooned fried potatoes and deer meat onto a plate and handed it to me. Yellow grease ran off the potatoes and meat and covered the plate. She always cooked everything in the same skillet at the same time, so I knew the potatoes would have no taste of their own, only the wild taste of the deer meat.

She filled her own plate and sat down at the table. We ate in silence. When we were finished eating, she went over and sat on the bed and began mending an old dress.

I cleared off the table, dreading the long, silent night ahead of me when I heard a welcome noise. We could hear whooping and hollering long before they started up the narrow path that led to the house.

Grandmother's eyes shone with anticipation as she hurried to the door and flung it wide open. I stopped what I was doing and rushed to her side.

We knew from the rowdy noise that my uncles had gotten together and made another batch of trade whiskey. It was thick and black and the next thing to poison, but guaranteed to get a person rip-roaring drunk.

Five of them exploded through the door. We stepped aside to keep from being knocked down. Grandmother and I both laughed at their drunkenness. My uncles roared and shouted and staggered around the room, bumping into everything.

Flint and Cloud started shoving each other, and finally the two of them slammed into each other and went crashing to the floor in a heap of arms and legs and fists. They rolled around like two bear cubs in the spring.

Grandmother smiled indulgently. Her sons could do no wrong in her eyes. It didn't matter if they broke a little furniture or even if they tore down the house. They were young men and they needed to let off steam.

The two finally struggled to their feet. Flint gave Cloud a hard shove and Cloud slammed into Flint with his shoulder. Flint spun around and came smashing into me, sending me hurtling backwards over a chair and up against the wall.

I doubled over in pain and couldn't breathe at all. The ache in my chest was almost unbearable.

Cloud and Flint each took an arm and dragged me to my feet and forced me to straighten up. Everyone was laughing.

"Got the wind knocked out of Crying Wind!" Grandmother said and reached for a bottle that was offered to her.

As soon as I had caught my breath, I was forgotten and left sitting on the bed in the corner of the room. My lungs still hurt. I had a bump on the back of my head. My elbows had been skinned raw when I had skidded across the wooden plank floor.

I kept smiling, and I laughed when anyone would say something funny, but I was hurting inside. It wasn't just the idea that when Flint had crashed into me I had taken a very hard fall and been hurt; that was an accident. What hurt most was that no one cared that I was hurt. I told myself I was being a spoiled child, and I should forget the burning tingle in my elbows and the throbbing headache and my sore rib cage. If I complained, everyone would laugh and make fun of me and call me a papoose.

I watched Grandmother as she accepted the drinks offered to her. She laughed at everything now and spoke almost entirely in Kickapoo. My uncles would argue and laugh and drink some more. They were all having a good time.

I faded into the dark shadows in my corner of the room.

These were my blood relatives, my family. Why, why did I feel so left out and alone? Why did I feel as if a circle had been formed, and I had been left out? Was it because I was a girl, or was it because I was a half-breed? Why was it I never seemed to fit in anyplace?

All of my uncles got up and left except Pascal, and things quieted down a little after the others had gone. The conversation was turning to more serious matters. Pascal seemed more eager to talk than usual and acted as if he didn't want to leave.

As the voices grew quieter, I pulled some quilts around me and turned my face to the wall. No one had remembered my birthday. No one was aware that, according to custom, I had become a woman today. I ached where my body had been hurt but even more I ached where my heart had been hurt.

Pascal's voice could be heard far into the night, but I no longer heard his words or cared what he said. I only wanted to sleep and forget this day.

CHAPTER FOUR

After my birthday I noticed that Shima Sani was limping, and I could tell she was in pain. We both pretended to ignore her trouble, but I was worried and knew she was, too.

She was getting worse all the time, and there could be no doubt that her feet hurt. It had been weeks since her feet were burned, and they had not healed. She spent as much time lying down as she could and avoided walking any farther than from her bed to the table to eat.

I had not seen her feet in a long time; she kept her tall moccasins laced up, and at night she wore heavy socks to bed.

Once when I came and caught her sitting in a chair, soaking her feet in a pan of egg whites, she told me to leave her alone. I went back outside to wait until she was finished. She had always used egg whites to draw poison out of an infected wound, so now I knew she had an infection in her feet.

She avoided talking about her feet, so I pretended not to notice how much trouble she was having getting around. I made sure I was outside at least an hour every afternoon in case she wanted to use her medicine without my seeing her.

At last she couldn't hide it any longer, and one morning she called me over to her bed. "My feet don't heal," she said. "I used all the old medicine I know. Nothing works."

I pulled back the covers on the bed, and as gently as I could, I began to unwrap the strips of cloth she had wound around her feet.

I had expected it to be bad, but nothing could ever have prepared me for what I saw.

The stench was almost unbearable. The rotten flesh hung loose around her toes. The skin was deep blue and green and black, and it was bloody. *Gangrene*. I gently wrapped some clean strips of cloth back around her feet, knowing there wasn't much time left.

"Grandmother—" I pleaded.

"No," she said flatly. "I know what it is, but I will have no doctor, no hospital, no one carving up my body. I won't go wandering forever, searching for lost pieces of my body. I will go to my grave as a whole person, just as I was born into this world a whole person. If I can't hold onto my life with my own two bare hands, I will let go of it."

We both knew she had just pronounced her own death sentence.

"Shall I go to my cave?" She smiled with a little twinkle in her eye.

"No, you don't need a cave, you have me," I said. She was

remembering the old days, when an old person who had become useless and was a hardship or danger to the rest of the tribe would take a piece of jerky, a wad of tobacco, and a little water and sit in a cave and wait to die. It wasn't just considered a noble way to die; it was an obligation. No one person had the right to endanger the entire tribe. No one made the decision for you; it was yours and yours alone to make.

I went outside and threw the filthy rags into a ditch and set fire to them. I knew Grandmother had not been making a joke with me. She had been giving me a way out if I had wanted to take it.

I wouldn't let her die alone. I couldn't keep her from dying but I could keep her from dying alone. I knew she was afraid. Maybe if I was with her when the end came she wouldn't be so afraid.

It was a dark day. Clouds had kept the sun covered, and I had overslept. When I finally did get out of bed, I was worried about it being so late in the morning, and I hurried around, making breakfast.

When the coffee was ready, I called Grandmother.

"Shima Sani, wake up. The sun slept late today, and so did we. Your coffee is ready."

She didn't move under the mound of quilts.

I walked over and put my hand on her shoulder. It was damp with sweat, and her skin was as hot as fire.

"Grandmother?"

Her eyes flickered open. They looked tired and dim. Her lips moved several times before any sound came. When she finally spoke, her voice was barely more than a whisper.

"Get Cloud," she breathed out. "I want my sons with me."

"What's wrong?" My voice trembled. "Grandmother?"

"I am not ready to die—I thought I was ready to die but I'm not—" Tears started to roll out of the corner of her eyes and across her wrinkled cheeks. "Get Cloud—get my sons!"

"I will. I'll run fast. Don't worry Grandmother, I will be right back with Cloud and the rest." I ran to the door and called over my shoulder, "Don't worry, Grandmother, I will bring them right back!"

Thunder Hooves was standing in the corral. When she saw me running she must have sensed the urgency, because she edged toward the gate and stood still as I grabbed the bridle off the fence post and slipped it on her. I jumped on her bare back and kicked her hard with my heels. She leaped forward so fast, I nearly slid off her back. I grabbed a handful of mane with one hand and drove my heels into her ribs again. She was in a gallop before we passed the barn. As soon as we crossed the creek, I began hitting her with the reins. She laid her ears back and switched her tail and ran faster, faster than I had ever forced her to go before, but it still seemed too slow. One mile. One mile to Cloud's cabin, but it seemed like a hundred. It could not have taken us more than a few minutes to reach the cabin, but it seemed like an hour.

As soon as his cabin came into view I began screaming out his name.

"Cloud! Cloud!" I couldn't tell if my voice could be heard or if the wind was just whipping my words away.

I could see Cloud standing in the yard, throwing a knife at a fence post.

At last he heard my screaming, and looked up. He began running toward me, and I yanked my horse to a sliding stop.

"Cloud!" I gasped. "Grandmother—something is wrong— she wants you now—she said she wanted all of her sons—"

"You go get Pascal. Tell him to meet me there." He took his cowboy hat and hit Thunder Hooves on the rump. "Go!" he yelled, and we were off in a gallop.

Cloud ran for his truck. I heard the motor grind and the wheels spin as he headed for Grandmother. Thunder Hooves ran for another mile, but she was slowing down. Foam dripped from her mouth, and she was drenched with sweat. My jeans were soaked with her sweat and itchy from rubbing on her hair. My side began to ache from the constant pounding, and my legs were cramping from holding on. I had to slow down. There was still another mile to Pascal's cabin. I pulled her down to a fast walk. She snorted and shook her head up and down and stumbled several times. The pain in my side began to ease up, so I urged her back into a gallop for the next half-mile.

I was in luck. Flint's pickup was parked at Pascal's cabin.

I rode up beside the house, tied my horse to a tree, and

pounded on the door. Pascal and Flint were upset when I gave them the message. They told me to leave Thunder Hooves tied where she was and to get into Flint's truck. The three of us rode back to Grandmother's house.

When we got there, Flint parked the truck beside Cloud's. "You stay in the truck!" he ordered. He and Pascal ran for the house, leaving me alone.

"Please let her be all right," I whispered over and over to the wind. "Please don't blow her breath of life away. Please don't send the Spirit Horse for her—" I must have repeated that a hundred times as I waited for someone to come back outside.

Just when I was sure they had forgotten about me, the door opened, and Cloud stepped outside and closed it behind him.

The look on his face told me the worst had happened.

He walked up to the truck and leaned against the door with his back toward me.

"She's gone, Cry. Shima Sani is dead." He took a deep breath. "It was the fever. She just slipped away. There was nothing we could do. She was weak, but she talked to us. She was glad to have at least three of her sons with her at the last.

"I should have been in there," I said hoarsely.

"No, Cry. It was better for you to be out here."

"Did she say anything to me? Did she leave a message?" I desperately wanted her to leave something behind for me to hang on to.

"No. Nothing. She just talked a little." He must have sensed how I felt, and he added, "She probably would have said something for you, Cry, but she ran out of time."

He turned around and looked at me. He could see I was seconds from bursting into tears. I was trying to fight it, biting my lip and blinking my eyes, but it couldn't be held back. My grief just had to come out.

"I'm going to get the rest of the family." He headed for his truck and left.

I knew it would be all right if I went inside the house now, but it seemed too late. She was gone, and there didn't seem to be any point in going in.

I sat in the truck and waited. Gradually other cars and trucks began to arrive, and my other aunts and uncles made their way into the house. It was nearly dark before I could finally bring myself to leave the truck and go inside.

Shima Sani dead? No, it was impossible. She couldn't be dead. She was not ready to die. I had seen her only hours ago and she had told me herself she was not ready to die!

I looked around the room at my seven uncles. They stood there, solemn and dry-eyed. There would be no tears shed for Shima Sani, at least not in public. It would show weakness to weep.

My oldest uncle stepped forward and made the announcement.

"Hear me. Our mother is dead. Shima Sani is gone forever

and her name will not be spoken again." Then he quickly walked out of the house, and one by one the others followed him.

I sat there in numb silence and looked at the bundle of cedar branches on the floor. Later tonight they would be burned so the smoke could direct Shima Sani's spirit to the place it should go. *What place,* I wondered, *and where is it? Would the cedar smoke really help her find it?* I looked at the bundle of branches which suddenly seemed small. I decided to go out and gather more. I wanted her to have enough smoke. I didn't want her spirit to get lost and wander in darkness.

For one year her name would not be spoken aloud by her family. If she heard her name, she could not rest and would return. At the end of the year, cedar branches would be burned again in case her spirit had become lost the first time and needed a second chance. After that she would truly be gone forever, and her name could again be spoken.

Now it would begin. First Grandmother's favorite bowl and cup would be taken to the burial ground. There, members of the family would use them to hollow out a place in the earth for her grave. The bowl and cup were old and fragile, and they were already chipped and cracked from many years of use. The gravediggers would have to be very careful as they scooped away a handful of dirt at a time with the bowl and cup. It took hours to dig a grave this way, but this is how it must be done. This is the way it was always done. A Kickapoo grave must never be dug with the white man's shovel or any of his metal tools. After the grave was dug, someone would stay behind and guard it. You couldn't leave an open grave unguarded; an evil spirit might jump into the hole and hide. Then it would carry away the spirit of the dead person after he was buried.

Two of my uncles had gone into the forest and searched until they found a hollow log large enough to place Grandmother's body inside. They trimmed it to the right length and carried it home.

Grandmother's body was taken care of by my aunts. They dressed her in her best clothing, and her white hair was plaited into two neat braids. Her turquoise and silver rings were placed on her fingers, and a pair of new moccasins were placed on her feet. Beads had been sewn on the soles of the moccasins to show that these feet would never again walk on the earth but would walk only in a land beyond here. A new, red blanket was folded and draped over her left arm, and a few of her favorite things were placed in her right hand: some beaver teeth; a tiny obsidian arrowhead; and a piece of beadwork she had been working on when she died, along with enough beads to finish it after she reached the end of her journey.

When my aunts were finished, my uncles gently lifted Grandmother and laid her in the hollow log. All seven of them stood shoulder to shoulder and carried her to the burial ground. She was placed in the grave, and her bowl and cup were smashed against the log so they could never be used again. Everyone pushed the dirt over her with their hands, and leaves and twigs were scattered over the surface until there was no sign of a grave being there.

A terrible feeling of loneliness swept over me. It wasn't fair! Grandmother and I had been on a journey together. We had been searching for an answer, and now she was gone before our journey was finished. She had gone on alone without the answer. She had died being afraid of death.

"Oh, Grandmother, where are you now?" I cried.

As I walked up the path to the house, I saw a mourning stick outside the door. It was a stick driven into the ground, and it had black crow feathers attached to it to tell others there had been a death in this house.

My aunts placed grandmother's personal belongings on the pile of cedar branches. A fire was started, and we all stood there in the darkness and watched the flames destroy the last of Grandmother's life here on earth. Her possessions would be sent to her on the smoke that was rising up to the stars. The fire snapped and crackled until I had destroyed everything and only a few dying embers remained.

After the rest of the family had gone to their homes, I stood alone and watched as the last hot coal flickered and died.

"I'm sorry, Grandmother," I whispered. "I'm sorry I took too long to find the answer for you."

She had been right. Spring had not come for her this year. It seemed impossible that she was gone. As I entered the cold, dark house, I lighted a lamp and sat down on the edge of the bed and looked around. Every trace of her had vanished. It was almost as if she had never existed. The only clothes hanging on the wall were mine. The quilts she had made were gone. All of her personal possessions were gone.

It was so quiet I could almost hear the snow falling outside. The room seemed dark and full of shadows. I turned up the lamp wick. The flame grew higher, but the room still seemed dark. I walked over to the stove and started a fire. My hands were red and stiff, and I was shaking from the cold. There was ice on the top of the water bucket, and it was over an hour before the fire warmed the house enough to melt the ice.

The wind had come up. He seemed louder than I had ever heard him. He was angry, and I could hear him beating against the house. I put more wood on the fire, but I couldn't get warm. I wondered if I would ever feel warm again without Grandmother here.

I crawled into bed with my clothes on, because it was too cold to take them off. I pulled the covers tightly around me, and still I shivered.

"Oh, Grandmother! I miss you!" I cried out. "The wind is so loud, the cold has never been colder, and the dark has never been darker. Are you somewhere safe and warm, or are you out there in the frozen night, with the wind blowing your spirit away?"

I stuck my fingers in my ears and tried not to hear the wind.

I would not speak to him. I was angry at him for letting Grandmother die. I wanted to fight back, but who can fight the wind? He whistled and blew the snow deeper around the house and taunted me. I lay in the darkness, alone and shivering in the empty bed.

As soon as I woke, I turned over to see if I had had a terrible dream and maybe Grandmother would be sleeping beside me, but she wasn't there. It was no dream; she was really gone.

I spent the morning sitting beside the window and watching the snow, but by noon I knew I had to find something to do. I dragged out the box of beads and set up the loom. It made me feel better to be busy. I worked quickly. Soon I had a piece long enough for a woman's belt. I decided to make some rosettes next. They always sold well, and I would need some money to live on. I didn't know if Flint or Cloud would help me, but even if they did, I didn't want to have to beg them for every penny to buy food. I would need a little money of my own.

I spent all day on beadwork. My neck and back were stiff, and my fingers were starting to drop some of the tiny beads. The sun was going down, and the house was getting dark. I lighted the lamp and pulled it closer to my work. As tired as I was, I didn't want to stop. It seemed important to keep doing something. Then I wouldn't think about how empty and lonely the house was.

It was late now, and I was making mistakes. I had to go back and restring some of my work. I would have to quit. I just hoped I was tired enough to go right to sleep and not lie in bed for hours, staring into the darkness.

At least I had gotten through the first day alone. I felt proud of myself for doing so much work. Tomorrow I would do this much again, or maybe more. I would keep busy. Before I went to bed each night I would make lots of plans for the next day. I would have something to look forward to, and things wouldn't seem so bad.

I finished the last row of beads on the large rosette necklace I was making. This necklace turned out better than any I had ever made. I would get a good price for it at the trading post. If the trader bought everything I made, I would have forty dollars. That was more money that I had ever had in my life.

I looked at the necklace one last time before putting it into the box with the other beadwork. My eyes were tired from working so long by the flickering light of the kerosene lamp. I blew out the flame and got ready for bed. As I walked past the window, I looked outside at the sparkling snow.

The moon was full and beautiful and reflected on the snow so brightly I could see clearly as far as the barn. Thunder Hooves and War Cloud were both drinking from the water trough, when a sudden gust of wind sent snow flying off the roof of the barn and across their backs. I laughed as both horses broke away and ran a short distance and then turned to see what had frightened them. Thunder Hooves was beautiful in the moonlight. Her neck was arched and her tail was held high and, even though I was too far away to see, I knew her eyes would be wide and wild-looking and her nostrils would be flared as she snorted in disgust that something had dared to bother her. So beautiful and so proud. I was lucky to have her. She was the one thing in this world I could love and call my own. I watched her a while longer as she pranced and pawed at the snow. War Cloud had gone back to the business of getting a drink, but Thunder Hooves still shied away from the area around the barn. The wind blew again, and she shook her head and trotted in a large circle. Maybe she smelled the scent of coyotes on the wind tonight. Maybe that was why she was nervous.

I was too tired to watch her any longer, so I threw another log into the stove and climbed into bed.

Tomorrow I would go riding. Thunder Hooves and I would run faster than the wind. With that picture in my mind, I fell asleep.

CHAPTER FIVE

I woke up early the next morning and my first thought was *This is my second day alone without Grandmother. Today will be easier than yesterday, tomorrow will be better than today.* I was looking forward to my ride.

Thunder Hooves would be good company today. She would make me feel better. Maybe we could ride up as far as Bitter Water Creek. I could pack a lunch and spend most of the day riding. I glanced out the window. The clouds were low and heavy with snow. A blizzard seemed to be coming. *I had better not try to go as far as Bitter Water today. If we are caught in a blizzard, it will be dangerous.* We could at least go up to the ridge and back; that wouldn't take long. I wouldn't need to take a lunch for such a short ride. I pulled on my leather jacket and tied a scarf around my hair and walked outside.

The bright glare of the snow blinded me for a few seconds. The air was so cold I lost my breath. I stood on the porch and looked toward the barn. I couldn't see any of the horses in the corral. I hoped they were inside the barn, because I didn't want to walk all over the pasture looking for them. The snow was too deep.

I stepped into the snow and felt it go over the tops of my moccasins. It was so cold, the snow crunched underfoot as I made my way toward the barn.

It wasn't until I climbed through the fence that I saw it. Red ice. A river of red ice around the water trough.

"What in the world is that?" I asked aloud. I stooped over and touched it with my fingers. "What would make the ice red?" Then I felt weak. Blood. Blood would make the ice red.

I stood up and walked around the corner of the barn, following the red river of frozen blood.

I wanted to scream when I saw it, but no sound came from my open mouth.

Thunder Hooves lay on her side, with three of her feet tangled in barbed wire. Blood was everywhere. The snow was red where she lay in a pool of blood.

I turned and ran, staggering and falling and running again. I ran until my lungs felt as if they would explode inside my chest. With every step I begged, "Let her be all right! Let Cloud save her!"

I couldn't get through the snowdrifts fast enough. They seemed to pull at me, sucking at me to slow me down. Time after time I fell flat, sprawling in the crusty snow; time after time I struggled back to my feet and ran again. I couldn't see anything but Thunder Hooves lying there, tangled in the wire, helpless and hurting.

At last I staggered up to Cloud's house and beat on the door.

"Cloud!" I screamed, and before I could hit the door with my fists again it opened, and there stood my uncle.

"Thunder Hooves is hurt!" I panted. "She's tangled in wire, she's bleeding. Help—help her!"

He grabbed his coat off a peg behind the door.

"Let's go!" he said and started to run back to the barn.

I ran after him as fast as I could, but I was exhausted and soon fell far behind him.

"He can save her! He can save her" I gasped with each breath. I had seen him save many injured animals. He had a gift for healing animals. He would save her!

Soon he was out of sight, and I knew he had probably already reached Thunder Hooves. My legs were shaking, and my throat was raw from sucking in the frosty air.

The barn came into sight. Cloud had seen me coming and was heading toward me.

He met me at the bottom of the hill.

"It's too late. She's dead,"

I shook my head. "No—I—ran—fast—you can—save her!" I gasped.

He shook his head again. "She's been dead for hours. She died last night. She was already dead when you saw her. It looked like she was running and hit some ice and slid into the wire—well, she bled to death."

I shook my head again. "No—" My lips formed other words but there was no sound.

"I'm sorry, Cry. If it helps any, she probably didn't feel any pain. It was so cold last night. She lost so much blood so fast—it couldn't have taken long."

I could hear myself screaming and cursing and screaming some more. I threw myself down in the snow and beat at it with my fists.

Grandmother and Thunder Hooves both gone in two days! No! No! It couldn't be happening! I had lost everything! Everything!

Cloud didn't speak. He just stood nearby while my grief and anger ran their course. I thought I would never stop crying, but finally I did. I just sat in the snow, numb and empty and sick.

Cloud reached down and picked me up in his arms as if I were a small child and carried me the long distance back to his house.

I rested in his arms like a limp rag. I couldn't move one muscle in my body. All the life had drained out of me, just as it had drained out of Thunder Hooves.

CHAPTER SIX

The blizzard came that night. The wind howled, and the snow piled up fast and deep. All I could think of was the fresh, white snow burying Thunder Hooves, covering her up in a white blanket of death, hiding the red ice, hiding her river of frozen blood.

The storm blew all night and all the next day and into the next night. I slept most of the time, drifting in and out of wakefulness and sleep. I didn't want to remember the ache inside of me. I didn't want to think about life being one loss after another, always losing something, never gaining anything. My mind mercifully blocked out everything around me and let me sleep. I remembered Cloud waking me up a couple of times and feeding me, but I don't remember what I ate or if we talked. I only remembered the storm raging outside as if it would last forever.

Somehow the next few days passed, and my heart hurt a little less than it had.

I didn't say it out loud, but in my heart I felt that the wind had killed Thunder Hooves. It was the wind that had frightened her into running. The wind had been angry at me and had punished me by killing the last thing I had in the world. That's what I thought, but I was too afraid to say it, for the wind might kill me next.

I began to wonder how we had gotten all the Indian gods in the first place.

"Cloud, where did we get our religion from?"

He looked surprised. "What do you mean?"

"Who started doing the ceremonies? How did they know what to do or when to do it? Who made up the songs and dances? How did it all get started?"

He shrugged. "How should I know? It is all old. The old, ancient ones started it a long time ago, I guess."

"How long ago?"

"How do I know?"

"A thousand years ago?" I asked.

"Maybe."

"What did the Indians do before that?"

"Who knows?"

"That's just it! Nobody knows anything about the Indians. Anthropologists say we came from Asia across the Bering Strait and started out as yellow-skinned people and somehow turned red halfway here."

Cloud laughed and joined in, "And others say we came from the South Seas and we had brown skin and turned red later. Funny how the experts think we can change the color of our skin." He laughed again.

"Where do you think we really came from?" I was serious again.

"I think the Indian people were created here." He waved his arm around him, meaning here in America. "I don't think we came from any other place or any other people. We have always been here, we are The People, The Land."

"Maybe that is true," I agreed, "but if there is only one Indian people, why are there so many Indian religions? Even in our own family, we don't use the true Kickapoo religion. We mix Navajo with Kickapoo because Grandmother and Grandfather never could agree on which was right. Is the Kickapoo religion better, or is the Navajo better, or the Sioux? Who is right? How can they all be right when they are all so different? I pleaded for an answer.

"You make me tired with all your questions. I don't know the answers. Stop thinking about it. What difference does it make, anyway?" He had had enough.

"Yes, I guess you're right. What difference does it make, anyway?" I repeated, but I had an uneasy feeling inside that what you believe made a very big difference, or it wouldn't bother me so much.

I had been staying with my uncle for two weeks. One morning he came in and sat down beside me.

"Cry, do you feel like talking?"

"What about?" I asked. I hoped he was not going to mention Grandmother or Thunder Hooves, because today was the first day I hadn't cried. I was afraid if he mentioned either of them I would start crying again.

"You know, you can't go back and live in that house alone. For one thing, you're too young, and for another thing—well, it's not a good idea," he said and started pulling off his coat.

I nodded. He was going to ask me to stay here with him! I was excited. I could cook and keep house for Cloud, and he could bring home food for us. It would be perfect. We wouldn't have to be alone. Before I could tell him how happy I was, he continued.

"Anyway, I've been thinking. You can't stay there by yourself, and you can't stay here with me because I'll be leaving soon—"

"Leaving?" I asked weakly.

"Yeah. Look, Cry, there's nothing here for either of us anymore. There was never very much, but now there is nothing. I can do a little hunting and a little trapping and barely support myself, but game is getting scarce, and the price of pelts has gone down again. I can't support both of us"

"I can sell beadwork!" I said eagerly.

He laughed. "Oh, Cry! You are thinking about a handful of dollars. I'm sick of being half-hungry all the time." He stood up and paced the floor. "Do you know that Indians live in the worst poverty of any people in America? This is our land. We were here first, and now we are living in worse conditions than any other people here. I'm sick of it, and I'm getting out. I've been thinking about leaving a long time. I think the signs are right to go now. You'll go too. There is nothing to hold us here."

"Then you are taking me with you?" I asked, afraid of the answer.

"No, because I don't know where I'm going or what I'll do. Flint is living in town now. I guess he is doing all right. That would be the best place for you, too. I'll sell everything we own and split the money with you. Then I'll take you into town and get you a place to live. You'll have to get a job, but until you do, Flint can keep an eye on you."

"I can't! I've never lived in town. I don't know how to do anything. How can I get a job? What will I do?"

"You'll manage, " he answered simply. "You'll learn how to survive, and Flint can help you out."

"No! I want to stay here!" I said stubbornly.

"You can't. You would starve to death, or else you would be fair game for any drunken Indians who knew you were up here alone." He looked at me meaningfully, and I got the message.

"How soon do I have to leave?"

"I'll ask the trader to come out tomorrow. I'll sell him everything I can. We should be out of here in a couple of days."

"Where will you go?"

"I don't know," he said.

"You must have some plans," I insisted.

"No. All I know is that I want to get as far away from here as I can. I want a fresh start, and I want to have some of the things that other people have!" he said with determination. "This is the best for you, too, Cry. You'll see. There will be something for you in the city. You'll meet people. You'll learn a new way of life. Maybe you'll find someone to marry. Whatever happens to you, it's got to be better than living like this." He picked up his tin cup and hurled it across the room. It hit the wall and clattered to the floor.

I looked at the empty cup for a moment and then asked, "Will you keep in touch with me?"

"Sure, you know I will. As soon as I find out who I am and where I'm going, I'll write to you. Maybe I'll send for you," he said.

I didn't believe him. As soon as he was gone he would be every bit as lost to me as Grandmother and Thunder Hooves. I would never see him again. I kept my eyes on the empty tin cup he had just thrown away. How very much I felt like that empty cup!

Cloud put his coat back on and went after the rest of my things and brought them back to his place. He began sorting out all he owned, putting things to keep into one pile and things to sell to the trader into another pile. He was keeping very little. All my beadwork was put out for the trader to buy. I had planned to sell it to the trader anyway, but now I wanted to keep it with me for a little longer. I didn't want to part with everything so soon. I picked out one bead necklace and put it on for a while, but when I saw Cloud looking at me, I took it off and put it back on the pile for the trader.

After the trader had left, taking everything with him, I felt that I had lost everything in the world. Cloud stood on the porch beside me as we watched the trader drive off with everything we had owned bouncing around in the back of his truck.

"We'll leave tomorrow morning," he said. "We'll go to town and find Flint first. He might know of a place where you can stay. I'll give you sixty dollars and that will get you started. After that, you are on your own."

I hardly slept all night. There had been too many changes too fast, and now I would be leaving here forever. This was the only place I had ever known, and I had never been more than a few miles from here. Now I felt as if I was being sent to another world, outside and far away.

As soon as it was dawn, Cloud loaded things into the back of his rusty old pickup truck. Sleepy-eyed I followed him down the path from the house for the last time.

Someday I'll come back here, I thought. *This is where I belong. This is my home.*

Cloud reached over and handed me a piece of jerky. "Here's breakfast. I hope you never have to eat such poor food again," he said. He started the truck. The motor was cold and growled over and over before it would start. I hoped it wouldn't start at all, and we could stay here at least for a few more days, but it did start. Soon we were on our way on the rough road that led to the highway that would take us to town.

We were almost to town before I realized I still hadn't eaten the jerky. It had been lying in my cold hands so long I had forgotten it. I bit off a piece and chewed it. It was as hard and dry as a piece of old leather. I might as well have been chewing on my moccasin for all the flavor it had.

It didn't take Cloud long to find Flint. He was working in a lumberyard. I waited in the truck while the two of them stood a distance away and talked. Occasionally one of them would look toward the truck, and I guess that Flint was not very happy about having me dumped on him. Finally both of them walked back to the truck.

I rolled down the window, and Flint bent his tall frame almost double to speak to me.

"I guess you'll be staying here," he said. "I know of a place down the road where you can get a cheap room. Cloud will take you there. I'll stop in and see you after work tonight."

I nodded in agreement. I had no choice, and we all knew it.

In a few more minutes Cloud pulled up in front of a place with several rows of small cabins. The sign in front read, "Pine Valley Court."

Cloud got out of the truck and walked into the office. In a minute he came back with a man and motioned for me to come along.

I hurried after them as they walked to a small cabin at the end of the row.

The man unlocked the door and pushed it open, motioning for us to go in first.

I stood in the center of the living room and looked around. It was about the size of the house Grandmother and I had had, but this was so nice. There was a rug on the floor and curtains on the windows. There was a small kitchen off to one side, with a gas stove and a real refrigerator. I could have hot or cold food any time I wanted! There was a bathroom with a real bathtub where I could stretch out in hot water instead of bathing out of an old tin washbasin as I had back home. The furniture was finer than any I had ever seen, and there was a big bed off by itself in another room.

"I'm sorry it's so small, but one person it would be all right." The manager apologized for the size, not knowing that it was the best place I had ever been in.

"It's completely furnished," he said. "Linens, dishes, everything. It's fifty dollars a month or twenty dollars a week."

"We'll take it," Cloud said.

"When do you want to move in?" the manager asked.

"She already has," Cloud replied. He paid the manager for two weeks' rent and handed me twenty dollars to live on. He left me there and went for my suitcase.

The manager gave me the key and left just as Cloud came back through the door with my suitcase. He set it down beside me and looked around.

"You'll be all right," he said. "Flint will come over later. If you need anything, tell him. Oh, one more thing. It might be a good idea to tell people you are eighteen years old instead of fourteen."

"I'm fifteen now," I said. "I had a birthday."

"Oh." He looked embarrassed. "I guess I forgot."

"Everyone did," I said.

Cloud couldn't wait to leave. I wanted to keep him with me just a little longer, but I couldn't think of any way to hold on to him.

"You're settled now," he said. "I guess I'll be going." He walked back outside and I followed him.

"Cloud—" I wanted to beg him to stay, but I knew he wouldn't, so I just said, "Be careful." That wasn't what I had wanted to say, but I couldn't find the right words to tell him how I felt. I wished I could reach out and touch him, hold him for one second; but that would be a sign of weakness, and he would hate it. So I folded my arms in front of me so I wouldn't be tempted to touch him.

"Good-bye, Cry," he said and climbed into his old truck. He gave me a quick smile and then drove away. I knew I would never see him again.

I watched until his truck was out of sight. When he had gone, I retreated to my cabin and closed the door behind me and locked it. I opened my suitcase and put my clothes in a drawer and hung my dress in the closet. In less than three minutes I was unpacked and moved in. I walked around and around the rooms, examining each and every little thing, turning the stove on and off, and opening the refrigerator time after time.

It was a good place, better than I had ever had before. I knew I would be here at least two weeks; the rent was paid for that long. I had twenty dollars, but I didn't know how much food twenty dollars would buy. I had never shopped for food anywhere except at the trading post. I had done that only a few times, so I wasn't sure how much things cost, but it couldn't be very much.

I spent the rest of the afternoon walking back and forth and peeking out the window, hoping Flint would come. About the middle of the afternoon, I heard tires grinding across the gravel driveway. I leaped to my feet and hurried to the window to look outside.

It was Flint! I tugged the door open and went outside to meet him.

He got out of his pickup, walked up to the cabin, and stuck his head through the door.

"Everything OK?" he asked.

"Yes. Cloud is gone," I said. I hoped he might say something about where Cloud was going.

"Didn't think he'd stick around." He leaned up against the door. "Guess you need some food. Get in the truck, and I'll drive you to a store."

I grabbed my twenty-dollar bill and my key and climbed into the truck beside Flint.

There was a store only a few blocks away. It seemed huge. It was ten times bigger than the trading post and full of bright lights and rows and rows of shelves of food.

Flint pulled out a wire cart and started pushing it down the aisles. At first I was so overwhelmed by so much food that I went down two rows without putting anything in the basket. We had to go back and start over. Then I started picking up everything that looked good and putting it into the basket.

"Hold on a minute. You don't have enough money for all that stuff," Flint said. He put a lot of it back on the shelves. "Just get what you need. After you get a job, you can buy what you want." He put a can of lard and a small bag of flour into the cart. "You can live cheap on fry bread and eggs."

I could see I was going to end up eating the same thing here that I had eaten back on the reservation. Things weren't going to be better, after all. I let Flint pick out the rest of the food, but my eyes were still on the bright cans and packages of wonderful things like peaches and chocolate candy and roast beef. The groceries in the cart cost seventeen dollars. Flint took my twenty-dollar bill and handed me the change. I couldn't believe everything cost so much. No wonder he hadn't let me buy all I wanted. It would probably have cost a hundred dollars.

He drove me back to the cabin and sat in a chair while he waited for me to put my food away. He was looking at a newspaper and marking in it with a pencil. After I had put my food away, he motioned for me to come and sit beside him.

"I marked some jobs for you to check tomorrow. You might have to try many places before anyone will hire you. Some people won't hire you because you're an Indian, and some won't want you because you've never worked before. You'll just have to keep trying until you get a job somewhere. You had better tell them you're eighteen years old."

"Cloud told me that, too," I said.

"Yeah. Well, we talked about it and figured if people knew you were only fourteen, it might cause trouble. Another thing—don't talk to any strange men, and don't invite anyone back to your apartment with you."

"Why?"

"Things are different here. You have to be careful. I'll keep an eye on you as much as I can, but I can't be around all the time. If you need help, you know where I work." He handed the newspaper to me and stood up. "I'll go now."

"Can't you stay a little while?" I asked.

He shook his head. "No, I have some things to do. You'll be all right. I'll check back in a few days," he said as he opened the door. "Keep your door locked all the time," he cautioned as he pulled it shut behind him.

I checked the door to make sure it was locked. "Everybody keeps saying that I'll be all right. I don't think they believe that any more than I do, " I muttered to myself as I went into my little kitchen to fix some dinner.

When I climbed out of bed the next morning, I was filled with dread. I had to start looking for a job right away, and I didn't know where to go or what to do after I got there. I put on the only good outfit I owned, pulled on my moccasins, brushed my hair, and picked up the newspaper Flint had left.

I walked sixteen blocks to reach the first place listed in the paper. I had hardly walked through the door before I was told the job was already taken. It was three more blocks to the second store that had an opening. I did a little better. At least I was allowed to fill out an application. It didn't take long; all I could put on it was my name, address and age. My age was a lie. When there is no education and no experience to write down, the page looks pretty blank.

The rest of the morning was spent the same way, walking from store to store, filling out applications, and watching people's eyebrows go up when they read my name, Crying Wind.

At the next place I applied, the personnel manager gave me a cold look over the top of her glasses and asked, "Who sent you here? Was it Equal Employment or Civil Liberties or who?"

I shook my head. I didn't have the slightest idea what she was talking about.

She dropped my application on her desk as if it were something dirty, put her hands on her hips, and said, "Well, you can go right back to whoever sent you here, and tell them we've already filled our minority quota. We don't want any more of you—you people!"

By "you people" I figured she meant Indians and that there was something wrong with being an Indian.

The eleventh store I stopped at was a large department store. There was an opening for a salesclerk in the kitchenware department. The man who spoke to me seemed to think I would be able to sell pots and pans and can openers, so he said I could have the job starting the next day. I would be paid thirty-five dollars a week.

I jumped at the chance. I didn't think I could face filling out any more applications. I was exhausted from walking all over town. I was grateful for any kind of a job. I knew that Flint would be relieved that I found work and could support myself.

It was twenty-five blocks from the apartment to the store, but I was so proud that I had a job, I didn't notice.

On the first day of my new job, I felt numb. I was sure I would do something wrong and be fired. I almost didn't show up, but I knew I would have to have money, so I gritted my teeth and went. Somehow I got through the morning. Finally my boss said I could go to lunch.

"Where do I go?" I asked.

"It's upstairs." He gave a nod of his head without looking at me. I saw a flight of stairs tucked away in a corner of the room. When I got to the top of the stairs, there were two doors. On one door there was a red sign that said, "Keep Out," so I carefully opened the other door. It opened into a huge dark room with boxes stacked all over. It was dusty and cluttered. Surely this couldn't be the lunchroom. There must be a door on the other side of the room. I worked my way between the rows of boxes and came to the opposite corner. Instead of a door, there was a pile of old, broken mannequins. Arms and legs and heads were stacked in a heap, with more heads lined up against the wall. I knew they were made of plaster, but I felt as if their painted eyes were looking at me. I backed up. I wanted out of there. I almost expected some force to pull the mannequin parts together to form a multi-legged monster that would chase me. I hurried back across the room without looking behind me. I was being silly; I knew that. After all, I was fifteen. Wasn't that old enough to be on your own in the world? Why was I so afraid of everything?

I heard voices coming from the door marked "Keep Out." I opened the door a crack and saw about a dozen women eating their lunches around a long table. I walked inside the room and tried to smile, but my face felt stiff. A couple of them looked up and nodded, but the others ignored me and went on eating and talking. I picked a seat in the corner and put my wrinkled brown sack on the table. I looked around and saw that everyone else had neat, little lunch boxes with flowers and bright colors. I took my sack off the table and held it in my lap.

I had a sandwich of two pieces of fry bread and a fried egg. I felt starved. When I bit into my sandwich, I discovered that I hadn't cooked the egg long enough. The yolk was cold and runny and dripped into my lap. I was so afraid that everyone was watching me, I wouldn't look up. I took a few bites, but the half-raw egg just would not slide down my throat. I gave up, wrapped my sandwich in my wrinkled brown sack, threw it all in the trash, and left.

I felt foolish. I wondered if any of them knew I had gone in the wrong door and had wandered around lost in a storage room. Me lost! I had walked miles and miles in the deepest forest and across dusty plains, and I had never forgotten a rock or a stick or a tree. I had never been lost. Now, here in a simple building, I had become confused and got lost. In the forest back home I could have found a blue-jay feather on a mountainside a mile away. Here in the city I couldn't find a lunchroom up one flight of stairs.

My clothing was the same as anyone else's—perhaps a little old-fashioned, but not so much that I looked odd. I wore gathered, cotton skirts, just a little longer than the other girls' skirts, with long-sleeved, cotton blouses. I was proud of my moccasins. I had made them from an elk my uncles had killed. I had carefully sewn them together and used leather thongs and a silver concho to fasten them. They were soft and comfortable. I would walk miles in them, and my feet would not grow tired. The moccasins were silent on the city pavement. It was comforting to look at them on my feet and pretend I was still at home, stepping carefully through the forest. Yes, my clothes were a little different, but I didn't mind looking a little different.

There was a girl at work named Betty, who was beautiful. Her clothes were expensive and fit perfectly. Whenever she was around, I began to notice that my blouses were too loose and my skirts too long. Her hair curled around her face. I was determined to look like she did, but no matter what I did to my hair at night, it would end up hanging straight down my back in the morning. After several sleepless nights of trying to rest with curlers and pins in my hair, I gave up and let my hair go its own way.

Betty wore very high heels, which click-clicked as she walked around the store. My elk-hide moccasins sh-shhhed. Suddenly the moccasins I had taken so much pride in looked out of place, and I began to feel foolish. One day a customer looked at my feet and laughed, and I was angry and embarrassed. During my lunch hour I hurried out and bought a pair of shiny black shoes with heels as high as the other girls'. From then on I click-clicked as I walked around the store, and no one laughed at my shoes anymore. At night, when I came home from spending eight hours on my feet in those high heels, I would kick them off as soon as I came through the door and put on my old, friendly moccasins.

One day a Cherokee Indian boy about my age came into the store. I was happy to see someone like me. We talked a few minutes, but by his words and actions it was clear he was what Indians call an "apple," someone who is red on the outside but white on the inside—someone who wants to be a white person. Sometimes I felt that I was the opposite, white on the outside and red on the inside. I wondered if there was any fruit like that, that I could be called.

Betty was nice to me and even gave me some of her clothes that she was tired of, but I never looked as good in them as she did. There is just no way you can make a hundred pounds of skin and bones look like anything except a hundred pounds of skin and bones.

Days ran into nights and the nights ran into days, and weeks crept by.

I lay on my bed and stared at the ceiling. I could hear the faucet dripping in the bathroom, but it seemed like too much effort to get up and turn it off. I would do it later. I turned over on my side. I saw the telephone shoved under the edge of the chair. I had lived here six months and never used it. I had never called anyone or received a call from anyone.

I got off the bed, knelt on the floor, and pulled the telephone out from under the chair. It was dusty, and I wiped if off. The telephone had come with the room, as had the rest of the utilities. I hadn't even thought about it. It was just something that was always in the way when I wanted to put a book or a glass of water on the night table, so I had stuck it under the chair and forgotten about it.

Now I wished I had someone to call. Betty! I could call Betty! I pulled the phone book out of the drawer and looked up Woodard. There were a lot of people named Woodard, but no Betty Woodard was listed.

I let the phone book fall shut, and then I opened it again—there must be someone in town I could call. Flint didn't have a phone, but there must be someone to talk to. I found the number for the time and temperature and dialed it carefully. I had used a telephone only a couple of times in my entire life.

"Hello?" I said when I heard a click on the other end. "Can you tell me—" It was a few seconds before I realized there was just a recorded message at the other end of the line. I listened to it three times, Time 7:30 PM—temperature 72 degrees—Have a good evening and when you are looking for a bank you can trust be sure and—"

I began looking through the yellow pages, starting with A and going from one advertisement to the next until I reached the C's, where the churches were listed. I had not realized the town had so many churches. My finger trailed down the page and rested on "Trinity Evangelical United Brethren Church, Rev. Glenn O. McPherson, Pastor." I read on down the page, but my eyes rested again on the church with the long name. Somehow that name seemed to stand out more than any of the others. I turned the page and looked at more advertisements, but in a few minutes I turned back to the church listings and hunted again for the church with the long name.

Maybe I will call that church, I thought. *I could call that man named McPherson and ask him something. Then I would have someone to talk to, not a recording. I can always hang up whenever I want. I can even give him some other name. I could ask him a question about something, maybe about his church.* I began dialing. One ring—two rings—

"Hello, this is Reverend McPherson speaking."

My mouth felt dry. Now what? Maybe I should just hang up.

"May I help you?" came the soft voice on the phone.

"I—I—I was just, ah, wondering what it was like—I mean—what you did there?" I sounded foolish. I shouldn't have done this. Whatever had possessed me to do such a dumb thing?

"We worship God the best way we know how." He paused. "If you could tell me exactly what you want to know I could be more helpful—"

"I don't know what to ask—" I blurted out. "I'm new here. I just saw your name in the phone book and—" I could feel my face burning. Why didn't I just hang up?

"You would be welcome to visit our church anytime." He sounded friendly.

"No, I don't think I want to do that. I don't know anyone—never mind. I'm sorry I bothered you."

"Wait—don't hang up. I could give you some booklets that explain what our church is all about. You can read them and decide if you would like to attend our church or not. I could mail them to you."

That sounded like a good idea. I could get some mail, and I could get off this telephone. "All right. My name is Crying Wind—" and I gave him my address.

"Oh, you only live four blocks from the church. You are just right up the street from us."

My heart sank. That was why the name of the church had stuck in my mind tonight, why it had seemed familiar. I passed that little brick church on my way to and from work. This was awful! I had called someone right in the neighborhood!

"I'm making a house call near you. If you aren't busy, I'll drop off these books on my way. You can have them tonight," he said.

"OK," I answered weakly. I should have told him I wasn't going to be home, but I hadn't thought fast enough.

I hung up the telephone and slid it back under the chair. That was where it could stay! My one and only phone call I had made since moving here, and it had gotten me into a big mess! Now what was I going to do? I hurried to my closet and got out my coat. I would leave and just not be there when he came. Then I stopped. He would probably come back another time, and I would have to go through this again. It was better to get it over with. I hung my coat back in the closet.

I didn't have to wait long until I heard footsteps outside and someone knocking on the door of the cabin next to mine. I held my breath. No one lived on either side of me, so I knew it had to be Reverend McPherson searching for me. He knocked on my door, and I jumped.

The door seemed to weigh a ton as I slowly pulled it open. A small man wearing glasses and dressed in a gray suit stood before me.

"I'm Reverend McPherson."

I nodded. "Come in."

Another mistake. I shouldn't have invited him inside.

I sat on the edge of the couch, and he took a chair opposite me.

"I won't take up much of your time. I'm sure you have something to do on such a nice evening." He smiled.

"No, I wasn't doing anything." *Another mistake,* I thought, *I should have told him I was leaving soon, and he wouldn't stay long. I'm doing everything wrong.*

"I brought you everything I could think of that might help you." He put a handful of booklets on the table, "I will try to answer any questions—that is, if you have any."

I twisted my fingers together and stared at him. He looked embarrassed, but I had the feeling it wasn't for himself. He was embarrassed for me. Somehow he knew how awkward I felt.

"How old are you?"

"Eighteen."

"You don't look eighteen. You aren't married, are you?"

"No."

"Good. Well, I just meant that eighteen is very young." He tried to look around the room without being obvious. "Do you have a relative or a girlfriend who lives here with you?"

"No."

"You aren't from around here, are you?" He already knew the answer.

"No. I just moved here a few months ago." I knew I wasn't saying enough, so I added, "I work at Hawkins Department Store."

"Oh, my wife goes there sometimes. Do you like your job?"

"It's all right, I guess."

He turned his hat over in his hands a few times, and silence hung heavy in the room.

"Who is your God?" I asked in a strange, tight voice that seemed far away and not my own at all. I couldn't believe I had asked that question. Surely it hadn't come from me!

He smiled. "That is a big question. I could give you a lot of pat answers or tell you what the great theologians say, but I don't think that's what you want to hear. To me, God is the Creator of everything. He made man, but man fell into sin. God loved man so much that He made a blood sacrifice of His only Son so man could be washed clean from sin and have everlasting life. I believe much more than that, but that is it in a nutshell—I'm sure you've heard that many times before."

I shook my head. "No, I haven't heard that before."

"Have you ever read the Bible?"

"I don't have one. I've never read it. Bibles are for church people."

"Bibles are for everyone. I'll give you one. I don't have one with me tonight, but I'll either bring you one or mail one to you. What church have you attended in the past?"

"None." I swallowed hard. "I've never been to a church."

He couldn't hide the look of surprise on his face. "I see." He was silent for a moment than asked quietly, "I don't want to embarrass you or to pry but would you like to tell me what you do believe, and then we could go from there?"

I took a deep breath and pointed to some of my drawings hanging on the wall behind him.

He turned and looked at the sketches of various Indian gods and signs telling their legends.

"I'm—" I didn't want to say half-breed. "I'm part Indian. My grandmother taught me about the old religions. I believe in the old gods. I believe in the wind."

I clenched my teeth and waited for him to laugh, but he didn't. I felt some of the tension drain from me.

"I'm very ignorant about this subject," he said, "I thought Indians believed in a Great Spirit."

I told him a few things about the old religion.

"I've often wondered about some of the Indian customs. Some of them seem very strange to us." And then he added, "I suppose some of our customs seem strange to you."

"Yes. There is even a story about that. A white man went to a Kickapoo funeral, and he saw the Indians putting food in the grave, and the white man asked when would the dead Indian eat the food. A Kickapoo thought for a moment. Then he asked the white man, 'Don't you put flowers on the grave of your dead ones?' 'Yes,' replied the white man. 'Well, then,' said the Indian. 'When the dead white man smells the flowers, that is when the dead Indian will eat the food.'"

He laughed, but not at me, only at the story.

He didn't say much more, and he didn't stay long. He said he had to leave and visit some more people, but he invited me to come to his church, and then he left.

I told myself I was lucky to get off that easily. It was nice of him not to embarrass me or try to convert me. He was probably a pretty nice man. One thing for sure though—I had learned a lesson. I would never use that telephone again! That little machine could get a person into a lot of trouble!

CHAPTER SEVEN

After Flint decided I wasn't going to be a pest, he started coming around more often. We were closer than we had ever been. Since I had no other family or friends in town, I looked forward to seeing him. I was always disappointed on the evening he didn't come.

The next time he did show up, it was to bring sad news.

"Your Uncle Pascal is dead," he said simply.

"Dead?" I tried to think of the last time I'd seen him. It had been when Grandmother had died. "I didn't know there was anything wrong with him."

"There wasn't." Flint shuffled his feet for a moment. Then the truth came out. Pascal had eaten dinner at a friend's house, he had played with the children before they went to bed, and he had sat and talked for about an hour. He hadn't said anything special, just talked about the past and how most of his friends were gone now and he was alone. Then about 10:00 p.m., he left and walked home. They figured within an hour after he had arrived at his house, he committed suicide by shooting himself in the head with his shotgun. Flint was kind enough to spare me the details, but some very ugly pictures flashed through my mind.

"But why would he do that?" I asked.

"He was lonely." Flint slumped into a chair. "We're all lonely."

"Yeah," I said almost in a whisper. Even now, loneliness hung in the air like a fog. Flint and I were together, yet we were two of the loneliest people who had ever lived.

We sat there for a long time listening to the storm outside. I was thinking about Uncle Pascal. I couldn't remember very much about him. I couldn't even clearly remember what he looked like, and now he was gone. I would never see him again. What was worse, I probably wouldn't even miss him. I looked across the room at Flint and was surprised to see how upset he was. He had lost a brother. They had been fairly close. They were both bachelors. Maybe Flint was thinking they had a lot in common and was wondering if he would end up like that.

Suddenly his eyes met mine and he gave me one of those funny, crooked smiles that didn't really mean anything.

"Know what I'm going to do, Cry?" He stood up.

"No, what?" I tried to sound casual.

"I'm going out and get drunk. I'm going to get drunker than I've ever been in my life and then—" he stopped.

"And then what?" I stood up and walked toward the door more in an attempt to keep him in than to let him out.

"Nothing," he said.

He stepped around me, put his hand on the doorknob, and looked back at me.

"He was right."

"Who was right?" I dreaded the answer.

"Pascal was right." His voice cracked and I knew I couldn't let him leave alone, or I would never see him alive again.

"I'm coming with you Flint," I said. I grabbed my coat. "I don't want to be alone." It was true. I didn't want to be alone, and I didn't want him to be alone either.

"Sure, why not? I'm not going far."

He drove to the nearest liquor store and left me sitting in the car while he went inside. He returned with several sacks, each containing a bottle of liquor.

Then he drove back to my apartment and handed me one of the bottles.

"Here kid," he said and shoved one of the sacks toward me.

"Don't leave yet, Flint. Please come inside." I picked up the bottles and opened the car door. "You can drink here as well as anyplace else, and it's nice and warm." I didn't want to leave him alone when he was this depressed.

Before he could say no, I hurried inside and took all the liquor with me. He didn't seem to have any will of his own left and followed me without an argument.

Flint opened the first bottle of whiskey, poured some into a glass, and handed it to me. He took the bottle with him and stretched out on the couch.

"Here's to a wasted warrior," he said and began pouring the liquor down his throat like he was trying to drown himself.

I had seen my uncles and my grandfather drink this way before. For many Indians, heavy drinking is a way of life. The stories about "red man and firewater" weren't far from the truth. Unlike the white man who drinks to be sociable, the red man drinks to get drunk. He drinks to forget that he belongs no place; that he is a relic of the past. The two largest killers of Indians are alcoholism and suicide. In that room that night we had all the makings for both.

I took a sip from my glass and blinked my eyes as the liquor burned my throat. I had a feeling that really I shouldn't be drinking, but I pushed it to the back of my mind. Why shouldn't I drink? Why shouldn't I? What difference did it make? Who cared, anyway?

By the time I had finished my drink, Flint had finished the bottle, and we were both feeling the false security that goes with alcohol. Our brains were numb. Flint would rattle on and on, and I would laugh at anything he said without knowing whether it was funny or not. Instead of passing time, the whiskey seemed to make it stand still, and instead of escaping the present, we were suspended in it.

My tongue felt thick, and my head ached. I was tired. "I'm going to bed now, Flint," I said sleepily.

"OK, kid, I'll leave." He picked up the last bottle and headed toward the door, but before he reached it, he crashed into a chair and fell, spread-eagle on the floor. We laughed until our sides ached.

"You'd better stay here tonight. You can sleep on the couch. I'll get some blankets for you." I wove my way to the closet. By the time I got back, he had passed out. He was in the same position as when he had fallen. One hand still had a firm grip on the unopened bottle. I didn't try to wake him; I just spread a blanket over him and left him asleep on the floor.

I didn't wake up until late the next morning. I knew before I moved that I'd made a terrible mistake. My head ached, my eyes hurt, my stomach was in knots, and I wanted to die. I had a hangover. I lay in bed for nearly an hour before I could get up and face the day. I hoped I wouldn't be fired for not showing up at work. I would tell them I was sick. That was the truth. I couldn't have felt worse if I had every disease known to mankind.

I walked unsteadily to where Flint was still asleep. It didn't look like he had moved all night, but then I saw that the bottle had been opened and was beside him, empty. Sometime during the night he had regained consciousness, finished drinking the last bottle of whiskey, and passed out again.

I left him alone. He would have to sleep it off. Besides, I didn't feel like talking to anyone now. I didn't think I could move my tongue.

I sat and held my head and drank coffee until noon, when Flint finally sat up and looked around.

"How do you feel, kid?" he asked and tenderly touched his head with his fingertips.

"Terrible."

"Yeah. But we had a good time, didn't we?" He gave me that crooked smile again.

I didn't answer. I hadn't had a good time. I was still lonely and afraid and so was he. On top of all that, we were both sick.

"I'll never drink again," I said and handed him a cup of coffee.

"Why not?" he asked and made a face as he swallowed some coffee.

"It's stupid. You drink all night, and when you wake up the next morning, nothing has changed."

"Well, it makes you forget," he said.

"I didn't forget anything."

He took another drink of coffee. "No," he said softly, "neither did I."

We sat there and stared at the empty bottles lying on the floor.

"What else is there?" he asked.

"I don't know, but there must be something." My head was starting to hurt again.

"There must be something else to life, Flint. Otherwise—otherwise, what's the point to anything?"

"That's the joke. There is no point to anything." He laughed harshly. "Pascal found that out."

I felt tears coming to my eyes. "Flint, why doesn't anyone love us?"

He swallowed hard. "I don't know."

I wiped my eyes on my sleeves. "It looks like somebody, somewhere would love us."

He reached across the table and tugged on my hair. "It's OK, kid. You and I will stick together and lick the whole world."

He stayed about an hour longer. We talked about the weather and hunting season and a dozen other subjects that didn't mean anything, but we kept our minds busy so we wouldn't think too much. By the time he left, I was feeling better, and he was too. He would get through today all right, and maybe this week, but one of these nights he would start thinking about Pascal again. Maybe he would have too much to drink and maybe—maybe no one would be around to stop him from killing himself.

What happens when you die? I kept asking myself. I thought I had run away from that question when I left the valley, but it had reached out and touched me again. Grandmother hadn't known; Uncle Pascal hadn't known. Did anyone know? You couldn't know what death was until you died, and then it was too late. Depression settled over me like a heavy fog. Death had struck too close to me again, and I wondered whether Flint would be next. I didn't want to die, but I didn't really want to live either. Life wasn't a precious gift to me. I was born by accident. I'd be here a short time and then gone. I remembered the snowflakes and how quickly they melted. Maybe I was melting now and didn't know it. The more I tried to figure it out, the more senseless it became and the deeper I sank into the black well of depression.

The early spring wind was howling outside, and I paced the floor. I wanted to break loose and run, but there are no hills to run to in the city. Besides, people would think I was crazy or in some sort of trouble. No, I couldn't run with the wind tonight but I could at least go for a walk. By the time I had walked a block, I was feeling a lot better. This was the first really warm spring evening we had had. There would soon be other warm evenings, but the first was special. I remembered how Grandmother used to go out on nights like this and put her ear to the ground. She would say she was listening for the first heartbeat of mother earth after she had slept the winter. When she was sure she had heard the earth's heartbeat she would say, "Mother earth is awake now. We can plant our garden soon."

The fresh air lifted me up out of the depression I had been living with. Without thinking much about where I was going I found myself only a block away from the church. I stopped on the street corner trying to decide whether to go on to the church and see Reverend McPherson or to turn back and go home. I stood there while the traffic light changed several times and finally decided to walk past the church. He probably wouldn't be there anyway. Even if he was, there would probably be some kind of service going on. I wasn't sure when the church services were or what kind they were, but I sure wasn't going to get involved in anything like that.

In a few minutes I was standing in front of the church. The building was dark except for the study. It was brightly lighted, and I could see Reverend McPherson sitting at his desk reading. He was alone.

I walked up the steps, went inside, and knocked on his door.

"Come in," he said. I heard him push his chair away from his desk. I opened the door part way. When he saw me, he stood up and smiled.

"Come in. I was hoping you would come and visit us."

"Are you busy?" I asked, still hanging onto the doorknob.

"No. Come in and talk awhile. How are you?" He sat back down and motioned to a chair for me.

I sat on the edge of the chair.

"My uncle killed himself," I said abruptly. I surprised myself because I hadn't meant to say that at all.

"I'm sorry to hear that. Is there anything I can do?" he asked.

"No." I sat there quietly for a moment.

Then I looked him straight in the eyes and asked, "What happens when we die?"

"A lot of things. It depends on what kind of life you led

here on earth and whether or not you knew Christ and what you did about it." He leaned forward in his chair.

"Who is Christ?" I asked. "You talked about God and about Jesus and now you have a new person named Christ. Do you have three Gods?"

He smiled. "There is God, the Father and Creator of all things, and His only Son, Jesus Christ, Our Lord, and there is the Holy Spirit."

"Yes, three Gods."

"No, they are called the holy Trinity, three in one."

"I don't understand."

"It's not easy to understand. It is something far beyond the touch of our small, human minds, but you don't have to understand something completely to believe in it. Anyway, that's not what I'd like to get into tonight. I want to answer your question about what happens when a person dies."

"I guess I already know. When you die, you die, and your body rots," I said. I could almost hear Grandmother's voice again. I wondered if my eyes had the same look of fear in them that hers had had.

"That would be terribly sad if that were true. Man is too precious to die the same, hopeless way a dog dies. You see, human beings have souls, and that makes the difference. Man can choose between right and wrong. He can choose to accept God or reject Him. He can choose heaven or hell."

"Those are only church words; they don't mean anything

to me. You can't say for a fact what happens to a person when he dies," I argued, feeling strangely stubborn.

"Yes, I can. God knew that man was afraid of death. He knew there would be questions in a man's heart, so He gave us answers. In fact, the very question you just asked me tonight was asked thousands of years ago by a man named Job. He cried out, 'If a man dies, shall he live again?'"

"Once a man dies, he can't live again. The Kickapoo prophet said that when he died, he would be raised up again, but he wasn't. He just stayed dead. Dead is dead," I said.

"But that's the miracle of it! Man not only lives again, but he can live forever! This life is short and full of trouble and heartache and pain. If the next life were like this one, no one would want to live forever. But the next life will be beautiful if you are a believer. There will be love and peace and no tears and no death. We will live in a beautiful place that God has made especially for us. I can't find words to describe the joy I feel in my heart when I think of what lies ahead for us!" His eyes sparkled.

"How do you know?"

"The Bible says so," he said and put his hand on his ragged, frayed Bible.

"The Bible doesn't mean anything to me. It is only a book."

He settled back into his chair. "Yes, I see the problem you are having. I always take for granted that people accept the Bible as the divine word of God. And I forget that there are many people who have never even seen a Bible." He looked at me. "Do you own a Bible?"

"No." I shook my head. "There's no reason for me to own a Bible. Do you own a war drum?"

He laughed, and so did I for the first time in a week.

"No, I don't own a war drum, but I do have a Bible I can give you. Then you'll be one up on me."

Before I could think of a reason for him not to give me one, he had gone to a shelf of his library and pulled out a Bible and written my name on it.

"Here, now this belongs to Crying Wind." He handed it to me.

"You shouldn't have put my name on it. Someone else might want it."

"I have other Bibles I can give other people. This one is special; it is just for you.

I reached out and took it. As soon as my fingers curled around the hard, black cover, I felt as if I had taken a step, made some sort of unspoken commitment. I didn't know to whom or to what, but I knew that when I accepted that Bible, things weren't going to be the same. It was too late to give it back to him; my name had been written on the inside cover. Like it or not, I now owned a Bible.

"But what about the medicine man? They have power to do things," I said.

"Yes, I'm sure they do. I believe the devil gives them power to do things so they can fool people into believing wrong things."

"But if Christians have power, and the devil gives other people power, how do you know who is right?"

"Because power from God always leads to good and power from the devil will always lead to destruction."

We talked about another hour. My mind seemed to be swirling with words and ideas that were new and strange to me. Some sort of mystery was unfolding, but I didn't understand any of it.

It was getting late, so I thanked him for his time and for the book he had given me.

"Don't be discouraged if you feel a little lost in what we talked about tonight. The wisest men in the world are confused about death and about the next life. It's probably the deepest subject you'll ever talk or think about. It takes time to understand it, but one of these days it will all fall into place for you, and you'll understand everything." He shook my hand. "Just remember that there is an answer to every question, and we can know for a certainty what lies beyond the grave."

I didn't answer as I opened the door.

"Don't stay away too long," he said.

"I don't think I'll be back. I don't believe what you say," I replied.

I expected him to be angry, but instead he only looked sad.

"If you change your mind you can always find me here," he said softly.

I turned my back on him and walked away. I wished he

hadn't given me that book, the one with *Holy Bible* written on it in gold letters.

As I walked home in the dark I kept saying to myself, *Stupid! I was stupid to go there tonight!* I felt depressed again, and an overwhelming loneliness swept over me. *What if he was right? What if there was another life after death?* When I got home, I shoved the Bible into a drawer. Tomorrow I would throw it away. I just wished he hadn't written my name on it.

I felt as if there were a raging fire hidden just beneath the surface of my skin. I wanted to smash things, to scream and yell. I wanted to kill my enemies and hold their scalps in my hands and scream to the skies that I had met my enemy and I was the victor! Oh, if only I could have lived a hundred years ago. Life would have been simple. If you hated someone, you killed him. You were not punished; you were praised because you had defeated your enemy. *Life made more sense then*, I thought. *Who was my enemy? Everybody*, I thought gloomily, and threw a pillow across the room.

I was on the warpath all the next week. I didn't speak to anyone unless I had to. At work I just tried to fade into the background as much as possible. I ate my lunch alone in the back of the dusty storeroom instead of joining the others in the lunchroom upstairs. As I walked to and from work, I kept my eyes on the ground and refused even to look at the sky or the trees or anything around me. I was angry, but I wasn't sure why.

On Friday afternoon as I was leaving work, I saw Flint waiting outside for me. He was leaning against the side of the building and didn't see me until I was beside him.

I was never so happy to see anyone in my life.

"Waiting for someone?" I asked. I could feel the depression and anger of the past week falling away from me like a blanket.

"Yeah," he said casually and straightened up. "I'm looking for a skinny, ugly, Kickapoo girl. Have you seen any around?"

"No, but if I see one I'll let you know." I laughed. "I'm glad to see you."

"I didn't have anything else to do," he said and started walking down the street.

I fell into step beside him. "What goes?"

"I heard about a sing out west of town tonight. I thought you might like to go with me if you didn't have any plans."

I tried to hold back my excitement. "Sounds good. I didn't have any plans." I never had any plans. I was sure Flint knew that and was just trying to make me feel good.

"I'll buy you some supper, and then we'll head out that way. Heard there is going to be a lot there. It's just for bloods," he said and climbed into his pickup.

By "bloods" he meant it was just for Indians, and it was closed to "no bloods" which meant white people. I was glad he didn't say anything about "mix-bloods," which is what I was. It was just a polite term for half-breed.

As we drove down the long stretch of highway, Flint kept increasing his speed until I knew he must be doing eighty miles an hour. He was talking and laughing. He seemed happier than I had seen him in a long time. Soon I could feel my spirits lifting too. I rolled down my window and let the fresh summer air blow against my face. I no longer felt tired; the wind was blowing new strength into my body.

The moon was full and the color of Navajo silver. It was almost as bright as day. I could see every fence post beside the road and every tree and house we passed.

I felt good. I was glad Flint had asked me to come with him. I let out a long sigh and leaned back in the seat. This was the way to be—free and with someone who was like you. I didn't need a new religion and a new way of life. This was where I belonged; with my own people on our way to a sing.

The faster Flint drove, the more miles he put between myself and my empty apartment and Reverend McPherson and his church. If Flint drove fast enough, I was sure I could leave everything behind, even the new God I had heard about.

Flint talked steadily, but I only heard part of what he was saying. I was caught up in the moonlight and the speed of the pickup and my own thoughts. My mind went back to the special ride I had had on Thunder Hooves. I felt a pang of loneliness and loss, knowing that some part of my life was over forever.

Flint slowed the truck down and turned onto a narrow dirt road. I sat up and looked around.

"It's only a few more miles," he said, and then he was quiet as he concentrated on the narrow, twisting road. He hit some ruts, and the wheels jerked hard. He slowed down a little more.

I could feel the mood of the evening slipping away. I tried to hang onto it. I looked over at Flint and saw that he wasn't smiling anymore.

I began wishing we had missed the turnoff. I wished we could have kept driving for hours and hours. I knew it was already too late to recapture the mood I had felt earlier, so I stopped trying and watched the road, which had turned into more of a trail than a road.

Flint slammed on the brakes. I was thrown forward but managed to put my hands against the dashboard and catch myself just before my head banged against the windshield.

"What's wrong?" I couldn't see any reason for him to stop.

"Up there, those rocks," he said and made a sharp left turn.

A pile of three rocks was visible by the headlights, one rock on top of another beside the road. No one would have noticed them. Even if someone had, he wouldn't have known the rocks were a signal to leave the road and cut across country if he hadn't known the silent language of the trail signs.

We had bumped across about a half mile of sagebrush and rocks, when we saw more than a dozen pickups and cars parked in a corral of scrub oak and giant tumbleweeds. The first people to arrive had made a rough, horseshoe-shaped corral, about four feet high and large enough to allow parking for about fifteen cars and trucks. In the old days, horses would have been kept there during the pow-wow. Tonight the corral's purpose was to conceal the cars and trucks from outsiders. No one was welcome here who wasn't invited.

Before dawn, after the ceremonies, everyone would leave quietly and quickly, a few at a time, fading away into the darkness. The fire would be carefully put out and the ashes buried. The corral would be taken down and the bushes and tumbleweeds scattered. By dawn there would be no trace that anyone had been here tonight. Unlike the white man who left empty cans and cigarette butts and candy wrappers behind, the Indians left nothing behind, often not even their footprints.

Flint shut off the motor. We got out of the truck and quietly shut the doors. Then he took the lead, and I followed him through the underbrush and up the steep hill until we reached the rim of the canyon.

Between us and the rim of the canyon were four dancers standing in a line beside the campfire. Beyond the dancers was only blackness that stretched from the Canyon of the Old Ones up into the starless sky.

I followed Flint and sat down beside him in the circle of Indians who were seated on the ground. Most of them were wrapped in blankets. I looked around for a familiar face, but they were all strangers to me. I could see by the different jewelry and blanket designs that three different tribes were represented. I was so absorbed in watching the others that I was startled when the shrill anguished cry of the dancers pierced the silence. I quickly turned my attention to the four dancers as they moved around the fire. Each step was measured and exact, just as the dance had been danced a thousand years ago on this same canyon rim by our ancestors. Their shrill cries imitating the coyote god were so successful that coyotes wailed in the distance.

Suddenly I shivered with chill bumps, and the back of my neck tingled. I inched closer to my uncle. He handed me his jacket. I pulled it tightly around my shoulders.

The dancers were moving faster. I felt as if my own heart were keeping rhythm with the drum. I had always thrilled at the sound of Indian drums, but tonight it sounded threatening and evil, as if it were stealing something from me. Most of the other Indians had joined in the chant. Their bodies were swaying in time to the drumbeat. It was as if we were all going into a trance.

Then I saw it beside the dancers! A thin white, almost transparent smoke. It was small at first, but it grew larger and larger until it was as tall as a man. It was spinning around like a dust devil. It had no shape or substance. I was frightened, but I couldn't take my eyes off of it. I sensed that it was evil and dangerous. I wanted to speak or move, but I felt numb. As the dance ended, the white whirlwind grew smaller and smaller and finally disappeared. When it was gone, I turned to Flint.

"What was that?" I whispered.

"What?" He leaned over to hear me better, but his eyes were still watching the fire.

He hadn't seen it or he wouldn't have had to ask what I was talking about.

"Never mind. It was nothing," I said and looked back at the glowing fire. I must have imagined it. There hadn't really been anything there or Flint would have seen it, too. But why did I feel so strange inside? I was glad I had Flint's jacket on so he couldn't see me shaking. I wished the dances would end. I wanted to go home. There was something not right here in the Canyon of the Old Ones!

I sat quietly through two more hours of dances. I wanted to leave, but I was afraid to complain because Flint might not ask me to go anywhere with him again. I tried to think about other things because I didn't want to see the white whirling thing again. I kept telling myself that maybe I was just tired, or maybe it had been a shadow, but I couldn't convince myself that I hadn't really seen it, so I avoided looking at the dancers or the fire or the rim of the canyon and kept my eyes on the toes of my moccasins and the ground around me. Countless times I caught myself thinking about Reverend McPherson and how it felt to be inside the church. I would ask him about that when I saw him next time; he would know what it was. Then I remembered that I had told him I wouldn't be back. I had made a bad mistake by ever talking to him or going to that church. Maybe tonight was a warning not ever to stray from the Old Way again. Yes, that must be it. I belonged here. These were my people; these were my gods they were singing about. But I didn't feel a part of things.

Flint sat motionless, completely lost in the movements of the dancers and the chants. He belonged here. He was part of this, but he didn't look happy. I glanced around the circle. No one was smiling; all the dark faces looked like carved stone. I guess an Indian doesn't have any reason to smile.

The last dance came to an end. There was nothing to signal that this was the end of the evening. The dancers simply walked off into the darkness, the drum stopped, people stood up and silently faded into the shadows.

I stood up and brushed the dust off myself.

"Come on, Flint," I said and tugged on his arm. "It's over. Let's get out of here."

He stood up and stretched. "No, I think I'll stick around," he said and nodded his head toward a clump of trees.

I turned to see what he meant. My heart sank. Hidden among the trees was a tipi. That tipi meant only one thing. There was going to be a peyote ceremony here tonight.

I hadn't seen it when we arrived. It must have been hastily erected sometime during the dances. Flint probably hadn't come here expecting a peyote ceremony or he wouldn't have asked me to come along. Now that he knew one would be held, he wanted to stay for it.

"Please, Flint," I pleaded and held onto his arm more tightly.

"I'm going to stay for the peyote ceremony," he said in a voice that wouldn't allow for any arguments from me. He pulled his arm free. We stood there in a deadlock, neither of us speaking.

I looked down at the ground and dug my heels into the soft earth.

He reached into the pocket of his Levis and took out the keys to the pickup.

"Look, kid. You take these and go wait in the truck. I won't be long."

I took the keys and started toward the truck. My throat hurt and my eyes burned. I turned around hoping he had changed his mind and I would see him following me, but he was already at the entrance of the tipi.

I walked back to the truck and climbed inside. It would serve him right if I just drove off and left him here.

I stuck the key in the ignition and slid behind the steering wheel. I sat there wanting to leave but unable to make myself drive off and leave him. He had known when he handed me the keys that I would be sitting here waiting for him when he came back.

I buried my head in my hands and cried. I cried because I was angry with Flint and the world. I cried because what had started out as a special evening had turned sour and because I was alone again. No matter where I went or what I did, I always ended up alone.

I laid down in the seat of the pickup and cried until I heard the drum begin to beat inside the tipi. I sat up and wiped my tears off on my sleeve and watched the tipi. Smoke was coming out the top—the ceremony was beginning. Even though I was never allowed to go to a peyote ceremony, I knew exactly what was going on inside the tipi just as well as if I were sitting inside next to Flint.

Peyote is a cactus that grows in the southwest. When it is eaten it is supposed to increase the senses. It dulls the consciousness and takes a person to a half-dream world where he can see visions and speak to the spirits. To the Indian, peyote represents the mother earth. According to legend, a long time ago a woman was alone and dying. She heard a voice that told her to eat a plant that was growing nearby. When she had eaten it, she was strong enough to find her way back to her tribe. She taught them how to have peyote ceremonies.

Most Indians call the peyote ritual "half-moon way," so that non-Indians won't know what they are talking about.

I saw the flap pulled shut over the entrance of the tipi. Everything had to be exact for the ceremony. The entrance was facing east. Four Indian men conducted the ceremony. The roadman is the leader, then the drummer chief, the cedar chief and the fire chief. To begin, the roadman stands in the center of the tipi, faces west, and lies down on the ground. He does this to rid himself of his pride and humble himself on mother earth's breast. He stretches his arms outward as far as he can and uses his fingertips to draw a half circle in the dirt to form the half moon. Then he draws a line along the top of the moon called the peyote road, or the road of life. The roadman sits opposite the entrance and the drummer chief sits at his right. The drum is a special one for peyote rites. It is made by filling a metal drum one-fourth full of water and stretching a wet deerskin over it. To the left of the roadman sits the cedar chief. He sprinkles cedar on the sacred fire during the night-long ceremony. The fire chief sits at the entrance of the tipi and cares for the fire and keeps outsiders from entering.

The sacred fire is built by placing pieces of wood in the shape of a V with the open top of the V facing east and the closed end facing the west. The other firewood is also laid in a special way. Sage is placed throughout the tipi. Flint and the other Indians would be sitting on piles of sage.

After everyone is settled, the fire chief sprinkles cedar on the fire and is given the single eagle feather that gives him authority over anyone entering or leaving the tipi.

Everyone removes his clothing except the four men in charge. They rub their arms, chest and body with sage to cleanse themselves. Sage has always been a healing plant. It is also a spirit plant that can drive away evil spirits.

When the peyote buttons are brought out and passed around, all the men take four each. Then the roadman takes "father peyote" from his beaded ritual box, holds it over the smoke from the sacred fire, and puts it in front of himself. The peyote button used for the father is a large, perfectly formed button. Sometimes an altar is made from buckskin or a beaded cloth and this peyote button is placed on it.

Other ceremonial objects are placed around father peyote, a whistle made from an eagle bone, a branch of sage, a gourd rattle with a specially beaded handle (peyote beadwork is different from other beadwork), an arrow, and the roadman's personal peyote feathers. He uses eagle feathers if he can get them. If he can't, he uses trimmed turkey feathers.

Then the roadman picks up the sage branch and an eagle feather in his left hand and the gourd rattle in his right hand and begins to chant a peyote song. The drum chief begins to play the drum. Each chant is sung four times. Four is a sacred number to Indians; it represents the four directions and the four seasons. Then the roadman passes his gourd and feathers and sage around the circle and some of the men take turns singing. If they don't want to sing, they pass it to the next man.

I wondered if Flint ever sang. I doubted it. I didn't think he wanted to participate in anything as much as he wanted to escape from everything.

At midnight more cedar was added to the fire, the midnight water chant is sung four times, and a pail of water is brought inside the tipi. Then Flint and the others eat the peyote buttons and drink the water. They keep at it until dawn.

I could guess almost exactly what Flint what was doing, but there was no way I could tell what kind of visions he was having. They might be good or bad. They might be about death and evil spirits, or the visions might be good medicine that would give him strength and help.

I knew he had used peyote many times before. He didn't talk much about it, but it seemed that the more anyone used it, the more he needed to use it.

The steady beat of the drum and boredom of sitting alone in the truck finally put me to sleep. I woke several times during the night. I could see the moon had moved far across the sky, and it would soon be morning. Each time I woke, I still heard the drum beating.

Just as the eastern sky was faintly lighted by the false dawn, I woke again and stretched my stiff, aching body. I was tired, hungry and thirsty. My neck hurt from sleeping in a crooked position.

I saw the morning water woman approach the tipi with a pail of water. She is usually a woman who is related to the roadman. She is invited inside to smoke some cornhusk and pray, then she gives everyone a drink of water from her pail and leaves, taking water with her. Then she stands outside the tipi and passes in the four sacred food; water, corn, nuts, and meat. These represent the life the Indians had before the appearance of the white man. Everyone inside the tipi eats some of the food. After all this, the sacred peyote objects are put away, the ritual box is closed, and the ceremony is over.

I watched the tipi entrance for Flint to come out. Two other men came out before he did. One of them laid down near a small tree and held onto it with both hands as if he thought the earth was shaking and he was going to fall off. The other man took only a few steps and became ill and vomited. As Flint stumbled toward the truck, I knew he wouldn't be able to drive. I opened the door on my side and slid over to the driver's side. I hoped he wouldn't get sick or pass out. He had to try three times before he could climb into the truck. His eyes were glassy and red, his lips looked swollen and parched, but he was smiling and singing to himself. He hardly knew I was there. I started the motor and hoped I would be able to find my way back to the highway. There was no point in asking Flint for any help with directions in the condition he was in. I got lost twice and had to backtrack, but I finally reached the highway and headed for home.

During the drive the night before, time and miles had passed swiftly. Today in the harsh daylight, I was tired and the miles seemed to drag. A couple of times I tried to talk to Flint, but he couldn't really hear me or understand anything I said. He sang peyote songs and talked about wild horses and flying on a huge bird, just bits and pieces of medicine dreams he had had.

I wanted to get home before the effects of the peyote wore off. I had seen people go through this before. For a few hours afterwards they were happy and peaceful. When the peyote wore off, they went down, down into a deep dark hole of black depression and stayed there for hours or even days.

Flint would fight the depression by getting drunk. That was

followed by a hangover, and then depression, and then peyote. And the circle of death would start over again. We were both caught in the circle. *There is no way out of the circle*, I thought. My head felt dizzy, and before I knew it, I had driven off the road. My tires hit the loose gravel along side the pavement. I gave the wheel a sudden twist and jerked the pickup back onto the highway and slowed down. My hands were sweating. I'd nearly had an accident. We could have turned over and been killed. *You die.* I thought. *That's how you get out of the circle.* I glanced over at Flint, but he wasn't even awake enough to know what had happened.

I sat up straighter in the seat and opened my window to get some cold air in my face. Had I just been tired and had that near wreck just been an accident, or had it been something else?

CHAPTER EIGHT

I felt like I was walking into a steel trap as I walked through the doors of the department store to start another day at work. I hung up my coat and tried to shut off my mind and not think of anything except the countless customers who would trail in and out of the store all day.

There was new stock to be put away. As I began taking the china out of the crate, I looked at the price list. One teacup was twelve dollars, one plate was eighteen dollars, and a complete set of this china came to hundreds of dollars. I thought of the cracked, chipped, mismatched dishes Grandmother and I had used. "Oh well," I said to myself," An eighteen dollar plate doesn't hold any more fry bread and beans than a ten cent plate from the trading post." But these people didn't eat fry bread and beans. They ate strange, expensive foods. They even ate fish! Grandmother had always told me that our people would never eat fish because fish contained the souls of dead women who had been evil during their lifetime.

I'd just finished putting up the last of the china on the shelves when Betty walked over and handed me a piece of paper and a pencil. "Would you like to sign this?" she asked.

"What is it?"

"Mrs. Montgomery, who works in the dry goods department is retiring this week. Everyone in the store is signing this paper. We'll put it in a nice card for her. She's worked in this store in the dry goods department fifty years. She started when she was only fifteen years old." Betty shook her head. "Can you imagine that? Fifty years in this place. Boy, I sure won't be working here fifty years. As soon as I find the right man, I'm getting married and getting out of here." She waited for me to sign the paper and then she left. I heard her say again, "Fifty years!"

I thought about Mrs. Montgomery. She was my age when she started working here and she had stayed, stayed all her life. Every day she saw the same things and the same people, everything always the same—

A customer walked over and picked up one of the teacups I had just put on display.

"May I help you?" I asked.

She looked up and her face went into a frown. "If you don't mind, I would rather have someone else wait on me."

I felt as if a bucket of ice water had been thrown on me. I turned and went after Betty. I tried to sound casual, but I knew the stiffness of my smile and the tremor in my voice gave me away as I said, "Betty, would you mind waiting on that lady over there?"

"Sure, but I thought you were taking care of her," she said, glancing at the lady.

"She asked for someone else," I shrugged my shoulders. "Maybe her great-great-grandfather was scalped by Indians." I turned my back toward the customer and finished marking prices on merchandise while Betty made the sale. The customer left, and Betty hurried back to my side.

"Don't let her bother you. She's the kind of person who doesn't like anybody."

The morning dragged by, and it was finally time for lunch. I didn't feel like I could face another lunch from my brown paper bag. I felt empty, but I wasn't hungry. I stood around a few minutes trying to decide what to do with the next hour if I didn't eat lunch. Maybe some fresh air might clear my head. I hadn't had much sleep last night. I was probably just tired, and a walk would perk me up and give me an appetite.

The second I opened the door, I knew I had made the right decision. The fresh air and sunshine made me feel good after being in the old, stuffy building. I began to walk away from the store, and with each step I felt better. I walked for blocks and blocks, not caring where I was going as long as I could get away from the store for awhile. Suddenly I came upon a small park. It was only a single square block, but it was like finding a wilderness in the middle of the concrete and steel city. I sat down on the soft grass and looked at the trees and flowers. I wished I was back on the reservation where I could walk on the earth and not the hard pavement and where coyotes were heard crying at night instead of traffic on the streets.

I hadn't been sitting there very long when a man in a uniform came up to me and said, "I'm sorry, miss. You aren't allowed to sit on the grass."

I stood up.

He smiled. "What I meant was, people aren't allowed on the grass. You're supposed to stay on the little pathways." He pointed to several winding cement paths.

I was embarrassed, my face felt hot. I didn't speak or look at him as I left the park. Always, always they want you to walk on the hard cement. Don't touch the grass. Don't feel the softness of mother earth beneath your feet.

Nearly an hour had passed as I came within sight of the store again. My lunch hour would be over in a few more minutes, but as I came to the store, my feet kept going. I didn't stop at the door; I just kept walking. I wouldn't go back there. I couldn't go back there. No more time spent in the steel trap. I wouldn't spend fifty years there! I remembered my coat still being inside, but I wouldn't go back even to get that. "Goodbye, coat," I said and kept walking in the direction of home.

Without a job, time passed slowly. I was bored and restless and longed for something to do. When Sunday come, I was so desperate I decided to go to church. What harm could it do?

My knees shook as I climbed up the steps and entered the church. I stood just inside the doorway, unsure whether to go inside or turn and run back down the steps. My decision was made for me as some other people came through the door behind me, and I had to move ahead to get out of their way.

A few more uncertain steps found me inside the main part of the church. Light streamed in through the stained-glass windows with pictures on them. One window showed a man with some sheep. Another window showed men sitting at a table eating together.

My knees were shaking so badly now that I had to sit down. I didn't know where to go. Perhaps special people had special seats on these long benches with the high backs. Perhaps there was no place for me to sit at all. The other people walked around me and found places to sit toward the front of the room, so I followed them and slipped into the third row and clung to the edge of the seat.

Soft music seemed to come from nowhere, and I heard voices singing songs I didn't understand.

My heart was pounding so hard I was sure other people could hear it. I wondered if all the people were looking at me and wondering what I was doing in their church. I sat frozen and terrified. Any moment I was sure someone would see me and ask me to leave. Perhaps they would all stand up and point their fingers at me and shout at me and chase me away! I wished I hadn't come here. I didn't belong; I wasn't part of these people. I kept my eyes on my hands knotted tightly in my lap. I was afraid I was going to do something wrong and call attention to myself.

After a while a man handed a flat plate to me with money on it. I looked at him and then back at the plate. My stomach had a sick feeling in it as I held the plate. What was I supposed to do with this?

The man smiled and leaned down and whispered, "Would you please pass that down the row for me?"

How stupid I felt! I handed it to the person next to me so suddenly she almost dropped it. I could feel my neck getting hot, and I felt like running away. I had to get out of this building and back where I belonged! I gathered my courage and stood up to leave. Suddenly everyone in the entire church stood up, too!

I was so startled I didn't move. Were all these people going to stop me from leaving?

Then Reverend McPherson appeared at the front of the church.

I let out a sigh of relief. He wouldn't let these people hurt me. He would let me get away!

He said a few words, and all the people bowed their heads as if they were ashamed. Then he said a few more words and everyone sat down. Without thinking, I sat back down, too.

I kept my eyes on Reverend McPherson. He was talking again about this man named Jesus. I wondered what Grandmother would say if she knew I was in a white man's prayer house. I didn't think she would like it.

Soon the end of church had come, and everyone was leaving the building. A few people stopped and shook my hand and told me their names and asked me mine, but I didn't tell them. Didn't these foolish people know that if an Indian says his own name out loud three times in the same hour his ears will wither up? *White people have so much to learn*, I thought.

Reverend McPherson was at the door shaking hands with people as they left. I timidly put out my hand and he smiled as he held it firmly in his.

"We were all so happy to have you here today. Can you stay and eat lunch with us?"

I hadn't expected this and didn't know what to say. The red-haired woman standing beside him stepped forward and slipped her arm around my shoulder.

"I'm Mrs. McPherson. You call me Audrey. We would be so happy if you would eat with us." Then, almost as if she had read my mind, she added, "After you've eaten you can stay as long as you like or leave whenever you want."

"All right." I agreed and followed them next door to their home.

It only took her a few minutes to have everything ready and on the table.

"We always thank God for our food," Reverend McPherson said. He and Audrey both bowed their heads, closed their eyes, and talked to their God for a minute.

Then Audrey reached over and took the lid off a covered dish.

I had to swallow hard to keep from choking. It was fish! A fish with eyes that looked right at me and made my skin crawl.

"How much would you like?" Reverend McPherson asked.

"I'm not hungry," I said weakly, unable to take my eyes off the eyes of the fish.

"Is anything wrong?" Audrey asked.

I started to repeat that I just wasn't hungry, but at the same second my stomach growled so loudly I knew they couldn't help but hear it.

"I—I can't eat that—fish. She is looking at me!" I said.

"She?" Audrey asked and leaned over for a closer look at the fish.

I felt miserable; this just wasn't my day. "My people believe that the spirits of evil women turn into fish. If we eat fish those spirits can live again in our bodies."

Without waiting a second more, Audrey covered the fish. I was glad her eyes were no longer looking at me. Audrey picked up the fish and carried it into the kitchen.

"I guess I will go now," I said and started to get up.

"We haven't eaten, yet, and you must be hungry. Are their any legends about ham sandwiches?" Reverend McPherson asked with a twinkle in his eye.

"No, there are no spirits in ham sandwiches," I laughed.

The strangeness between us was melting away. We talked about many things. I could never remember laughing so much or talking so much.

The afternoon was gone in a flash.

"Why don't you stay for dinner and go to the evening service at church?" Audrey suggested.

"Do you have church at night, too?" I asked. "Isn't that too often to talk to your God? Maybe he doesn't like to be bothered so much with people. Maybe He would rather sleep."

"Our God never sleeps," she said.

"Then He must get awfully tired. Even the wind sleeps sometimes," I said.

"Our God never gets tired. He is always eager to talk to us and hear our prayers."

I thought about that for a moment. "Is night church like morning church?"

"No, not exactly. There are not so many people there and it is more informal."

"Does that plate get passed around?" I said.

"No. That's only in the morning service." Audrey laughed.

"What are you supposed to do with that plate anyway?" I asked.

"It's passed around so people who want to can put money in it to help support God's church and His work."

"I don't have any money," I said. "I didn't put any in the plate this morning. How much do I owe you for going to church?"

"Going to church is free. No one ever has to pay or give money if they don't want to. God is happy when people come, even if—especially if—they don't have any money."

"We'd like to have you stay," Audrey said.

I hesitated, and Reverend McPherson said, "Please."

"OK, I'll stay," I said. After all it hadn't been too bad this morning once I'd gotten used to it.

It was a quiet service. Fewer people came, and the plate wasn't passed around. I stayed for awhile, and then I decided I was tired of hearing about Jesus again. It seemed to me like they could find something else to talk about, so I got up and left. Audrey had a puzzled look on her face, but she smiled and lifted her hand slightly to wave good-bye.

For the next few days I did nothing, and then I realized I had only two dollars left. I would have to get a job now or go hungry. I knew I didn't want to work as a clerk again and have customers refuse to let me wait on them because my skin was a different color. No more of that! Maybe I could find a job where I wouldn't have to be with people, something I could do alone.

I checked the want ads in the newspaper and saw an ad for a night cleaning woman for an office building. It sounded perfect. I didn't even finish looking at the rest of the ads. I tore the address out of the newspaper and left.

I had expected a big, tall building with a dozen offices, but it was a small building with only six offices and an entrance lounge. After I told the receptionist I was there about the job, a middle-aged man in a black suit motioned me into his office.

"You look awfully young," he said first. "We were really looking for someone older."

"I'm eighteen," I said. I had told that lie so many times that I almost believed it myself. "I can work very hard. Maybe I can work faster because I'm young," I said hopefully.

He laughed. "It isn't a glamorous job. The salary is small and the work is dirty. You would come in after nine at night and dust, vacuum, and empty wastebaskets, and do whatever cleanup was necessary. You would leave whenever you were finished. One night you might work two hours, and another night you might have to work five hours. It's not really a job for a young girl."

"It's just what I want. I would work hard," I said seriously. I was anxious to have a job where I would be hidden from the public.

He studied me for a moment and then stood up. "All right. The job is yours. Come in at six tonight, and the lady will show you what to do. Starting tomorrow night, you'll be working alone."

Finally something was going my way! I was really glad the job had been so easy to get. I had dreaded going from one place to another, only to be turned down. This job would be perfect. I would be alone. My hours would depend on how fast I worked, and the work would be fairly easy. It seemed too good to be true.

I stopped by the church one night to say hello to the McPhersons and tell them about my job.

"That's a rough neighborhood. Be very careful," Reverend McPherson warned.

"We wish you had a job in the daytime," Audrey scolded. "You are too young to be out late at night!"

"I'm not too young," I said. "I'm fifteen."

"Fifteen!" Audrey groaned. "I was worried enough about you when I thought you were eighteen. Now that I know you are only fifteen I feel like I should take you under my wings and protect you from the world. You are too young to be on your own. You are only a baby!"

"Well, I feel like I'm a hundred years old," I said jokingly. I could tell by the look on her face that she didn't think it was funny.

"It's a sad thing to miss your childhood and grow up too soon."

I had been working my new job three weeks. Each night I left my place about eight and walked to the office building. I arrived there about nine. Most nights I finished my work by midnight and was home again by one.

As I was on my way to work one night, I suddenly became aware of footsteps behind me. There weren't many people out walking this late at night, especially since all the stores and offices were closed. I don't know what alarmed me. Maybe it was an age-old instinct for danger, but whatever it was, I quickened my steps slightly. When I heard the footsteps behind me become faster, I was sure I was being followed. There was no one else on the street, not even a passing car. It was still another block to the office building, and there was an alley between where I was now and the office building. I knew that if anything was going to happen, it would be when I walked past that alley. I tried to tell myself that it was probably just some harmless little old lady walking home from visiting a friend, and if I turned around to look I would see how foolish I was being. But I couldn't make myself turn around and look. I was afraid that what I would see behind me would frighten me so badly I would be paralyzed and helpless, so I just kept walking.

The entrance to the alley was just ahead of me. It looked like a big, black hole. The footsteps had started to gain on me! I waited until I was almost to the alley entrance, and then I broke into a dead run. I ran as fast as I could. I felt as if my feet were flying above the pavement. At any moment I expected to be grabbed around my throat, but I didn't look back. I just kept running. As I ran I took the key out of my pocket and held it in my hand, ready to unlock the door as soon as I reached it. I leaped up two steps at a time, jammed the key into the lock, gave it a sharp twist and kicked the door open, and yanked the key out. I shoved the door shut behind me, slammed the bolt down, ran down the dark hallway into the first office, and shut that door behind me, too.

With my heart pounding and my legs shaking, I stood in the darkness. I listened to hear if anyone was trying to get the door open. There was nothing but silence.

Well, I thought, *it was probably just a little old lady after all, and she's wondering what kind of a fool young girl runs down the street at night.* But I didn't believe it, not for a minute. I stood there a few minutes longer, unable to move. I knew I should forget about it and start working, but I was afraid to turn on a light. If anyone was out there, a light would tell him which office I was in. Maybe he would try to break in, or maybe he would wait until I was through and on my way home—at midnight.

I was scared. I couldn't remember ever being so scared. I wanted help, and I only knew one person to call. I reached for the telephone and dialed the operator and asked her to get Reverend McPherson.

Please let him be home! Please let him be home! I repeated over and over to myself as his phone rang.

When he picked it up and I heard his voice, I nearly collapsed from relief. "This is Crying Wind," I said in a shaky voice. "Please, please come and get me. I'm afraid—I'm sure someone is following me. I'm in the office building now, but I'm afraid he is outside waiting for me."

"I'll be right there. I'll honk the horn when I drive up. Stay where you are!"

I heard him hang up but I didn't want to let go of the phone, so I still held it to my ear.

"Please hurry!" I whispered into the phone even though no one was there to hear.

I tried to imagine how long it would take him. I tried to

picture in my mind where he was. *By now he would be turning onto 30th Avenue. Now he would be at 29th Avenue, unless he had to stop for a red light. No, please let all the lights be green! Now 28th Avenue. Maybe I should call the police.* Maybe the man who followed me was gone now, or maybe he had somehow gotten into the building. Maybe he was going from room to room looking for me—my neck ached from the tension. I wondered if there was anything in the room I could use for a weapon. I was sick with fear. The only sound was my breathing and then I found that I was unconsciously holding my breath so there was no sound at all. Then I thought I heard something. Was it a footstep? I strained to hear it again. It was a horn! It was about a block away! There again, closer! I let out the breath I had been holding. Now the horn honked out front. It took me about two seconds to get out of the building and into the car beside Reverend McPherson.

"Are you all right?" he asked as he pulled quickly away from the curb.

"Yes." I was shaking all over. "Yes, I'm all right. How did you get here so fast?"

"I guess I ran a couple of red lights and drove over the speed limit, but I think God will overlook it this time."

"Did you see anyone? I was sure someone was after me."

"I didn't see anyone, but that doesn't mean much. If there were someone after you, he wouldn't let anyone else see him. I think we should drive to the police station and make a report. If there is someone on the prowl tonight, it would be a good idea for the police to know about it. They could send a squad car out here to look around."

I laughed nervously. "But what if it wasn't anything? After all, nothing really happened."

"That's OK. The police don't mind, and there's no reason to take any chances. Better safe than sorry. We have a built in warning system that tells us when we're in danger, even if we can't see anything. I think you did the right thing to call me."

He drove to the police station, and we made a report. The police said they would take a look around that area.

"Would you like to stay with Audrey and me tonight? Maybe you'd feel safer," he offered. "You know you are welcome."

"No, I'll be fine. Thanks anyway."

"I wish you could get a daytime job—"

I didn't let him finish. "Don't worry. I'm going to call in the morning and quit! I'll never go through this again! I don't think I've ever been so terrified in my life. You know, I've always thought I could take care of myself until tonight. Tonight I felt helpless and so scared." I was still shaking.

"Then you've learned something important tonight—everybody needs somebody sometimes, and we all need God all the time. Mankind was never meant to face anything alone. Maybe God allowed you to be frightened tonight to teach you not to try to depend only on your own resources. Audrey and I have been so worried about you working nights.

She'll be glad to know you won't be working there anymore. It wasn't really the right job for you anyway. You need a job that has some kind of future for you. What would you really like to do?

I shrugged my tired shoulders. "I don't know. I've never thought about it. As long as I can eat I guess I don't care." Just as he drove up in front of my apartment I asked, "Were you and Audrey really worried about me?"

"Of course we were," he said. He waited until I was safely inside of my apartment, and then he drove away.

I kept telling myself I wasn't afraid anymore, but I checked several times to make sure the door was locked. I left all the lights on all night.

I didn't understand the city or its dangers. At home the night hadn't been dangerous. When the moon was full and the wind was high, I would go out for a ride on Thunder Hooves. We would gallop up and down the dark valley and across the shadowy hills. I hadn't been afraid of the darkness. It hadn't bothered me that I couldn't see, because Thunder Hooves saw for me. Only the coyotes were out that late at night, and they wouldn't harm us. As I remembered the midnight rides and Thunder Hooves, a pain stabbed through my heart because I would never again go on one of those rides with her.

Here in the city I stayed behind locked doors at night because it wasn't safe for a lone girl to be out late after dark. Yet the city was supposed to be civilized. The country was the wilderness, but in the wilderness with the wild animals I had been safe! It didn't make sense.

I didn't sleep much that night as I thought about two things Reverend McPherson had said. I wondered why he thought I needed a job with a future. After all, it was plain I was nobody going nowhere. I had been lonely and unhappy all my life. I was that way now, and I knew the future held more of the same. Then I wondered why he and Audrey would worry about me. No one had ever worried about me before. Sometimes he said things that puzzled me, but one thing was sure, tonight I had asked him for help and he had come running.

It was back to the want ads again. One ad asked for someone to make pottery, and my hopes soared. If there was one thing an Indian could do it was make pottery!

I hurried to the address. As soon as I walked into the office I said, "I've come to get the job making pottery."

"Fine. Fine. Have you ever worked with pottery before?" asked the lady as she handed me the forms to fill out.

"Well, my grandmother knew how, and when I was a small girl she showed me how to make pottery, but it was a long time ago. I've forgotten a lot of what she taught me, but maybe it would come back."

"That's OK. We'll train you to fit in. Follow me," she said and turned down a long hall. I walked closely behind her. She stopped at two large, heavy doors with little glass windows in them.

I looked beyond her and through the windows and caught a glimpse of huge machines and pipes going from one to another. As soon as she opened the door, the most deafening noise I ever heard in my life made me instinctively put my hands over my ears to shut out the sound.

She looked at me and laughed. "Haven't you ever worked in a factory before?"

I could hardly hear her above the noise, but I shook my head.

"It's all right. You will get used to the noise, and you won't notice it at all."

I felt as if there were a thousand drums beating in my head. How could anyone get used to that?

She pointed at a long row of switches and levers. "This is what you will operate. You will be told when to punch the switches or move the levers. You must not do anything unless that man in the apron over there tells you. It all depends on times and temperatures and the thickness of the clay for the pottery. He will tell you all you need to know. Just do exactly as he tells you." She waved at the man in the apron, and he came over to explain my job to me.

I stood there pushing, pulling and punching. The noise seemed to grind its way into the center of my mind. I tried to shut it out by thinking of other things. I remembered how Grandmother showed me how Indians make pottery in the old days. She would take a little gourd, fill it with water, pour it on the ground, and get down on her hands and knees and watch the water soak in the ground. Then she would add a little more water and say, "Now you must be gentle, for you are scratching skin from the breast of mother earth." She would dig into the mud with her fingers and take the wet earth in her hands. She formed it and worked it and re-formed it until it became a small, uneven bowl. When she was satisfied with it, she would put it on a tree stump to dry in the sun. The hot summer sun would bake it hard as stone. It was a simple, natural way to make pottery, using earth and water and sun. It had been quiet, not noisy like this place. I wished I could once more be back scraping the mud into my hands with Grandmother.

Far down the line a machine was stamping a design on some of the finished pottery. Stamp. Stamp. Stamp. Each one alike. I remembered seeing Indian women painting their pottery by hand, using yucca brushes that had only three or four bristles. It took them hours and sometimes even days to finish painting one bowl. They were proud of their work. There was no pride in this.

I closed my eyes and curled my fingers, aching to feel mud from that day so long ago. Instead my fingers curled around a cold, steel lever. I opened my eyes and looked around. This was not the way to make pottery. This was not the way for an Indian to live.

I pushed the heavy doors open and walked down that

long hall and outside the building. It was quiet outside. My head stopped pounding with the noise of machines. I reached down beside me and scraped a small piece of dirt up between my fingers. Mother earth was still here. It was the same mother earth as back on the reservation. Why did everything seem so different here?

I walked home. This job had lasted two hours. What was wrong with me? Why couldn't I just go to work and put in the time and go home like other people? Why did I remember the past? Why did I think about mother earth and the sun and the seasons?

As I was walking home, a car honked behind me and pulled over to the curb. I turned around and looked. Audrey and Reverend McPherson were motioning for me to come over to the car.

"We saw you walking and wanted to know if you had any luck job hunting today," Audrey said.

"Yes, I found a job. I worked two hours," I told her as I leaned against the door of the car.

"Two hours? What happened?"

"I quit."

There was a mixture of amusement and disappointment on her face.

"What now?" she asked.

"I don't know," I answered.

"Dear child!" she said. "You can't spend the rest of your

life changing jobs every few weeks. You need a purpose, a plan, some kind of goal for yourself. Isn't there anything you want in life?"

"No, I guess not." I stood up and walked away from the car.

"Can we give you a ride home? You look tired."

"No, I think I'll walk."

"Is there anything we can do to help you?" she asked.

I didn't answer this time. I just shook my head and walked away.

The wind had come up. It made me feel cool and relaxed. After I got home, I opened all the windows to let the wind blow fresh air into the apartment. I got out some beads and began working on a necklace, looking up sometimes to watch the curtains blowing back and forth. I worked until dark. My eyes were so tired I went to bed and watched the stars out of my window. The stars seemed smaller here, farther away. It was not like back home, where you could almost touch the stars, where they were just a little higher than the mountain peaks.

The wind had become very strong just before dawn, and the curtains had blown against the lamp beside my bed and knocked it over. It woke me up. I got up and started to close the window and go back to bed, but the sight of the black, shadowy tree limbs being tossed back and forth by the wind caught my attention. I stood at the window, watching the wind play with the trees.

When I did crawl back into bed, I noticed my cheeks were wet from tears. I hadn't even known I was crying.

"Oh, if only I could go back home—if only I could go back home—" I whispered to myself, over and over.

CHAPTER NINE

As the wind blew louder, I could hear his voice calling me, calling me back home, back to the reservation, back home to the hills and valleys I knew and longed for.

I grabbed a pillow, yanked off the pillowcase that was still damp from my tears, and started filling it with things I needed. I put in all the food I thought I could carry, and on impulse, I put in a kitchen knife in case I needed protection. Living in the city had made me wary. I wrote a note to Flint and stuck it on the door as I left. I told him that I had gone back home and that he should bring the rest of my things and some food.

I walked as fast as I could for the first hour, anxious to arrive home by dark and afraid that if I stopped to rest I might lose my nerve and turn back.

During the second hour, I walked slower. By the fifth hour my feet were dragging, and the pillowcase felt like it had a ton of rocks in it. I'd gotten so overheated that I'd taken off my coat and stuffed it inside the pillowcase. Now I was cooler, but my pack was heavier. My hands cramped from carrying it so many hours.

It had taken eight hours to walk home, but now I was within a few minutes of being there. For the past hour I had been walking through the forest I knew and loved. Each tree was a familiar old friend; each rock a marker along the trail. No, I could never get lost here; not like in the city with all of its look-alike streets and tall buildings that blocked out the sun.

I reached the crest of the hill and looked down toward the valley to see our house.

It was gone! The house was gone! There was nothing left but a few scattered logs, charred black from a fire.

Forgetting how tired I was, I ran down the hill with my bag bouncing against my back.

I stopped where the front door should have been and looked at the twisted rubble in front of me. There was nothing left. It couldn't have taken long for this old shack to burn to the ground.

I kicked through the ashes. It had been burned down months ago, probably right after Cloud and I left the valley.

I knew it wasn't an accident. Someone, either one of my uncles or one of Grandmother's Navajo friends had set a torch to the house, thinking that since she had died inside, her spirit could be trapped in the house and unable to find its way to the next life.

I slumped down in the ashes. I had come home, but there was no longer a home.

It was getting dark. I didn't want to spend the night out in the open. If I hurried, I could make it to Cloud's cabin before nightfall. At least I would have some shelter. I forced myself to my feet and threw my bag back over my shoulder, staggering under the weight.

I avoided looking in the direction of the barn and kept my eyes focused on the path in front of my feet.

"I shouldn't have come back," I told myself. "It was stupid. There is nothing here anymore. Everything is gone; the people, the animals, the house. All are gone now. Only I am here, wandering around like a lost spirit haunting the valley.

I reached Cloud's cabin just as the sun sank out of sight.

I took a candle and some matches out of my bag. I lit the candle. It didn't give much light, but it was better than this awful darkness.

I sat down on the floor, opened a can of beans, and leaned against the wall while I ate them.

The trader hadn't left anything behind when he bought Cloud out. There was nothing but an empty room. Not one stick of wood or scrap of paper remained.

I was exhausted now and couldn't keep my eyes open any longer. I reached into my bag one more time and pulled out the knife. I rolled my coat into a pillow, blew out the candle, and lay down on the floor, still holding the knife tightly in my hand and wishing I hadn't tried to come home.

I woke up stiff and cold in the early morning. There was a faint hint of frost on the ground, and patches of fog were hanging low in the valley waiting to disappear as the sun climbed higher.

I ate a can of cold chili for breakfast and I put my things back into my bag. After a last look around, I headed back to town.

As I walked, I tried not to think about the pile of ashes that used to be my home. I tried not to think about anything except putting one foot in front of the other.

My feet were aching when I walked up to the door of my apartment, eight hours later. My note was still on the door. Flint hadn't been there. As I pulled the note off the door and wrinkled it up in my hand, I was glad Flint wouldn't know about my plans to go back home. I didn't want him to know what a fool I'd made out of myself.

What was I going to do now? I couldn't go back home; it was gone. I didn't belong in the city.

Why had the wind called me back to the reservation when he must have known there was nothing left to go back to? Was he playing a joke on me? Yes, that must be it. The old Indian gods often played cruel jokes on people, and he had played a joke on me. He must be angry at me about something. I was doing something wrong and he had punished me. What had I done, what? Then it came to me. The wind didn't like me going to church. That had to be it. I would have to stop going to church or he would do something terrible to me. This had only been a warning.

I took my things out of the pillowcase. It was filthy from the dust along the road where I had dragged it behind me the last mile, too weary to carry it any longer.

I sank into a steaming, hot bath and let it soak the aches out of my tired body. I was thankful for the luxury of a hot bath. City life had spoiled me. I would have missed the hot running water and the electricity and the refrigerator and stove. City life was making me soft and lazy.

The next few days were empty and long. When it was dark, I went to bed. I said, "At last, another day is over." I dreaded the next dawn. I hated to wake up in the mornings. I pulled a chair up in front of the window and sat in it for hours, watching people walking past or cars going down the street or sometimes I just stared into space not seeing anything at all.

I don't remember when I first noticed it, but I caught myself watching a flashing sign about two blocks away. "LIQUOR." "LIQUOR." It flashed many times a minute. Pretty soon I was watching it more than I was watching anything else.

Then I remembered that Flint had left a half-full bottle of whiskey in the kitchen cupboard the last time he was here. The more I thought about it, the more I was tempted to drink it. I didn't really like to drink. The liquor tasted bad and made my head ache, but Flint drank a lot of it and so did my other uncles, so there must be something to it. Maybe I just hadn't drunk enough. Maybe it took a lot to make you feel good.

I left my chair by the window, went to the cupboard, and took out the bottle of whiskey. I held it in my hands and looked at the pale brown color. When I opened it, the fumes made my eyes water. I almost put the cap back on, but decided I might as well go ahead and drink it. After all, I had nothing to lose. Maybe it would pass the time and make me feel better.

I poured a small amount into a glass. It took me several minutes to finally choke it down. It tasted bad and burned my throat, but I kept at it. The next drink went down faster, and I was feeling warm and sleepy. *I must be on the right track now,* I thought. I poured another drink.

The room started to reel and the light hurt my eyes, so I crawled into my bed and turned off the lamp. In seconds I was asleep. I didn't wake up until late the next day.

I felt awful when I woke up and decided to drink a little more whiskey to make my head stop spinning. I passed the day by taking a drink, taking a nap, taking another drink.

Somewhere between the drinks and the naps, depression started creeping up on me. Questions echoed in my head, *Why keep trying? Why not give up?*

I don't remember leaving the apartment, but I found myself standing on the edge of the curb of the street. In the foggy haze of my mind, I kept thinking *Pick a fast car and step in front of it and it will all be over.* Then I saw a car coming much faster than the others. I closed my eyes tightly, took a big breath, and stepped off the curb!

There was the screeching of brakes and the squealing of tires as I waited for the car to hit me.

It was taking too long! I should have already been run down. I opened my eyes in time to see the car swerve around me. As it passed, the driver shook his fist at me and yelled, "Stupid, drunken Indian—" his car motor drowned the rest of his words out as he sped down the street.

I was suddenly very sober and standing in the middle of a very busy street. Horns seemed to be honking all around me as I made a mad dash for the curb.

With very weak legs I walked back to the apartment. I would have to find some other way to kill myself. I finished the rest of the whiskey and threw myself across the bed. I tried to think of a quick, easy way to die. I didn't have a gun or any sleeping pills. I had heard of people drinking themselves to death, but that could take years. I didn't want to be around that long. I was in a hurry to get it over with.

All the next day I tried to think of a way to end my life. I thought of dozens of ways to die, but I came to the conclusion that there is no easy way to die. Dying is hard.

I also came to the conclusion I was too poor to die. I was too broke to buy a gun or sleeping pills. I lived on the ground floor, so I couldn't jump out a window. I didn't own a piece of string, let alone a rope, so I couldn't hang myself. Indians have very little body hair, so I didn't even own razor blades. The stove in the apartment was electric, so I couldn't use gas to kill myself. The only way I could afford to die was to jump in front of a car, and I had lost my nerve. I couldn't go through that again! I was too poor to die. I would have to get a job and save some money to buy something to use to kill myself! It was so funny I had to laugh about it. Living was hard, but dying was harder.

CHAPTER TEN

T he next day I visited Reverend McPherson.

"Do you have a job?" he asked.

"No." I didn't tell him that I wasn't even looking.

"I was just thinking I could use some help here in the office. It would only be for a couple of days and I couldn't pay you much," he said.

"What kind of work?" I asked.

"Well, for one thing, all the books in the church library need to be listed. Some need repairs and new labels. I need some missionary letters sorted and filed. Things like that."

I thought for a moment and then he said, "Thanks anyway, but I don't think he would like it."

"Who wouldn't like it? Your uncle?"

"The wind. The wind wouldn't like me working in another god's house."

"There is only one God," he said.

"But if the wind isn't god, then who is the wind? Or what is the wind?" he asked.

"That's hard to say. I guess scientists could give you some sort of answer about high and low pressures and cold fronts and such things, but I know that's not what you're looking for." Then his eyes lit up, and he smiled. "I don't mean to be frivolous, but I just remembered a poem I knew as a child. It was written by Robert Louis Stevenson. He apparently had his own questions about who or what the wind was—let's see if I can remember it, it's been many years since I was a child—"

I saw you toss the kites on high
And blow the birds about the sky;
And all around I heard you pass,
Like ladies' skirts across the grass—
O wind, a-blowing all day long,
O wind, that sings so loud a song!

I saw the different things you did,
But always you yourself you hid.
I felt you push, I heard you call,
I could not see yourself at all—
O wind, a-blowing all day long,
O wind, that sings so loud a song!

O you that are so strong and cold,
O blower, are you young or old?
Are you a beast of field and tree,
Or just a stronger child than me?
O wind, a-blowing all day long,
O wind, that sings so loud a song!

"What was that last part again?" I asked as soon as he had finished.

He repeated it slowly so it could sink in.

"Was this man an Indian?" I asked.

"No, he was an Englishman. He wrote the poem over a hundred years ago."

"He should have been an Indian. He understood the wind." I repeated the lines I could remember, "I felt you push, I heard you call . . . O you that are strong and cold, O blower, are you young or old? Are you a beast of field and tree, or just a stronger child than me?" I nodded. "I like that. Do you know any more poems about the wind?"

I twisted my fingers together and chewed on my lip. "What is your God really like?"

"He is everything to everyone. The Bible says, 'As a father pities his children so the Lord pities those who fear Him.'"

"My father abandoned me," I said. "I don't like to think about God being like a father."

"It also says, 'As one whom his mother comforts, so I will comfort you,'" he quoted.

"My mother ran off and left me years ago. I've never heard from her since," I reminded him.

He is a friend who sticks closer than a brother," he said.

"I've never had any friends, and I don't have any brothers or sisters," I challenged him.

He shrugged and smiled, "Well, it also says, 'Husbands love

your wives as Christ loved His Church,' but since you are not married, that won't mean much to you, will it?"

"No. I guess none of that applies to me," I said.

"Maybe none of these verses, but somewhere in the Bible there is one verse that will be special to you, and when you hear it, it will unlock your heart and your mind to the spiritual truths of the Bible. Then it will all fall into place for you. Once you hear that verse your life will be changed. You will never be the same again. We will keep searching until we find that special verse that was written there for Crying Wind." His hand fell gently on his Bible.

"I don't believe there is a verse in there for me."

"There is a verse in here for everyone. The Bible speaks to every heart."

"It doesn't mention the wind," I said. Certainly I was right this time.

"It mentions the wind many times."

I leaned forward. "What does it say?"

"I can't remember all of them, but I could look up every time it's mentioned in the Bible and make a list. Then you look up the verses when you have time."

"All right. I guess it wouldn't hurt to know what your book had to say about the wind." I shrugged casually, but I was interested. When he made out the list, I folded it carefully and put it into my pocket.

Later that night, after I had gone to bed, I propped myself

up with some pillows and began hunting through the Bible for every mention of the wind. *After all,* I thought, *it isn't as if I were studying about this God. I was just trying to learn more about the wind.*

It took a long time to find all the verses, because I didn't know the order of the books of the Bible, but I finally had all the verses looked up and written down.

The first mention of the wind was in Genesis 8:1, "And God remembered Noah, and every living thing, and all the cattle that was with him in the ark: and God made a wind to pass over the earth, and the waters assuaged."

In Exodus 15:10 it read, "Thou didst blow with thy wind."

Job spoke of the wind twice: "My life is wind" (Job 7:7), and "the words of thy mouth be like a strong wind" (Job 8:2).

Over and over I read the verses about the wind, and there were a few that seemed to reach out to me.

"Who hath ascended up into heaven, or descended? Who hath gathered the wind in his fists?" (Proverbs 30:4).

"Lo, he that formeth the mountains and createth the wind . . . The LORD, the God of Hosts, is His name" (Amos 4:13).

It spoke of the Lord sending out a great wind into the sea, but when I read Matthew 8:26 where it said Jesus "arose and rebuked the winds," I knew I'd found something!

Why had the wind allowed this other God to rebuke him and to order him to be still? You didn't give orders to someone unless he was under you and you didn't follow orders unless the person giving them was stronger or wiser or had authority and power. I was becoming curious about this new God. Was it possible that He really could have created the wind?

It was beginning to seem that the only time I was even halfway happy was when I was at the church talking to Reverend McPherson or Audrey. I told myself it was only boredom and loneliness that drove me back there time after time. After all, they were the only people I knew except Flint, and he seldom had time for me. I was beginning to show up on the doorstep of the church more and more often. I liked sitting in Reverend McPherson's comfortable office with its shelves of books and the cluttered desk and flowering plants beside the windows.

"How are you today?" he greeted me.

"I don't know," I said truthfully.

He smiled knowingly. "You would be surprised how many people feel exactly the same way you do. They know something is bothering them, but they don't know what it is. Maybe if you talked about how you feel—maybe I could help?"

I sat in silence for several minutes. "It's no use, I can't find the right words. When my heart is full, my head is empty. When I am alone I can think of many things to say. All the way here as I walk along, I practice what I will say when I see you. Then when I come through the door, my words stay outside and the wind blows them away." I swallowed hard. "I am just wasting your time."

"No, you aren't wasting my time. Sometimes it's good to be with someone even if you don't say a single word. Sometimes you can learn more about a person by his silences than by his words." He paused. "Do you think it would help to write your thoughts and questions down? You could carry a little notebook, and when you thought of a question or had an idea you wanted to discuss, you could write it down. If you felt like sharing it with me, I could read the notebook when you came back."

He began rummaging through the clutter of his desk. "Ah! Here it is! I'll even get you started with this little notebook. I bought it the other day. I hadn't had time to use it yet so it's new, for some new ideas from Crying Wind." He smiled and leaned across the desk and handed it to me. He reached into his shirt pocket and pulled out a pen. "Now you have the notebook, and you have the pen. I know you have the ideas. All you have to do is get the three of them together."

I reached out eagerly and took the gifts he offered and smiled as I fanned through the notebook and saw the clean, fresh pages waiting to be filled.

"I think I'll go now." I stood up. "I want to go home and write something."

"I'll be looking forward to reading it." He walked me to the door.

"Maybe I'll see you sometimes," I said.

"I hope so."

I was reluctant to leave. "Maybe Friday," I added.

"Anytime you feel like coming, you are welcome."

We shook hands, and I walked down the church steps. When I reached the bottom step, I turned and looked back. He was standing just inside the door, watching me.

I waved with my hand that held the notebook and pen and hurried down the street. When I was almost half-way home, I was so eager to get home, I ran the rest of the way. I was completely out of breath by the time I reached my apartment. I yanked off my coat and sat down at the table and opened the notebook. I took the pen in my hand and wrote "Crying Wind" in bold letters across the front page.

I paused only a second, and then it seemed as if the pen was magic. Words and ideas poured from me. I wrote several pages before I stopped to read what I had written. Writing was so simple, such an easy thing to do. You could write anything that was in your heart or on your mind. Why did speaking have to always be such a hard, painful thing to do?

I wrote some questions that I wanted to ask Reverend McPherson about this man Jesus and His Father, God. I remembered that Reverend McPherson had asked me who I thought the wind was, so I began to describe the wind on the paper. Then I wrote about the Spirit Horse. There seemed to be thousands of unused words in my heart, waiting to be set free. I couldn't write fast enough to keep up with my thoughts.

I wrote until the last page was filled. I put the pen down and looked at the clock. It was two o'clock in the morning. I noticed how stiff my fingers were from holding the pen all these hours, and I stretched my muscles that were tired from bending over the notebook so long. I felt good. Thoughts and feelings that had been buried in silence for years had finally fought their way to the surface. I smiled as I fell asleep, and I knew that I couldn't wait until Friday to see Reverend McPherson. I would see him tomorrow.

As soon as I saw him, I handed him the poems I had written. I waited anxiously while he read them. It was important to me that he like them.

THE WIND
by Crying Wind

The Summer wind is warm, passionate, and alive. She caresses the flowers until they tremble with emotion. The trees whisper the mysteries of the forest, and the wild roses blush at the secrets told. A swing moves gently to and fro as if the ghost of a small girl of ages past still laughs and plays beneath the same tree.

Time has slipped away now. The wind is older, wiser, perhaps a little crisp and angry because it cannot fight its fate.

It carelessly tosses around the dried leaves of autumn in the same way a jilted lover might toss aside his dreams. The brown grass scratches against the broken stems of flowers whose faded blossoms have long since been blown away.

Now Winter is here. The wind is old and bitter and as cold and lonely as a widow. The leaves are covered with snow, and the moon is brittle and bright as it gazes at its beauty in ice on the pond.

The swing is now still, weighted down by snow that holds it prisoner in silent bondage.

It blows again, but the spirit and strength are gone. The wrinkled old woman screams around the houses, begging to be let inside so she might warm her chilled body by the fire. She rattles the windows and bangs at the doors, but none will answer her, and she is left alone in the night. In anger she tugs at the swing and releases it from its slavery.

Then the old woman wind moves slowly down the valley and disappears into the night. She goes without a sound; silently, mournfully. The trees make no move to wave goodbye. They only stand, watching, perhaps a little sad, perhaps with no feeling at all.

ALONE

(Written for Pascal)

It's too late, but now we'll mourn;
Some will speak of him with scorn.
Perhaps if once someone had said,
"I love you," he would not be dead.
Time is marked by days, months, or years,

It's marked by emptiness and tears.
Was he really so very bad?
Or was he only lonely and sad?
He lived alone and died that way, too.
No one cared, not even a few.
No one will know the reason why,
He shut out life and preferred to die.
People passed him by on the street,
He wasn't important, no need to speak.
Killed himself, that's what they said.
If some had loved him,
He wouldn't be dead.

SPIRIT HORSE
by Crying Wind

There will be no sleep for me tonight,
The wind is crying and the moon is bright.
It's only then that you come to me,
When the moon is silver and the wind is free.

Wild-eyed and prancing, you stand on the lawn,
To carry me away and return before dawn.
The raging wind is your fiery breath,
Your hooves make thunder as we race with death!
You carry me to the edge of the sea,

The fierce, pounding waves crash around me.
I feel the salt spray against my face,
Then you gallop away at your deadly pace!
Up through the foothills and valley we go,
And stand on top of mountains with the whole world below.
Then across the desert through the dust and sands,
Onward we roam to strange, distant lands.

Your hooves keep pounding, and I feel your power,
You quicken your pace at the midnight hour.
With your neck outstretched your mane flowing white,
We gallop on through the stormy night!

My heart grows heavy as you turn around,
And we head back over familiar ground.
I know that soon there will be an Eastern light,
And our ride will be over until tomorrow night.

Spirit Horse, come back to me. Don't leave me here alone.
I won't fear death if I ride with you, into the great unknown.
Wild-eyed and prancing, you stand on the lawn,
To carry me away and return before dawn.

He finished reading them and he smiled when he looked
up at me.

"They are good. They are really good and I like them. In

fact, "Spirit Horse" is beautiful. I could tell there was a lot of you in it. I think we are finally finding out the secret of Crying Wind." He handed the notebook back to me. "You should try to get these published."

"No one would want to read anything Crying Wind wrote," I said.

He leaned back in his chair. His eyes met mine and held them.

"Who is Crying Wind?" he asked. I could tell by his voice he was expecting an answer.

"I'm the accidental offspring of two people who hated each other. I never saw my father's face because he abandoned my mother before I was born, and she hated him for it. My mother was young and didn't want to be tied down with a baby she hadn't wanted in the first place, so she left me with my grandmother on the reservation. It didn't matter anyway. I didn't need parents. Grandmother took care of me, and my uncles were around. We did all right." My jaws seemed to tighten as I spoke. "I'm a worthless half-breed; two people trying to live in one body." I added bitterly, "That's who Crying Wind is—nobody."

His fingertips touched lightly together, and he spoke softly. "Then I know more about Crying Wind than you do. You paint pictures—that makes you an artist. You write beautiful poetry—that makes you a poet. You are a lovely young girl with a keen mind who could have an unlimited future. Your parents did not create you—God created you! The same God who created the heavens and the earth created you. You are not what your parents made you. You can be whatever you want to be. You have a special worth; you are unique. There is not another person in the world exactly like Crying Wind. God made you and you are valuable to Him. You are worth more to Him than a star, because He has millions of stars, but He has only one of you! You are worth more to Him than the mountains or the rivers."

It was more than I could understand. "Worth more than a star shining in the sky at night?" I asked.

"Yes!" he said. "Worth more than the very life of His own Son. In the Bible it says, 'For God so loved Crying Wind that He allowed His only Son to die in her place so that she could have eternal life!"

"It doesn't say that," I argued, knowing my name was not in the Bible.

"It could say that because you are so valuable to God, that if you were the only person in the whole world, Jesus would still go to die on the cross for you. Never say you are nobody, because you are somebody special. You are special to God and to Audrey and me. I have the feeling that someday thousands of people are going to hear from Crying Wind. I don't know God's plan for your life, but I do know this; He has a special plan for you. Maybe He'll use your artwork or your poetry or some other talent that is buried now but will come to light later. God has His hand on you, and when you stop fighting Him and let Him guide you, great things will happen!" He paused. "Would you like me to pray for you?"

"No," I answered quickly. "I don't want to believe in your god."

He smiled. "I think you believe in Him already, or you wouldn't be so afraid that He would answer my prayers that you would become a Christian."

I studied him closely. He really believed every word he was saying. He thought I was worth something. Was I really worth more to God than a star? On the way home that night, I watched the stars and thought, *maybe I really am worth something after all!*

CHAPTER ELEVEN

Flint was waiting for me when I got home.

"Where have you been?" he asked.

Without thinking I answered, "I went down to a church and talked to the minister—" I stopped. I knew I had been wrong to tell him.

"You've been in a church!" he exploded.

"Yes." I admitted but added quickly, "But I didn't go to a real church meeting. I was only talking with the minister." It was too late to undo the damage.

"You must be loco! Why did you do that? You are an Indian. You don't need any Long Robes!"

Flint was using the Indian term for missionaries. The first missionaries to our people had been Catholic priests who had worn long robes. Ever since then, any white religious leader was called Long Robe.

Flint's voice was hard. His eyes were full of hate.

"The Kickapoo have never accepted the white man's religion. More Kickapoo have hung onto the old ways than any other tribe. We are proud that the white man has never taught his religion to us or taught our children in our schools. We've always burned down his schools, and in the old days, we burned down his churches, too. We killed the Long Robes who came into our land! Why were you talking to a Long Robe?"

"I don't know," I said weakly. "I just don't know anyone else here. We just talked about poems and things."

I'd never seen Flint so angry before. His jaw was set so tight that the muscles in his neck stood out and his hands were clenched into fists.

"Now you listen and hear my words!" he said between tightly clenched teeth, "I never wanted to take care of you in the first place, but Cloud dumped you in my lap. I am stuck with you. I promised to keep an eye on you because you are family. Up until now you haven't been much trouble, but I'm warning you—no niece of mine is going to get mixed up with those snake-in-the-grass white people or that crazy religion of theirs! Don't you ever go back there again, or I'll skin you alive!" With those words hanging in the air, he stomped out and slammed the door behind him.

At first I decided to obey Flint. After all, he was my uncle. I would stay away from church. After a few days passed I realized how much I missed my visits with the McPhersons. Up until now I thought I could take it or leave it, but without Reverend McPherson's friendship and Audrey's warmth, there was a big empty hole in my life. I missed church and wanted to return, but I was afraid to go against Flint.

Late in the afternoon the phone rang, and I jumped at the loud noise. I had never had a phone call before.

"Hello?"

"Is this Crying Wind?"

"Yes."

"This is Audrey. We've missed you dear. Are you all right?"

"Yes."

"We were hoping you might come to the church tonight. There is a special service for Christmas. We really would love to have you with us."

"OK," I said and hung up. After I hung up, I wondered if she had finished talking, or if I just cut her off. I would never get used to speaking into a machine and talking to voices without faces. You should see a person when you speak to him, not talk into a machine.

If the church had seemed beautiful to me before, now it was overwhelming. Candles seemed to be burning everywhere. Pine boughs and poinsettias decorated the altar and the area around the altar. The altar itself had a manger scene.

I walked up to the altar to get a closer look. Snow fell off my coat and dropped on the carpet, leaving a little trail behind me.

On the altar was a small stable with donkeys and cattle and sheep. In one corner was a man and a young woman who were bending over a newborn baby laying in a manger. The flickering candles made them look alive. I had heard the story of the

Nativity before, but it had never seemed like anything except a church legend. Now, as I stood here looking at these tiny figures, I suddenly knew they represented real people. Mary and Joseph had been real people, and if that was true, then the baby Jesus had really been born. The wise men and the shepherds had believed it and had come to see the Christ Child. It wasn't just a pretty story any longer. It was true!

I slowly reached out my hand. I wanted to touch the baby in the manger, but just as my fingers were about to feel it, I heard the door open and people coming in. I went back to the benches and sat down. A moment later a woman sat down beside me. She leaned over and whispered, "We are so happy to have you here tonight. My name is Sally."

"Sally?" I repeated. White people had strange names. They were only sounds instead of words. It was easy to remember a name like Song Bird or Gray Fox, but a name like Sally gave no pictures to the mind.

She smiled, "Do you care if I sit with you? I don't like to sit alone. It is so much nicer to sit with a friend."

When she said the word *friend*, our eyes met, and I knew she meant me. She smiled again, and I knew now that I would never forget her name, Sally.

The service was starting. Reverend McPherson stepped behind his pulpit, opened his Bible, and read the story of the birth of Christ. The choir sang songs more beautiful than anything I had ever heard; "O Holy Night," "What Child is This," and others.

I stole glances at some of the people as they sang. It was plain from their faces that they believed every word they sang. At the end of the singing, Sally closed the hymnbook and said, "I love Christmas carols. I wish we used them more than once a year."

"But why do you use your best songs only once a year?" I asked. " I would sing these songs all year. They sound good."

"Yes, they do sound good, don't they?" she agreed.

The service was over and everyone left for home too quickly. I still felt a warm peace from the service as I walked home.

Fresh snow was falling and looked like sparkling little stars. My footprints were the only ones in sight. I felt as if I were the only person who lived in this clean, white world of snow.

As I turned toward home, I saw that there were fresh tire tracks leading up to my apartment. The snow had been cleaned off my doorstep, and there was something on it.

It was a large cardboard box with my name written on it.

I unlocked my door, flipped on the light, and hauled the box inside. It was heavy and hard to move.

I shut the door, took off my coat, dropped to my knees beside the box, and carefully opened the lid.

Inside the box were a dozen cans of soup, vegetables, and fruit, and a small canned ham. There were also two packages wrapped in bright red paper. I picked up the largest package and tore the paper off. It was the most beautiful red sweater I had ever seen. I touched it to my cheek. How could anything feel so soft? I put it on and buttoned it; it fit perfectly. I reached for the next package and opened it. It was a book about Christian Indians. As I opened the cover, an envelope fell out and landed in my lap. I put the book down and opened the envelope. It was a Christmas card; a beautiful card with the manger scene on it. Inside was ten dollars, and the card was signed, "Merry Christmas from your friends at church."

I held the card in trembling fingers. All this? All this for me? No, it couldn't be. It was a mistake. I checked the box again. That was my name on it, but why? Why would the people at church want to give me anything for Christmas? I was a stranger to them—but the card had been signed "friends." Were they really my friends? Why would they do it? I had nothing anyone could want.

I sat on the floor, still wearing my new red sweater, and took each can of food out of the box and looked at it, knowing how good the food would taste. I looked at the book again and put the ten dollars back inside the cover.

I propped the Christmas card up against the lamp beside my bed. The manger scene, Mary, Joseph, and Baby Jesus, was just like on the altar at church.

I carefully folded my sweater and put it away, touching it one last time before I closed the drawer. Then I put the canned goods away, stacking them on the shelf in neat little rows. So much, and all for me!

Early the next morning there was a knock on my door. It was Flint.

"Hi," he said. "I just thought I'd drop by to see how you are doing."

"I'm so happy to see you! What have you been doing? I haven't seen you for a while. Will you stay and have lunch with me?

He ignored my questions, but I put some food in the oven to cook. He wouldn't pass up a hot meal. He was silent for a while, and then he said, "I quit my job. Never liked it much anyway, so I decided to quit."

"What will you do now?" I suddenly found myself sounding like Reverend McPherson did when I told him I had quit my job.

"Oh, I don't know. I'll find something. One job is as good as the next. I can always get a job wrangling horses on the Circle L Ranch. It's only ten miles from here." He paced the floor, stopped, and tapped the cardboard box with his toe.

"What's the box for?"

"Some people gave me a box of things for Christmas," I said. I wanted to tell him who it was from and how wonderful it had made me feel, but I knew I didn't dare. I was glad he dropped the subject.

As we ate, we talked about people we knew and about our family. I asked him if he had heard from Cloud. He said he hadn't and didn't expect ever to hear from him again. That made me feel sad because I missed Cloud. I still hoped he would come back someday.

After he had finished eating, he leaned back in his chair and patted his stomach. According to Indian custom, he belched loudly to show his appreciation.

"That was mighty good Cry. You're not a bad cook. Too bad you can't get a husband to cook for, but you're too skinny to be worth much."

"I'm worth more than a star," I said.

"What are you talking about?" he asked.

"Oh, nothing. Can you spend the day with me?" I asked.

"No, I have to go now. Thanks for the grub." He stepped out the door, and the wind blew snow inside.

"Please come back soon Flint. Don't stay away so long this time."

"Sure. I'll see you sometimes," he said and headed for his truck.

I waved good-bye, knowing "see you" sometimes could mean a couple of days, a couple of weeks, or even several months. I wished he would spend the day with me. It would have been nice to have someone to talk to.

I sank into a soft chair and reached for the book from the church. Soon I was deep in the story.

A few nights later I walked to the church to thank Reverend McPherson for the Christmas gifts. We only talked a few minutes when he said, "Well, it's nearly time for the service to start. I'd better get the lights turned on in the sanctuary. You would be more than welcome to join us."

"What are you going to do?" I asked.

"Tonight is a healing service. We pray for those who are ill, hurt, or in trouble."

"I'm not sick. I don't need healing," I said as I put on my coat.

"I think there is a little child in you who needs healing from many hurts in the past. I think that little child was hurt so many times by so many people that you have locked her away behind a stone wall so she wouldn't get hurt anymore. Don't you want to let her out?"

I didn't answer.

He went on quickly. "There will only be a handful of people here tonight. They are all very nice people, good Christians. They would like to help you if they could. You could just sit quietly in the back if you wanted. You wouldn't have to do anything or say anything."

I almost said yes. I wanted to stay, but for some reason that I didn't understand, I just shook my head. I could see he was disappointed. After I got outside and stood on the front steps of the church a few minutes, I almost talked myself into going back inside, but then I heard singing in the sanctuary. The service had already started. I had waited too long to make up my mind. I walked home feeling like I had missed out on something.

CHAPTER TWELVE

I thought about it all week and decided that next Wednesday night I would go to church. I would stay and sit in the back and listen to what the people said and watch what they did. If I sat in the back, I could always leave anytime I wanted.

When Wednesday night finally came around, I was just getting ready to leave for the church when Flint drove up. It was the first time I hadn't wanted to see him. I knew if I invited him inside I wouldn't get to church, so I met him on the steps and shut the door behind me.

"Hi. You leaving?" he asked as he climbed out of his pickup.

"Yes, I didn't know you were coming tonight, and I already have plans."

"Date?" he asked.

"No." I couldn't tell him I was going to church.

"Can I drive you someplace?" he offered.

"No. I want to walk. Thanks anyway. Maybe you could come over tomorrow night and eat with me. I'll make some fry bread for you." I knew how he loved fry bread. I was hoping he would start thinking about tomorrow evening and forget about tonight.

"OK." He got back into his truck. "Sure I can't drop you off someplace?"

I shook my head, and he left. I was glad to see him turn down the street and go the opposite direction of the church.

I hurried along, not paying any attention to anything around me. If I had been watching I would have noticed a truck following about a block behind me.

It wasn't until I cut across the parking lot next to the church that I heard someone driving behind me.

My heart sank when I turned and saw Flint. He had followed me to see where I was going.

"Hi," I said. I wished he didn't look so angry.

"Is this the big secret?" he nodded toward the church. "This is why you aren't home half the time. You've been coming to this place."

"But it's a good place, Flint!" I argued.

"How can it be a good place when it turns you against your family and against your own people and your own gods?" he said sharply.

"I'm not turning against anyone. I'm the same person I've always been."

"No, you're not! You're different, and I don't like the change. The rest of the family isn't going to like it either! Whatever lies they've been teaching you in there, you had better forget them and remember who you are! That religion is for the white man; let him keep it. You stay where you belong and stop trying to be someone you aren't."

"Why are you so angry? What difference does it make if I come here? I'm not a believer, I just come because the people are nice and I like to hear the stories and the music. It's better than sitting at home all the time."

"You can come with me if you're lonely."

"You never go anyplace except bars and peyote ceremonies," I said. I regretted it as soon as I saw the look in his eyes.

"Peyote is the father god of your own people!" He was angrier than I had ever seen him. "These people are poisoning your mind. Now get in the truck and come with me. Don't you ever come back here again!"

He reached out and grabbed my arm and started pulling me toward his truck. I yanked free and started toward the church.

"You come here!" he shouted after me, but I kept walking. I heard a door on the truck open and thought he was leaving, but before I had taken three more steps he was beside me.

"I'm warning you, Crying Wind, if you don't come with me now you'll be sorry!" He shook his leather horsewhip in my face. I'd seen him use it on horses before, but I knew he would never use it on me. It was just a threat.

"Leave me alone," I said and started to turn away. Flint cracked the whip. It came down hard across my left shoulder and my arm. I staggered backward under the blow. When I saw him raising the whip again I turned my back and hunched my shoulders and waited for the next stinging blow. The whip sliced across my back. I felt a chill go through my body like ice was being rubbed across my skin. After a couple more blows, the whip didn't hurt anymore. The shock of it made my body numb. I felt as if I were somewhere outside my body, and Flint was beating someone else. I don't know how many more times he hit me. Finally he stopped.

I waited for another blow. When there wasn't one, I straightened up and faced him.

Flint stood there with his arms hanging limp at his sides. The whip looked as if it were about to fall out of his half-open hand. He shook his head a few times and stepped backwards.

"Don't go there anymore," he said in a hoarse voice, but there was no power in his threat. He seemed like a shell standing there. This man wasn't the uncle I had known. This man in front of me looked thin and tired. His eyes looked like the eyes of a hunted animal who was too tired to run anymore and just waited for death.

I hadn't uttered a sound. My throat was too dry to speak.

Flint turned and walked away. In a few seconds I heard the motor of his truck as he drove away.

I walked around the corner of the church and climbed up the steps. The numbness had gone, and my back felt like it was on fire. Every move I made sent fresh flames of pain across my shoulders. It took all my strength to pull open the heavy door and ease inside. The lights seemed too bright and the floor seemed to be moving. Reverend McPherson was coming toward me. My legs turned to water, and I sank to the floor. The floor felt cool against my face. I closed my eyes and let the spinning darkness catch me.

"I think she is waking up." A voice from far away spoke quietly.

I tried to open my eyes.

A cool hand touched my forehead. "How do you feel?" asked the voice.

I finally got my eyes open long enough to see Audrey standing over me.

I was lying, on my stomach, on a soft bed. I started to move. The fire started burning my back again, so I laid still.

"Your back is hurt pretty bad. I put some medicine on it and some bandages. You probably should see a doctor," she said. I could feel her gentle fingers rubbing something cool across my back.

"No." My voice was weak. "No doctor."

"What happened? We can help you. No matter what it is, we can help." She finished wiping my back and took the bloody pieces of cotton and dropped them into the waste-basket. "If you are up to it, my husband wants to talk to you."

"I'm all right," I said. She helped me sit up on the bed. She went to the closet and took out a blouse and helped me slip into it.

"This will be too big for you, but yours is—is torn," she said, and her voice cracked. After she helped me put on the fresh blouse, she picked up my torn, bloody one and dropped it into the wastebasket on her way out of the room.

I sat on the edge of the bed and held onto the bedpost to keep from shaking.

There was a knock on the door and I heard Reverend McPherson ask, "May I come in?"

"Yes."

"My wife is making some hot tea for you. She'll bring it in a minute. How are you feeling?"

I started to shrug my shoulders and pain shot across my back and the look on my face showed exactly how I felt.

"Can you tell me what happened?"

"My uncle—" I took a deep breath, "My uncle and I got into a fight—he won." I would have smiled but I couldn't manage it.

"I don't understand," he said.

"My uncle has been warning me not to come here. Tonight he was waiting outside the church. He tried to make me leave with him. I wouldn't go, so he beat me."

"Do you mean to say that your own uncle beat you for coming here?"

I nodded.

"I don't believe it! While I was sitting inside the church praying for tonight's service, you were being beaten less than a hundred feet from my door! Things like this just can't happen. Not in America. Not in this day and age! He can't do that to you! We'll call the police and have him arrested!"

"I can't do that," I said.

"Of course you can! No one can treat you like that and get away with it!"

"He's my uncle; I can't have him arrested. If I did that— well, it's just a family feud. Things like this happen all the time back on the reservation—"

"You're not on the reservation now," he argued. "You deserve protection. You have a right to go to church." He acted like he wanted to say more but was too angry to find the words.

"It doesn't matter. It didn't really hurt that much," I said lamely, knowing it had hurt more than anything I had ever known. Maybe it wasn't the sting of the whip that hurt as much as knowing Flint had held the whip.

He took a deep breath. "I've never been so angry."

Just then Audrey came with a cup of hot tea. The two of them sat in silence while I drank it. When I was finished, I handed her the cup.

"I'd better go now," I said.

"No," they both said together. Then Audrey said, "We can't let you leave in your condition. You're hurt, and you shouldn't be alone. You'll stay here with us until you're better. Besides, I don't think it is safe for you to return to your apartment tonight. What if your uncle showed up?"

"Don't worry about me," I said.

"We have to worry about you because we love you," Audrey said.

Her answer took my breath away. Never in my life had I heard those words spoken to me. "We love you," she had said.

She went to her dresser and pulled out a nightgown. "You'll stay with us," she said firmly. "In the morning I can go to your apartment and get some of your things. You can stay as long as you like, and we won't let anything happen to you."

I didn't argue. It was possible that Flint might be back home waiting for me, and I really did want to stay here where I was safe. Safe—such a nice word.

Reverend McPherson left. Audrey helped me get ready for bed and tucked me into a fluffy, warm blanket.

"Good-night, dear," she said. She leaned over and kissed my forehead.

Something inside me crumbled, and I burst into tears and threw my arms around her.

She sat on the bed and held me tenderly while I hung onto her for dear life. I had been used to rough treatment all my life. Tonight, for the first time in my life, two people had said, "We love you." Someone had tucked me gently into bed like a small child and kissed me goodnight. Someone had worried about me and was angry because I had been hurt. Two people had taken me into their home and gently wiped the blood off my back and bandaged my wounds. Now they wanted me to stay here so they could protect me. It was true, they did love me! At last, someone finally did love me! I sobbed and hung onto her while she brushed back my hair and gently rocked me back and forth and spoke soothing words as if she were talking to a small child.

"It will be all right," she had said. "Everything will be all right. We love you and God loves you, too. You aren't alone. You're safe."

I wanted her to say it a thousand times—I was safe, I wasn't alone—

Finally I fell asleep in her arms. When I woke up for a few minutes during the night, I found myself lying on my side with a pillow placed next to me so I wouldn't roll over and hurt my back.

"Oh, Cloud, I wish you were here. You would never have let Flint beat me." I whispered and fell back to sleep.

The next few days were the happiest I could remember in my life. For the first time someone was giving me all the tender care I had never had as a child. Audrey was fast becoming the mother I never had and Reverend McPherson was taking the place of the father I had never known. There was peace and love in this house, and I was accepted as a member of the family.

One evening after dinner, we were sitting in the living room watching television when an old western movie came on. Practically the first scene showed the cavalry shooting down Indians.

"Why is it when the Indians are killed it's called a battle, but when the Indians kill a white man it is called a massacre?" I frowned.

"You are still fighting a war that ended a hundred years ago," Reverend McPherson said. "Stop fighting, Crying Wind. The war is over. The real war you are fighting is not in the battlefield; it is in your heart."

I would have liked to have stayed with the McPhersons forever, but I knew I had to go back home sometimes. I decided I might as well get it over with. I had already been here a week.

After I moved back, I kept a constant lookout for Flint. I imagined him lurking behind every bush and watching me from every corner. After two weeks passed I relaxed. Maybe Flint wasn't even here anymore. Maybe he had gone to Mexico where there were still many of the Kickapoo.

On my way home from church one night, he was waiting for me.

"You've been to church again, haven't you?" he said as he walked slowly toward me.

"Yes," I said, feeling strangely brave.

"If you don't give it up—" his voice dropped to a threat, "we'll sing your death chant."

My breath was taken away. "I don't believe it," I said, but I knew it was too serious for him to say unless he meant it. It was the worst thing the family could do to me. The family would have a meeting, and they would sing my death chant. No one would ever speak to me again. As far as they would be concerned, I would really be dead. All ties would be cut off forever.

"Dead?" I whispered. I almost felt dead when I said it.

"You have until Saturday to clear your mind and know who you are, to make your choice."

For an instant he was my uncle again, and his voice was softer, "Come back, this new stuff you're mixed up in isn't worth losing your family over. We're all you've got."

My head hurt, and I felt tired. I didn't want to think about this. I didn't want to make a decision. Why couldn't I just keep on like I had been? Why couldn't I go to Indian ceremonials when I felt like it and go to church when I wanted? I shouldn't have to make a choice between them. After all, wasn't I half Indian and half white. I had one foot in each world. Didn't that give me the right to go back and forth between them?

I couldn't have my family turning their backs on me forever, erasing me from their lives like the wind blows away footprints, gone as if I had never existed. No, this Jesus man wasn't worth that, He couldn't expect a person to give up his family for Him. I could remember Reverend McPherson saying something about anyone who wanted to follow Jesus had to love Him more than his own father, or mother, or wife or children, or anyone—no, Jesus wanted too much from a person. I wouldn't follow Him.

I didn't see Flint again. I had no way of knowing whether he carried out his threat or not. For the first time, I was glad Cloud wasn't here. If Flint did go ahead with his threat, I didn't like to think of Cloud going along with it. I didn't want to hear Cloud sing my death chant.

CHAPTER THIRTEEN

I decided what I needed was to talk to the wind. It was that wild goose chase he had sent me on that had caused all the trouble. He was angry with me, so he had withdrawn his favors and was going to make my life miserable until I got back on his good side again.

I decided that as soon as it was dark tonight, I would go out and seek the wind.

I waited anxiously for the sun to set. I started walking to a rocky hill on the outskirts of town. It seemed to take a long time. I felt like giving up, but I knew if the wind was angry with me, he would be sure to punish me until I was back in line.

At last I reached the little hill and climbed it. It wasn't a big hill like the one back home, and it didn't have the sacred circle of rocks on top. I didn't have much hope of the wind hearing my prayer, but I went through all the motions and called his name. Then I waited and waited for a sign that he heard me and would answer me, but there was no wind blowing, not even a faint breeze. Not even a leaf rustled, all was still. Was the wind so angry he refused to speak to me, or was it that the wind had stayed behind on the reservation? Was he out blowing across the hills and valleys, talking to other Indians? I used to think the wind could be everywhere, but he wasn't here, not tonight, not when I needed him. I remembered what Reverend McPherson had said about his God, that He was everywhere all the time. It would be nice to have a God like that.

After a while I knew the wind was not going to speak tonight, so I gave up and started the long walk back home.

I was more tired than I could ever remember being in my life, but I knew even after I went to bed there would be no rest for me. There was never any rest for me. Kickapoo—he who moves about—standing here and then there—moving, searching. That was the way of the Kickapoo. I walked past my apartment and on toward the church. As I got closer, I walked faster. I was less tired now. My heart seemed to beat faster, I felt in a hurry. Something important was about to happen, and I couldn't be late! I was nearly running now, even though an hour ago my feet had been dragging.

I ran up the steps to the church and burst through the door. Reverend McPherson was standing at the rear of the church listening to the choir practice. He turned and saw me hurrying toward him.

"Crying Wind!" He seemed to sense that this was not an ordinary visit.

"I went to talk to the wind—he wasn't there. He didn't

answer. I want a god who is always there; who always answers. Whenever I try to talk to the old gods, your new God keeps getting in the way. Your God is always coming into my thoughts, and I don't even know who He is!"

"I think you know who God is. I think you've always known in your heart. That's the reason you were always so restless, why you had so many doubts and questions. God kept calling to you, but you wouldn't answer Him."

"Why can't He just leave me alone!" I rebelled one last time.

"Because God loves you too much to just leave you alone! He cares about you. He loves you, and He won't give up on you just because you are stubborn. There is no place you can go to escape God's love. He has called your name, Crying Wind. He wants you to follow Him. He wants you to accept His love."

I stood on the threshold, uncertain. Then I heard the choir singing the words of a hymn and its message touched my heart,

> O Love, that wilt not let me go,
> I rest my weary soul in Thee.

It was like the gentle flutter of a butterfly's wings in my heart. A quiet stirring, almost so soft that it went unnoticed, but I had felt it. I knew it was there.

God loved me! Whether I was good or bad, I didn't have

to be anyone special or important, He loved me just the way I was right this very minute.

> O Love that wilt not let me go,
> I rest my weary soul in Thee.

Yes that was me! My soul was weary from searching, it longed for rest. Yes, God loved me too much to leave me alone. He had protected me as a child. He had saved me too from taking my own life, He had led me to this church and the McPhersons. He had allowed Grandmother's house to be burned down so I would be forced to live here in the city where I would learn about Him. I could see so much now—so many things leading me, guiding me right up to this very moment.

"Do you want to pray?" Reverend McPherson asked in a quiet voice.

"I don't know what to say."

"Say whatever is in your heart."

"God—God—God, can You hear me? Do You know who I am? I'm Crying Wind. I used to belong to the wind, but now I belong to You—if You want me."

And then the tears came. I kept talking and crying, but I can't remember what I said. Time had no meaning as I talked to God for the first time. It was almost too much to accept all at once. God loved me—me—me! Jesus died for me—me! Now I was saved. I was a Christian, a child of God! I looked over at Reverend McPherson. He was smiling and wiping his eyes with his handkerchief.

"Praise God," he said quietly. "Praise His holy name. At this very moment the name of Crying Wind is echoing throughout heaven. Audrey and I have prayed for you so many times. Now our prayer has been answered. God has something great and wonderful planned for your life. You were such a rebel. He worked so hard to claim your soul that He will have work for you to do."

"I wonder what my future holds now," I said, feeling, for the first time in my life, that I really had a future.

"I don't know what the future holds, but I know who holds the future," he said.

We talked awhile longer, and then he left me inside the church while he went after Audrey. They drove me home. There was a new richness in our friendship now—now I was truly a member of their family. A few hours ago I had had nothing; now I had everything.

I went inside the apartment and knew it was different. I didn't live here alone anymore, Jesus lived here with me. I would never be alone again!

I read the Bible until I couldn't hold my eyes open any longer. I lay in bed, thinking about Grandmother and wishing I could have told her about Jesus. Then I thought about my mother and father and found no bitterness in my heart for them. There was no anger left in me. The burning war fires had been quenched and would never be lit again. This was good. My weary, restless soul had at last found peace and rest.

I fell asleep and slept like an infant in its mother's arms. When I awoke the next morning, the world was fresh and new, and so was I. The sun was bright, and life had never seemed so good. I found myself smiling all the time and singing Christmas carols, because they were the only hymns to which I knew the words.

I began looking for a job. I wanted to work now. I wanted to stay here, close to my church and my new friends. I spent the morning looking for a job with no luck at all. At noon I stopped at a small café to get a sandwich and a cool drink and to rest. While I was eating my lunch, I noticed a man staring at me. Every time I would look up, he would be watching me. Just as I was about to leave, he got up from his table and came over to me.

"Excuse me, miss, I know I've been staring and I apologize, but I was admiring your beautiful beadwork necklace. I was wondering where you bought it."

"I made it myself," I said.

"Did you really? It's lovely. I have a jewelry store a block from here. I sell Indian jewelry, mostly Navajo silver and turquoise, but other kinds, too. It's seldom you see good beadwork these days." He looked at my necklace again. "I don't suppose you have some to sell?"

"Well, I do have a couple of necklaces—" I said, my hopes rising.

"Do you think you could bring them by my shop so I could have a look at your work?" he asked and reached inside his pocket and handed me a business card.

"Yes. Do you think you might buy them?" I asked. "I used to sell beadwork to the trader."

"If your other work is as nice as this, I'm sure I'll want to buy it." He smiled and turned to walk away. Suddenly he stopped and came back.

"I just had a thought—it just occurred to me," he chuckled. "I don't suppose you would be needing employment?"

My mouth dropped open, "Why yes, that's what I'm doing today, looking for work."

"You know, this is the strangest thing. My wife and I run the jewelry shop. Besides the jewelry, we sell Indian paintings and Navajo rugs. Well, I've been trying for months to get an Indian silversmith to work for us, but we never seemed to find anyone. Our idea was that he could help wait on customers, and when business was slow, he could make jewelry. A moment ago I thought, 'Instead of a Navajo silversmith, why not an Indian girl doing beadwork?'" He stopped to catch his breath. "Why don't you come and talk to my wife? She can tell you all about the job."

I was too excited to speak, so I just followed him to his store.

During the next hour his wife showed me around the store and told me what I would have to do. It was a miracle! I would be selling things I loved and understood instead of pots and pans and china. I would be selling beautiful Indian rugs and jewelry. When business was slow, I would do beadwork, and it would be sold for me right here in the store. This time, people wanted to hire me because I was an Indian and not in spite of it! They seemed to be happy to give me the job, and I was happy to take it. It was perfect.

I agreed to start the next morning. As soon as I left their store I called Reverend McPherson and Audrey.

"Do you want to hear about a miracle?" I asked. I told them what God had done for me on the very first day I was a Christian.

That night I went to church. It was a small, informal prayer meeting and afterward many of the people stayed behind to visit.

Sally was there, and I told her the good news and that I would be joining the church soon. She was overjoyed.

A lady beside us said, "We are happy to have you join our church, but it's a pity to turn your back on your culture and your heritage. I always thought the Indians were 'children of nature' and that the Indian religion was beautiful. After all, haven't you always worshiped the great spirit? Isn't he the same as God?"

I squirmed in my chair, I wanted to speak, but I was afraid. Then I saw Audrey and Sally and Reverend McPherson giving me encouraging smiles, and I found the courage to speak.

"The Indian religion is only beautiful to outsiders. To those of us who know the terror, hopelessness, and fear, it is not beautiful. I remember a young man who lost his bride, and went to a medicine man for help. I remember him running through the night screaming and terrified. No one ever saw him again. If the Indian religion is beautiful, why do more Indians commit suicide than any other race or people? Why are there more Indian alcoholics? The great spirit I called to was not the true God. People say it does not matter what name you call God, but it does matter or God wouldn't have said, 'Neither is there salvation in any other; for there is none other name under heaven given among men whereby we must be saved.'" I looked around. Everyone was watching me. I had said too much.

The lady spoke again. "But isn't there any way to save the Indian culture by incorporating it into Christianity? Couldn't the Indians have a church and use their symbols and change their legends into Bible truths? Don't you think that would help more of them feel at home with Christianity?"

"No, I think that would be a mistake. I cannot see peyote beadwork without thinking of the drug peyote that it represents. I cannot think about Indian legends or symbols without thinking of the past. People must be willing to turn their back on the past and change to be Christians. The symbols and beadwork of the old way are not just decorations, they represent false gods. The Indian will have to be willing to give up something. God gave up His Son. Heritage is important, but not more important than salvation. Preserving the past is important, but not more important than where you will spend eternity."

"Yes, I can see you are right," she said. "I didn't really understand before. Could you come and talk to the Women's Missionary Circle and tell them what you've just told me?"

"Oh, I couldn't do that. I could never speak in front of anyone," I said.

"You just did," said Sally, "and you did a beautiful job. If you would teach us about your people, maybe we could do more to help them."

I agreed to talk to the Missionary Circle next Thursday evening. A chance to help my people!

I went to bed that night a happy person. It seemed that until now my life had been a dried up bud on a dying vine. Then someone had poured life-giving water on me, and I was bursting into bloom.

I didn't know how I had the courage to speak up in church, but I was sure the words had been God's.

"Thank You, Jesus," I prayed. "Thank You, Friend."

CHAPTER FOURTEEN

Mr. and Mrs. Megel were easy to work for, and I really liked my job. Nothing could have been better. Each morning I woke up happy and eager to start the day. I was always anxious to get to work. I looked forward to seeing the customers and showing them the beautiful work the Indians could do. Sometimes if a customer seemed interested, I would tell them a legend or give them information about one of the tribes that made the rugs or jewelry. They seemed to enjoy it. My life was full. I never missed church. Often Sally or one of the other church members would come by the apartment and visit me.

I didn't see Flint anymore. After that last night, he had disappeared. I called his apartment but they said he had moved, and they didn't know where. I missed Flint. I knew he was sorry for the things he had done and said, and I wanted to tell him I wasn't angry and that I understood and had forgiven him.

I thought about Cloud a lot, and wished I knew where he was. He had been gone over a year now. I had kept hoping he would come back or get in touch with me, but as the time passed, it seemed less likely that I would hear from him again. Maybe he was dead. I hoped not; I didn't want him to be dead. I wanted to tell him about Jesus and about the changes in my life. Oh, Cloud, why did you have to go away?

One day when I got home from work, I saw a letter in my mailbox. As soon as I saw the simple, round writing, I knew it was from Cloud. The return address on the envelope said he was in Oregon. I was so excited that when I ripped it open, I tore off a corner of the letter.

The letter read:

> *Dear Cry,*
>
> *I hope you are all right and will forgive me for walking out and leaving you alone. I had to write and tell you about something that has happened to me. After I left you I just wandered around for a long time and I ended up here in Oregon. I met a girl. She was so beautiful and so good. Well, she kept telling me about this man named Jesus. At first I didn't listen to her, but she kept telling me I needed to give my heart to this Jesus and then one day I knew she was right. I can't write the words that I want to make you understand, but the old religion is all lies. It is wrong. There is only one God. Cry, there is so much I want to tell you. Mary, this girl, and I are going to get married this summer. I found everything I was ever looking for. I even have a good job here. I work at a sportsman's lodge and*

teach men how to hunt and fish. I am a guide, too. My life is good and I am happy. I want to share this happiness with you, Cry. I am sending you a book called the Bible. Please read it. Do it for me. Do you know where Flint is? Please write and tell me how you are.

Love, Cloud

I held the letter against my heart, and tears of joy ran down my cheeks. Cloud had found Jesus Christ, too! It was a miracle! We had been looking, searching for something, and we had gone in opposite directions. Then, almost at the same time, hundreds of miles apart, we had both found God!

I sat down to answer Cloud's letter right away and tell him the story of my own special miracle. I could see his face smiling as he would read my letter. For hundreds of years there hadn't been one single Christian in our family. Now in a matter of weeks, there were two of us!

CHAPTER FIFTEEN

INDIANS TAKE OVER WOUNDED KNEE, SOUTH DAKOTA

The newspaper headlines were frightening in that early spring of 1973. A handful of Indians, armed with old hunting rifles, had declared war against the United States. I was afraid for them. This small band of Indians was standing up against the strongest nation in the world, a nation with a multi-billion dollar defense system, millions of soldiers, tanks, missiles, bombs—surely the Indians would be wiped out and destroyed by the government. What chance did they have? Hadn't the government always killed Indians? The Indians could only lose, just as they had always lost.

Each day I scanned the papers and expected to read of the second Wounded Knee Massacre, but I never did. Days turned into weeks and the tension mounted, but still the handful of Indians held their ground.

Some American Indian Movement (AIM) members had occupied Wounded Knee to get the attention of the American people and wake them up to the poor treatment of the red man. Years of treaties and peaceful negotiations had gained them nothing. Now many Indians felt it was time for drastic measures.

Many Indians were fired up with old hatred and a strong desire to dig up the old, half-buried hatchet. Who knew how many other Indians in the country felt that way? How many would get into cars and drive to Wounded Knee, looking for revenge? Dozens? Hundreds? This generation of Indians was tired of reservation life, tired of corrupt agents, and fed up with the BIA (Bureau of Indian Affairs). They wanted changes, and they wanted changes now. That's how AIM got started, and right or wrong, it was at least getting people to take notice of the Indians.

I hadn't seen or heard from Flint, and I wondered if he was in South Dakota. I knew he would want to be in on this. He wanted to be a warrior. I had heard him cry "Indian Power?" and pretend to shoot an imaginary bow. I had heard my uncles give the war cries that meant "It's a good day to die!"

I went to church early so I could talk to Reverend McPherson before the Wednesday evening service started. "I am confused about my feelings," I said. "I am proud of the Indians at Wounded Knee. At the same time, I am afraid for them. I even find myself wishing I were there to help them fight. I know they will be killed. The government always kills Indians. That's the way the story always ends." I felt miserable.

"I can't pretend to understand all your feelings about this,"

Reverend McPherson answered, "but I know how tragic it would be for anyone to die. You must remember that this isn't 1890. The cavalry isn't charging in and slaughtering helpless women and children in a bloodbath. The very fact that the government hasn't taken drastic action shows things have changed. The government is trying for a peaceful settlement."

"Why do I feel so angry?" I asked. "I'm a Christian now. I have changed my heart. Why do I feel old blood boiling up until I want to run up there and fight and scream and say, 'Look at us! We are brave! We will die for our cause!'"

He smiled. "First of all, even Christians get angry. Being angry is human, and I would say that the Indians have a right to be angry and discouraged and frustrated. I don't think you should grab a spear and go charging off, but there are other things you could do to help."

"How can anyone help a lost cause?" I mumbled.

"No cause is lost as long as someone believes deeply in it. The first thing to do is pray."

I looked up.

"We can pray for the Indians to use sound judgement; we can pray for the government to be reasonable and just; and we can pray for God's guidance for all those involved. After that, we can write letters to other churches, to senators, and to anyone we can think of who can help." His voice showed his enthusiasm. "You can help your people, Crying Wind, but haven't you heard that the pen is mightier than the sword?"

"Or spear?" I smiled.

As the prayer service started, I expected the usual requests for people in the hospital or people who were having problems. Instead, Reverend McPherson called for a special prayer service for those involved at Wounded Knee. My eyes filled with tears as one person after another came to the altar and prayed for a handful of Indians they didn't know and probably didn't agree with. I knew there had been no prayer service for Indians in 1890. Times were changing. People did care, but they had to be told what was happening. There was such a lump in my throat that my own prayer had to be silent, but I prayed; "Please, God, don't let anyone get killed. Let me help if I can, and please, don't let Flint be up there. But if he is, take care of him."

Weeks passed. I began to wonder if it would ever end, but it finally did. A Methodist minister helped make the arrangements to bring a close to Wounded Knee.

I let out a big sigh of relief. The government hadn't killed all the Indians. Things really were changing!

My phone rang early one morning and woke me up.

"Hello," I said sleepily.

"Is this Crying Wind?" A strange voice asked.

"Yes." I waited.

"Are you related to a man named Flint Pakotah?"

"Yes, he is my uncle." I was beginning to feel afraid.

"We found your name and phone number in his billfold.

He has been injured in a highway traffic accident. He has been taken to Memorial Hospital."

"I'll come right away," I said, and hung up, still not knowing who had called.

I arrived at the hospital and asked to see Flint. I was told to wait until his doctor could talk to me.

It was nearly an hour before a man in a long white coat came and sat down beside me and told me about Flint. He had been driving fast, too fast, and had missed a corner. His truck had rolled down a steep hill and crashed at the bottom. Luckily, someone had seen the accident and reported it, and an ambulance brought him here. He was banged up pretty badly. He had three broken ribs and a broken leg, but he was lucky to be alive. I wanted to see him, but the doctor told me he was asleep and I should come back the next day.

When I returned the next afternoon and walked into his room, I was unprepared for how bad he looked. His eyes were black and nearly swollen shut, there was a bandage across his nose and another on his forehead. There was tape across his chest, his left leg was up in a sling, and he seemed to have bruises on every inch of his body.

"Hi, Flint," I said and eased over toward the bed.

He pressed his lips together and shut his eyes.

"Do you hurt bad?" I asked, knowing he would never admit to feeling pain.

He wouldn't answer.

My spirits sank. He had gone ahead with my death chant, as far as he was concerned I was dead.

"Can I do anything?"

No answer.

I stood there a minute and decided I might as well leave. As I left, I told him, "If you need anything, have someone call me. I'm sorry you were hurt."

I told myself there was no point in wasting my time. He would never speak to me. I would not go back and see him.

But try as I might, I couldn't get him out of my mind, so the next day I went back to see him. Again he refused to speak to me. I left and was determined I wouldn't go back again. I held out for a week, but I couldn't stay away any longer.

"Hi Flint." I tried to sound cheerful.

He was silent. I was getting ready to leave when suddenly he said, "What are you doing here?"

I was so relieved to have him speak to me at last!

"I wanted to see how you are doing." I walked closer. "You don't look too good."

"How did you know I was here?" he asked, but avoided my eyes.

"Someone found your wallet. My phone number was in it."

More silence between us.

"What happened?" I asked.

"I was coming back from a peyote ceremony—" he looked up at the ceiling, " I thought I saw a huge eagle coming at me, and I swerved to miss him—there was no eagle."

"Peyote!" I shook my head. "It will kill you."

"Why don't you get out of here?" he snapped and closed his eyes.

I left without saying anymore.

The next day I had a head cold and felt so bad I didn't even go to work. It was several more days before I felt well enough to try to see Flint again.

This time when I walked into his room, Flint raised up and looked at me.

"I didn't think you would be back," he said.

I shrugged my shoulders, "I care about you."

He looked at the cast on his leg and then said quietly, "I'm glad you came. I'm sorry about what I did, Cry."

I had never heard Flint say he was sorry for anything he had ever done in his life.

"Forget it." I quickly changed the subject. "How are you feeling?"

"Rotten. I hate being tied up here like an animal."

"When can you leave?"

"Not for a couple of weeks, she says."

"She says?" I asked. "I thought your doctor was a man."

Flint looked embarrassed. "He is. I meant one of the nurses told me it would be a couple of weeks."

"Are they taking care of you? Do you need anything?"

"I'm OK. She brought me some books and loaned me this

little battery radio to listen to." He nodded toward a small radio beside his bed.

"She?" I asked.

"One of the nurses," he said, and this time he changed the subject.

Now that he was talking to me, I visited him every day after work. His leg was healing, and his ribs were better. He was looking like himself again, but he wasn't acting like himself. He seemed lighthearted, and he smiled and joked more than he ever had.

One day while we were talking, he asked, "Cry, do you remember the story your grandmother used to tell about why the Kickapoo hate the Pawnee?"

I had to think for a moment. "Yes, I remember."

"Tell it to me, I've forgotten."

"The Kickapoo and Pawnee have always been enemies. The Pawnee were sneaky and they were afraid of Kickapoo warriors. The Pawnee would wait until the Kickapoo warriors went hunting, and then the Pawnee would attack the women and old people left behind in the camps. In the hot summer of 1845, some Pawnee stole horses from a Kickapoo hunting party at Little River. The Kickapoo were so angry they chased the Pawnee, ran them down, and killed them all. The Kickapoo took back not only their own horses, but all the Pawnee horses, too." I could hear Grandmother's voice telling the story. "They made a vow then and there, to seek vengeance on the Pawnee from that time on. To seal their vow, they cut off the arm of one of the Pawnee braves and sent it back to the Pawnee as a warning."

"That was 130 years ago." Flint sighed, "A long time ago. A long time to be angry."

"What do you mean?"

"Oh, nothing, I guess. There is a nurse here. She is Pawnee. I knew the Kickapoo hated the Pawnee, but I couldn't remember why. Now I know it is because of horses stolen 130 years ago." He laughed. "I will have to tell her that."

I couldn't help but notice he spoke more and more often of "that nurse."

"What is her name?"

My question caught him by surprise. "Oh, I don't know, I forget. Autumn Rose, I think."

"That's a beautiful name," I said. "Is she as beautiful as her name?"

"I didn't notice. She's just a nurse." He began to talk about the weather.

I wanted to tell Flint that I had heard from Cloud, but if I did he was sure to ask what Cloud said. Then I would have to tell him about Cloud becoming a Christian, and about myself, too. I knew he wasn't ready to talk about that, so I kept it in my heart and saved it for another time.

Flint was getting stronger and looking better each day. He now welcomed my visits. We had nice long talks, but both of us carefully avoided mentioning the church or our fight because neither of us wanted to cause trouble between us.

One night when I entered his room I knew right away something was wrong by the angry look on his face. "What's wrong?" I asked. I saw his untouched dinner tray beside his bed.

"Nothing," he said in a tone of voice that meant something was very wrong.

"Are you worse?"

"No. I'm OK."

"I can see that you aren't."

"Oh, it's nothing. It's not important," he said.

"Flint?" I pushed on trying to find out what it was.

"I found out I would be getting out of here soon and, well—I asked that nurse if I could call on her after I got out of the hospital."

Before I could speak the door opened and a nurse came in and picked up his tray.

"You should have tried to eat something. Perhaps you'll feel like eating later," she said cheerfully and went out the door with the tray.

"That was her," he whispered, in case she was still within hearing distance.

I couldn't believe it! Flint had fallen for a girl, and a Pawnee girl at that!

He shrugged his shoulders. "Nothing to worry about anyway. She won't go out with me." He tried to look as if he didn't care, but I could see in his face that he was hurt by her refusal.

"Why not? Because you are Kickapoo?"

"The truth is—" He swallowed hard and turned his face away from me. "The truth is—I asked her out and she asked me if I was a Christian."

"What!" I walked around to the other side of the bed so I could see him.

"She asked me if I was a Christian." He shook his head. "I said to her, 'what kind of a question is that?' She said she was a Christian and didn't date men who weren't Christians."

I stood there in silence trying to think of something to say that might help. Flint must really think she was something special to be so miserable about being turned down by her.

Before we could talk any more, the bell went off to end visiting hours. I promised to be back tomorrow and then I left.

At the end of the hall I could see the nurse Flint was talking about. She was waiting for an elevator and I walked up and stood beside her.

I wondered what it was about her that Flint thought was so special. She was short and a little overweight, her dark brown eyes looked like the eyes of a fawn, and her black hair was cut very short. She was a Pawnee. A year or even a month ago Flint wouldn't have considered speaking to a Pawnee, and here he was now longing to court a Pawnee girl. He was changing, just a little, but he was changing.

She saw me watching her and she smiled. When I saw her smile I knew that was what had captured Flint. In her smile was all the warmth and gentleness of a summer day.

I smiled back and then I noticed something else about her. Around her neck on a small gold chain was a tiny gold cross. I knew it was that cross and what it meant to her that kept her from going out with my uncle.

"You are Flint's niece, aren't you?" she asked. "He told me you were coming to visit him."

I nodded. "Yes, he is my uncle. I am worried about him. Will he be all right?"

"Yes. He can probably leave the hospital next week," she said. There was a long pause of silence.

"He likes you," I said boldly.

She lowered her eyes and said shyly, "I like him, too." Her fingers moved upward and gently touched the little cross on her necklace, "If only—" she stopped.

The elevator arrived and the doors opened, and she stepped inside.

"Up or down?" she said.

"Neither. I forgot something. I have to go back and see Flint for a few minutes," I said.

"Maybe I'll see you again," she said, and she let the elevator door close.

I had a feeling we would be seeing a lot of each other.

I walked back to Flint's room.

He was surprised to see me back again.

I pulled up a chair beside his bed and put my hand on his arm.

"Flint, my uncle." I took a deep breath. "Cloud and I have a story we want to share with you—"

He looked at me with a deep, lonely hunger in his eyes.

I smiled and began. "You see, there was this man named Jesus—"

MY SEARCHING
HEART

The Cross

On a hill there stood
Two strips of wood
To form a hated cross.

The ground was red
From the blood Jesus shed
On that hated cross.

That ugly cross,
That hated cross,
Where Jesus died for me.

That glorious cross!
That beautiful cross!
Where Jesus set me free!

—Crying Wind

TABLE OF CONTENTS

Whatever happened to Uncle Flint?" was the first question people asked when they met me after they read my first book, *Crying Wind.*

I was amazed at the overwhelming response to my book. When my phone started ringing and letters started pouring in from people who wanted to know more about the people in the book, I knew I would have to dust off my typewriter and finish my story.

In *Crying Wind* I told of the struggle of my family, who belonged to a different culture and believed in the old Indian gods, and what happened to us when we heard of Christianity for the first time. I tried to share the terror and loneliness of believing in a false religion.

Some of my experiences were left out of my earlier book because I felt they were too personal or too embarrassing to share. Now, since so many people have shown loving concern and interest in the details of my life, I have decided to share my deepest secrets in the hope they will be read with understanding and compassion. Being human, I've often said and done things that I wished later I hadn't. Because of this, I have changed some of the names and places to protect the privacy of those involved. It is not my wish to embarrass or criticize anyone. Time sequences were sometimes changed to make the story more interesting, but the details of the events were kept as accurate as my memory can recall.

If some of my experiences sound strange or impossible or just plain foolish, please remember that as a new Christian (with no church or Bible background), I matured very slowly and often found it hard to adjust to my new way of life. However, all the events in this book have actually happened to me or to those I love.

I'm very grateful to my good friends and patient husband who have helped me to grow and to find my place in the world, and especially to all those who read *Crying Wind* and cared enough to ask, "Whatever happened to Uncle Flint?"

CHAPTER ONE

Looking for Freedom

Rifle shots rang out in the distance like thunder on a still night, and dust kicked up around my feet where the bullets hit the dry earth. I stood frozen in place. To move now, even one inch, could cost my life. Two more shots echoed down the valley, and again dust kicked up near my feet.

A nerve-shattering scream knifed through the air. "Today is a good day to die!" A young Indian man let out his war cry and whipped his horse into a breakneck run that ended in a sliding stop less than three feet from where I stood.

The Indian man wore only jeans and moccasins. His dark chest was bare to the hot sun, and his long, black hair fell loose to his shoulders. He had a gun stuck in his belt and held a rifle in his right hand. He threw his right leg over the horse's neck and slipped easily to the ground, allowing the horse to step off and search for grass.

My gun was cold and heavy in my hand as I slipped if from my holster and leveled it at the man walking toward me.

"Is it really a good day to die?" I asked.

He laughed as he stooped down to pick up an empty pop bottle and set it on his head.

I squeezed the trigger, and a bullet shattered the bottle into hundreds of tiny pieces. My Uncle Flint laughed and brushed the glass out of his thick, black hair.

"Good shooting, Crying Wind. Now it's my turn."

I picked up an empty tin can and held it in my hand. An instant later my uncle jerked his .44 Magnum revolver out of his belt and fired. The can flipped up into the air with a hole in the middle. He pulled the trigger again, and it had a second hole in it before it hit the ground.

"I wish it was hunting season," Flint said as he took a couple more shots at the can. "In the old days there were no hunting seasons. When you got hungry, you shot something and ate it. I'm bored with shooting cans—and at you," he added with a grin.

"Are you going bear hunting this year?" I asked.

"Yeah, I saw lots of tracks less than a mile from the ranch. You want to come?"

I shook my head. There was nothing I feared more than a bear, and I was sure that someday I would be killed by one.

Flint threw a can into the air, and I grabbed his rifle and fired. He picked up the can and looked at the hole in it.

"You're one of the best shots I've ever seen, Crying Wind," he said.

I felt great pride rise in my heart. It was seldom that my uncle had a compliment for me.

"You taught me how to shoot when I was five years old.

You gave me my first gun when I was eight years old," I reminded him.

"Yeah, and the first thing you shot was Grandfather's truck!" He roared with laughter.

I wished he would forget that! Grandfather had beaten me for not doing my chores, and in anger I had shot his old truck full of holes. It had never run again. It had sat in the yard and rusted, a constant reminder of my black temper.

Eager to change the subject, I said, "I guess we've used about ten thousand bullets shooting together."

"Maybe. Never stop practicing, Cry. Someday your life will depend on how well you use your gun."

"In the old days, but not now," I said.

"Yes, now!" he snapped. "Times change, but people don't! People are dangerous. People are the same today as they were a hundred years ago, and they will be the same a hundred years from now. Mark my words, Cry, never let anyone take your gun away. Someday your life will depend on it. An Indian is no good without a gun." He reloaded his rifle. "There's too many laws around here! I can't breathe! I want to be free! I hear in Canada they treat Indians better than they do here. Do you think it's true?"

"I don't know. Couldn't treat them any worse, I guess."

"I want to go someplace, maybe back to the reservation, find something to do there. Maybe find freedom." He got a hopeful look in his eyes.

"What about your girl friend, Autumn Rose?" I asked.

Autumn Rose was a Pawnee girl Flint had met in the hospital after he had nearly been killed in a car wreck. She had nursed him back to health, and he'd fallen for her.

"I don't see her anymore. She's always wanting me to be a Christian and give up the old Indian gods. I won't stop being an Indian for her. She's Indian, she should understand!" he said bitterly.

I was silent. I had been a Christian for only a few weeks, and I knew it was hard to give up the old gods and the old way of life. It was a heartbreaking struggle; and even though I had accepted Jesus as my Savior, sometimes the past sneaked up on me and I could still hear my old Indian god, the wind, calling my name and I wanted to answer. I still did not have my roots deeply planted in the Christian faith, and I often felt confused, frightened and lonely.

"I'll find an Indian girl who lets a man be what he is and doesn't try to change him. A good, obedient wife who will give me many sons, and she will grow old and fat and keep me warm in my old age." He nodded, agreeing with himself.

"And I will marry a strong, handsome Indian man with arms like two oak trees and long hair like a raven's wing. He will have hooded eyes like an eagle, and he will wear buckskin and beads!" I said, and my heart prayed that someday there would be such a man. A warrior, his name would be Winter Hawk or Running Wolf or Lightning Eyes.

"Flint, why is it we don't fit into this world?" I asked the question for the thousandth time. "What's wrong with us?"

"We're not wrong, we're just different. There's war drums in our blood, Cry; you and me, there is a dangerous fire always burning in our hearts. Sometimes only a tiny flame, but then it explodes into a wildfire, burning out all reason and caution and driving us to destruction. You and I are the kind who die for lost causes. We're driven. I see it in you when you are angry. Your eyes flash and you look like a wild animal. If you were cornered, you'd fight to the death before you'd give up."

"You're wrong."

"No, I'm not wrong. I know about you because I know about myself, and we are alike." He kicked the rock out of his way. "I feel fighting mad. I've been pushed enough! In the old days I'd have been a gunslinger," he said. He ripped his gun out of his belt and fired six shots so they sounded like one. "There's no glory or freedom in life anymore. Now there are only laws and rules. 'Don't do this, don't do that, don't be a man, don't think!' I can't breathe anymore!" Flint tossed a can to me.

"On your head!" he commanded.

The fear of appearing scared was greater than the fear of dying, and I obeyed. He shot the can off my head, and we both holstered our guns. We were both deadly accurate shots, and we never missed; but if we had, it wouldn't have made much difference. Life was cheap to us; we had very little to live for. We were both lonely and drifting, and death was less frightening than life.

My seven uncles were my only family. My own parents had abandoned me when I was born, and Grandmother had taken care of me until she died shortly after my fifteenth birthday. Since then, I had been on my own, working here and there at countless jobs, earning just enough to survive.

Flint and I had had bitter feuds, and several times he had beaten me for attending a "white man's church" and turning my back on the old ways. After his near brush with death we had become close again, and we both avoided bringing up anything that would cause trouble between us.

After Grandmother had died, my seven uncles had scattered from the reservation. One uncle had committed suicide; one was in prison for robbing a bank. Uncle Kansas was always getting into trouble wherever he went, and two uncles had disappeared and we never heard from them again.

My favorite uncle, Cloud, had gone to Oregon, fallen in love and become a Christian. He worked as a guide at a hunting and fishing lodge.

Everyone was far away now, and only Flint and I were left. Flint and I mounted our horses and headed back to the ranch where he worked. We let the horses walk slowly along the worn trail, neither of us eager to end the day.

"Crying Wind," he said suddenly breaking the silence, "let's go home!"

"Home? We don't have a home." I shrugged.

"I mean the Kickapoo reservation! Let's go back to the reservation!"

"Do you mean it?" I was afraid he was teasing.

"Let's go tomorrow. I'll pick you up early. Pack all your stuff, you won't be back. We're going to be free!" He let out a war cry and jabbed his heels into his horse's sides, sending it into a wild gallop.

I let out a yell and whipped my horse into a run. We were going to be free!

My horse trailed far behind Flint, and I watched him up ahead of me, the sun glistening on his bare back, his muscles straining with the horse as they raced for freedom.

Freedom! Was it possible? Could we go back to the reservation and live the way we wanted to?

Excitement pounded in my chest, and I leaned down low on my horse and kicked it until it caught up with Flint. We raced side by side, yelling and laughing and filled with the hope of a free life.

That night in my apartment, I packed my few belongings into a cardboard box and prepared to leave. I didn't own much, and I was packed in fifteen minutes.

I started to call my boss to tell him I wouldn't be in the next day, I decided not to bother. I was probably going to be fired soon anyway. I had already had eight jobs so far that year.

I pulled on my leather-fringed coat and walked to my

church. I had to tell Reverend McPherson and Audrey good-bye. They were my best friends and had stood by me when I needed them. They had taught me about Jesus, and that had changed my life. It would not be easy to say good-bye to the only friends I ever had.

They knew as soon as I stepped in the door that I had something on my mind, and I didn't waste time on small talk.

"I came to say good-bye," I said.

"Good-bye?" Audrey asked.

"Where are you going?" Reverend McPherson closed his Bible and folded his hands. He had heard me say good-bye many times since we had first met, and always after a few days or a few weeks I would be back again.

"Flint and I are going back to the reservation—going back for good. I won't see you again, but I'll write and let you know how I am." I was trying to take the sting out of the good-bye.

"What will you do there, dear?" Audrey asked, looking worried.

"Oh, I don't know. Maybe a little hunting, a little farming. We'll do all right."

"Do you really think this is the best thing for you? Your Uncle Flint, will he—" Her voice trailed off. She was remembering the terrible fights we had had in the past.

"Oh, he's OK. We don't fight anymore."

"But is there a church on the reservation? You must remain strong in the Christian faith. Don't go back to your wind god. You've only been a Christian a few weeks—you'll need Christian friends and a church."

"Don't worry, I'll take the Bible you gave me, and even if I don't get to church I'll read it."

Audrey's shoulders sagged. "Crying Wind, you must be careful. God has a plan for your life. You must not spoil His plan for you. You are so careless with your future; you never make plans."

"Yes, I do," I argued. "I plan to go to the reservation."

"Then what?"

"Then we'll figure out what to do next," I said, hoping Audrey wouldn't give me her usual lecture about getting a good, steady, job with a future. She couldn't understand why I couldn't hold a job more than two months or why I changed apartments every four months. She didn't know what it was like to be restless and lonely. She was a good friend, but she didn't understand Indians.

"Crying Wind, do you really have to go? This is so sudden. Can't you think it over awhile? You have a pretty good job and your apartment is nice," she argued.

"I don't like my job, and my rent is only paid until the end of the week."

"Oh, my dear child! When will you ever settle down?"

"Never, I guess. The wind calls me, and I answer. I need to be free. Don't you remember that even the name of my tribe, Kickapoo, means 'He who moves about'?"

"But you are a young girl! It's different for a girl. You can't just pack up and run off all the time."

"But I'll be with my Uncle Flint."

"But—oh, Crying Wind!" she sighed.

"We are going looking for freedom," I explained.

Reverend McPherson broke in, "Freedom is not something you go look for, it is something you feel in your heart. Who owns your heart, Crying Wind?"

"The wind owns my heart." I knew I should have said that God owned my heart, but old ways were hard to break.

"If you need anything, write to us or call collect, and we'll help you in any way we can. We are always your friends. You can come back here anytime you want to." Reverend McPherson shook my hand.

"We will miss you, Crying Wind, but if this makes you happy, then good luck and Godspeed," he said.

Audrey hugged me, and with tears in her eyes she said, "God bless you! Keep in touch with us."

"I'll write as soon as we're settled," I promised and hurried out into the night, anxious to get away from them before the lump in my throat grew any larger. I missed them already. I owed them my life. When I had felt deserted and all alone, I had attempted suicide, and they had picked up the pieces. I had depended on them for so much. Now I wouldn't have their strength or friendship to lean on, and I wasn't sure how far I could fly on my own wings. ☀

CHAPTER TWO

Easy Money

I was already sitting on my box of clothes outside my door when Flint drove up at dawn. I threw my cardboard box into the back of the truck and climbed in beside him.

"Is that all your stuff?" He jerked a thumb toward my box.

"Yeah, I don't own much. Where's your stuff?"

"I own less than you do. I'm wearing most of it, and the rest is under the seat. How come we work so hard and don't have anything to show for it?"

"I don't know," I said. "I guess we spend it too fast. I never could figure out how people could save their money. I'm always broke."

"Well, don't worry about it. Back on the reservation we'll do better." He raced the engine and the truck roared down the road toward home.

Thirteen hours later we drove onto the reservation, tired, dusty and hungry.

As the pickup bounced and rattled down the muddy ruts in the narrow road our spirits sagged. The reservation was nearly deserted. Most of the shabby, two-room wooden houses stood empty. There was no livestock to be seen; tumbleweeds had taken over the pastures.

"Where did everybody go?" I whispered.

Flint drove down the back roads where our family and friends used to live, but no one was left.

Finally we spotted an old man plowing with a mule. Flint stopped the truck and walked across the freshly plowed field to talk to him.

I could see the old man shake his head no to everything Flint asked him, and in a few minutes Flint came back to the truck.

"Everybody's dead, moved away, or gone to the reservation in Oklahoma. The old man said there are only about fifty families left on the reservation now, and they are mostly old people like himself, who are too old to leave. He said just pick an empty house and move in." Flint didn't look as happy as he had earlier.

"What about the Banakee family?" I asked.

"All dead."

"But what about the Cadues?"

"Same. All dead."

"The Charlie Big Horse family?"

"Moved to the reservation in Oklahoma. I don't think we know anybody here anymore," Flint said.

"Flint, have you ever wondered about what happens to all the Indians after they leave the reservation?"

"They get lost in the crowds, I guess. They change their names, cut off their hair, buy a suit, and pretend to be something besides Indians."

"Flint—" I swallowed hard. "I passed for white once," I confessed with shame. "I wore clothes like everyone else, dyed my hair a light color, and changed my name."

"What happened?" he asked.

"It was awful. I looked like a freak, I made some enemies and I was miserable! The worst part was that after I came to my senses and saw how stupid I was and decided to be myself again, the people who knew me when I was passing for white wouldn't believe I was Indian! Even now people will say, 'I used to know you—you aren't Crying Wind, you are a white girl named Linda. Why are you trying to be Indian?' It confused a lot of people. Some people said I was Indian, some said I was white. I guess since I'm a half-breed they were both right. It just goes to show you that you never really know everything about anyone. You only know what they want you to know, just the outside." I felt ashamed. "I wish I'd always just been myself and not tried to be somebody else."

"I know. My friend Black Hawk tells people he's a Mexican and calls himself Jose Gonzalez. He says it's better to be a Mexican than an Indian."

"Is it better?" I asked.

"He's drinking himself to death. I guess that's the answer," he said grimly. "We'd better find a house before dark and move in." He turned down another narrow road and before long stopped in front of an old house.

We got out of the truck and walked inside the house.

Pack rats scurried across the floor, and I quickly scurried back to the truck.

"I'm not staying here!" I said.

"It's getting dark. You sleep inside the truck, and I'll sleep in the back. Tomorrow we'll look for a good place to stay."

Flint climbed into the back of the truck and pulled his coat over his shoulders. I rolled up in my blanket and, trying not to get my feet tangled up in the steering wheel or bump my head on the door handle, lay down on the seat. Somehow this wasn't how I had pictured our homecoming. I was the glad the McPhersons couldn't see me now, and I wished I had a nice, warm bed and something to eat.

I looked out the windshield and watched the stars come out one by one. Finally the moon decided to wake up and climb into the sky. There was a new moon that night: it tipped so you could hang your powder horn on it and keep it dry. The rain would be held up in the sky all night. I was glad Flint wouldn't get wet as he slept in the open.

At last I began to grow sleepy, and I folded my hands and prayed, "God, this is Crying Wind talking. Did you see that I moved back to the reservation? Help Flint and me. Good night." I hadn't had much practice praying, and I didn't know God very well yet, so my prayers were short and without any fancy trimmings.

The next morning Flint sent me after a rabbit. It is easy to run down rabbits, because they run a little way then stop, run and stop. They do this three times, and after they stop the fourth time they make a sharp turn to the right or left. You don't have to outrun them, you only have to outguess them. After a couple of misses, I caught one by the nape of his neck and carried him back to Flint. We cooked him over an open fire. He was a skinny rabbit, but at least we had some breakfast.

We began driving down all the back roads, and just before noon we found a house that hadn't been empty long. We moved into it before the pack rats did. It had three small rooms, no furniture, no water, and no electricity. Flint drove into the trading post and bought some food and supplies, and by evening we were fairly comfortable and enjoying a hot supper.

The next day Flint got a job breaking horses on a nearby ranch, and I began planting a garden. We had a home; we were going to stay. Things were looking good for us. Now I could write to the McPhersons and tell them they didn't need to worry about me anymore.

A few days later I was planting some onions in my garden when Flint drove into the yard and stopped in a cloud of dust. He yelled out the truck window, "Cry, I know where you can pick up a fast twenty dollars."

"If it's such easy money, how come you don't pick it up yourself?" I laughed. Flint always knew a way to pick up easy money, but it never worked out. As often as not, he would end up working for nothing or losing money.

"Out on the ranch where I'm working there's a new colt the boss wants broken. I'm too heavy. He wants someone light on its back the first time."

"Oh, no thanks! I remember when you were riding in the rodeo a couple of years ago and entered me in the wild burro race! You said I was a cinch to win, but the burro I drew went everywhere except forward, and I came in last! I don't think I want any of your easy money!"

"This is different. It's just a nice little bay colt. You shouldn't have any trouble staying on him at all. You used to ride Thunder Hooves like you were glued to her. I know you can handle this horse."

Memories of Thunder Hooves flashed through my mind. It was a long time since she had died, and I hadn't ridden much since then. Flint took my silence as assent.

"No time like now. Let's go on out to the ranch and give it a try," he said and opened the truck door for me.

An hour later I was sitting on a corral fence looking at the little bay colt. Except he didn't look so little, and he was older than a colt.

"Flint, I don't think I want to do this. He looks mean," I said, backing down off the fence.

"He's as gentle as a lamb. Just let him know who's boss. Come on, Cry, you're acting like an old lady."

Flint patted the horse on the neck, and the horse tossed his head and shied.

"I don't feel good about it, Flint. The horse will know it, and I'll get thrown."

"Cry, it's just a little horse. Just get on him and ride him around the corral a couple of times so he can get the feel of somebody on his back. They you can collect your twenty dollars, and we'll go back to town. Besides, I already told the boss you'd do it."

I walked slowly over to the horse and touched his back. He shivered and snorted. "What's his name?" I asked.

"What difference does it make? You don't have to be introduced to walk around the corral one time," he answered impatiently.

"What's his name, Flint?"

"Cyclone."

"What? You have to be crazy! I'm not getting on a horse named Cyclone!"

"It's only a name. We can call him Powderpuff if it will make you feel better. A dumb horse doesn't know what his name is."

I patted the horse and swung up onto his bare back and took the reins from Flint.

The horse shook and stepped sideways. Then his ears lay back and I dug in with my knees. Cyclone pitched forward and bucked three times, kicking his hind legs out behind him. Then he seemed to remember his name and spun around and exploded in all directions at once! He tucked his head so far back between his front legs that his neck disappeared, and I went flying over his shoulders, neck, and head. I hit the ground headfirst and started rolling head over heels across the corral until I hit one of the fence posts. I felt my neck pop, and I lay in a crumpled heap.

Flint grabbed the rope on the horse and tied him snugly to the gate. Then he gave the rope a final jerk and came running to me.

"Cry! Are you all right?" He kneeled down beside me.

I looked up at him, but everything was spinning around so fast I closed my eyes to make it stop. "My neck! My neck's broken!" I yelled.

"Can you straighten it? Can you move your head?" Flint asked.

I tried to move my head, but it hurt so much I thought I was going to be sick. "It hurts too much. I can't move!" I could feel my head resting on my right shoulder, with the muscles pulled tight on the left side.

"Can you move your arms and legs?" Flint was starting to sound scared.

I moved my arms and legs a few inches.

"You're neck isn't broken if you can move—it's just bent. I'll pull it back into place." He reached over and put one hand one each side of my head and tried to straighten it.

Everything went white and I screamed with pain. "No! No! Don't touch me! Flint, my neck is broken!"

"No, it's not, you just had a bad spill. You'll be all right." He picked me up and carried me to his truck, but when he tried to sit me up in the seat I started to get sick, so he carried me around and laid me down in the back of the truck. "I'll get you home and into bed. You'll be all right in a while."

As the truck bumped along the dirt road back to the old house, every inch of my body ached, and I could feel a large bump swelling up in the middle of my back. "I couldn't hurt this bad unless something was broken," I groaned.

After we got home Flint held hot, wet towels on my back while I held them on my neck, which was still bent at an angle.

"Flint, when I get well—if I ever do—I'm going to kill you" I said through clenched teeth.

"It was just a bad spill. You'll be fine tomorrow. You can take it, Cry, you're tough." He took away the hot packs from my back and looked at the swelling. "Cry, do you think you need a doctor?"

"Does it look bad?" I was glad I couldn't see it.

"It doesn't look good." He put the hot pack back on.

"Let's wait an hour. Then we'll decide."

We both looked at the clock fifty times during the next hour. My dizziness was gone now, and my stomach was reminding me that I hadn't eaten all day. Flint cooked some bacon and eggs for us, and I began to feel as if I might live.

I stayed in bed the next day. Each day my neck got a little straighter, and by the end of the week it was back in place again and I was no longer looking at a crooked world.

Flint got over being worried, and in two weeks he was thinking up more ways to get us some "easy" money.

The first Sunday I was on the reservation I dressed up, took my Bible, and walked a mile to the little wooden chapel.

There was no one around when I arrived, so I sat down under a shade tree to rest and wait for the others to come. I kept thinking I had come too early, but after a while I realized no one else was coming.

I walked down the hill for a closer look. The white paint had peeled and chipped. The tower held a silent bell, and just below the cross was a small, crooked sign that read, "KICKAPOO BIBLE CHAPEL."

The doors were nailed shut, so I walked around to the side of the building and peeked through the dirty windows. Inside were rows of dusty pews, and the pulpit was lying on its side. The chapel was empty. It hadn't been used in years.

"Closed due to lack of interest," I whispered. What had happened to all the people who had built such a fine church? Where were they now? I knew many of the younger people were going back to the old Indian religion, but surely, somewhere on the reservation, there must be a few Christians. Why had they closed up their church?

I felt sad as I looked at the empty chapel. It looked like an old woman sitting there. All her children had gone away and left her alone to die on the prairie. ☀

DESERTED CHAPEL

Chapel on the plains,
Beaten by wind and snow and rains,
Sad and lonely standing there,
A silent monument to prayer.
Weddings, christenings, funerals, and praise
Marked the memories of your days;
Now dust blows through the broken door,
Weeds grow through cracks in the floor.
The pews are now empty, they once were filled;
The voices of praise have long been stilled.
The people are gone, the houses are too;
Time has taken all but a few.
The old wooden cross reaches up to the sky,
As a welcome to strangers who may pass by,
But no one comes here anymore,
No weary travelers will stop by your door.
Chapel on the plains,
Beaten by wind and snow and rains,
Sad and lonely standing there,
A silent monument to prayer.

CHAPTER THREE

Alone and In Danger

We had been back on the reservation a few months but knew very few people, so I was surprised when there was a knock on the door late one evening. When I answered it there was a man holding a paper bag of fresh garden vegetables.

"Is your uncle home?" he asked, looking past me into the house.

"No, he's gone out tonight," I answered trying to remember if I had seen this man before.

"He asked me to bring these by, but since he's not here, I'll just leave them with you," he said and held the sack out in front of him.

I opened the screen door and reached for the sack, but he threw it aside, spilling the vegetables across the porch. He grabbed my wrists and shoved me into the house. Once we were inside he let go of my wrists and quickly looked around to make sure I was alone.

I was in trouble! I had made two mistakes: I had told him I was alone, and I had opened the door for him! How could I have been so stupid? I glanced around the room to see what I could use for a weapon. There was a poker by the stove, but I wasn't sure I could hit him hard enough to knock him out. What if I just hit him hard enough to make him angry, and he killed me?

I backed up a step. "So you are a friend of my uncle. Do you work with him?" I asked, trying to keep my voice from shaking.

"What?" He turned around to face me, and then I could tell he was drunk.

"I asked if you met my uncle at the ranch. He'll be home soon now. He'll be glad you stopped by." I knew that if Flint had a date that night it would be hours before he came home, and I hoped it didn't show on my face. In my heart I was praying, *God, help me! God, help me!*

He took a step toward me and my heart turned to ice.

"It's so hot in here. Why don't we go out on the porch for a minute and get a breath of that cool evening air?" I smiled at him and stepped out the door. He was right behind me as I walked to the edge of the porch.

"Oh, look!" I said, pointing off to his right. "Is that your dog?"

Without thinking, he turned to look, and I leaped off the porch and headed for the trees at a dead run.

Please, God! Don't let him catch me! I prayed as I ran for my life.

I could hear cursing behind me as he staggered through the underbrush. I made as much noise as I could as I ran through the trees. It was very dark, and he was drunk; if he would follow me far enough, he would probably get lost. Now I began to move as quietly as I could. I wanted to make a circle and get back to the house. He could get lucky and stumble across me, or maybe he wasn't as drunk as I thought. I couldn't underestimate him.

I silently worked my way back toward the house. Then I was out of the trees and running across the open yard. If I could just get inside the house! I reached my bedroom window and climbed through it. I shut the window behind me and hurried to my closet. Even though it was pitch black, my hand reached inside and found the shotgun.

Now I waited. Would he try to get back into the house?

There! A noise on the porch! He was back! I watched the doorknob and waited for it to turn. Nothing happened. I could hear vegetables rolling across the porch. I knew he was out there!

I took a deep breath. "Get out of here or I'll shoot! I yelled. I slid the bolt into place and held the shotgun waist high. "This is your last chance!"

I counted to three and fired at the door, splintering it.

A few seconds of silence, and then an engine started! I looked out in time to see a pickup truck pulling away.

I ran out onto the porch and fired the shotgun after it. *Blam!* One of the taillights went out. *Blam* again! But he was out of range. His wheels were spinning, and the air was thick with the dust he was kicking up. I shot again. *Blam!* He was far down the road now. He must have been driving ninety miles an hour.

I went back into the house, locked the door, and reloaded the gun—just in case. I let out a shaky breath. "Thank you, God," was all I could say.

When Flint came home hours later I spilled out the story of the frightening nightmare.

"Well?" I said after I had finished. "What are you going to do?"

I expected him to grab a gun and go after the man.

"You handled it all right," he said and pulled off his boots. "Guess I still think of you as a kid. I never thought about any man giving you trouble. Better keep an eye on you from now on," he yawned.

I was disappointed. I felt that he should have been angry, but instead he was calmly getting ready for bed.

"If a man came and stole your rabbits, you would punch him in the nose! If a man tries to steal me, you don't do anything! I'm worth less than a rabbit to you!" I was angry.

He smiled. "Cry, you are safe. You probably scared that man so bad he drove down the road, and had a heart attack. You probably scared him worse than he scared you."

"I doubt that!"

"I can't do anything tonight. Tomorrow I'll ask around and see if I can find out who he was. Then I'll decide what to do about it. Now forget it and get some sleep."

I went to bed, but it was a long time before I fell asleep.

The next night when Flint came home he was smiling the smile of someone who knows a secret. "I heard a couple of the men talking today," he said, grinning.

"What about?"

"About a man who needs some repair work done on his truck. It seems some wildcat shot his truck full of holes," he laughed. "I told them he was lucky the holes were in his truck and not in his hide! I said to pass the word that if he ever showed up here again, his hide would be nailed to our barn, and that went for anybody else who has any ideas about my niece." He threw his hat at the table and missed. "Nobody will bother you again."

The next morning my hammering caught Flint's attention, and he walked to the front gate to see what I was doing. He stood behind me and read aloud the sign I was nailing up. 'BEWARE OF BAD DOGS.'

"We don't have any dogs," he said.

"You don't have to have a dog to put up a sign," I said. I reached into a sack and took out three large soup bones and dropped them on the ground in front of the sign.

"That won't work," he laughed. "People aren't afraid of signs."

"Yes they are," I said and picked up my hammer and nails and headed toward the house. "It will keep bad people away."

He fell into step beside me, still laughing and shaking his head.

Before we had reached the house we heard a horn honk and turned around. A large, red car had pulled up, and the driver was waving for us to come to him.

"What can we do for you?" Flint asked, walking toward the car.

"I'm Bright Star's cousin. She said you'd sell me some rabbits," the driver said.

"How many do you want?" Flint asked.

"Four."

"Come out back to the hutch, and I'll let you pick out the ones you want," Flint said.

"No thanks! I don't hanker to get chewed up by your dogs."

"Dogs?" Flint asked.

"I saw your sign. That's why I honked instead of getting out of the car. I'm too old to outrun a pack of bad dogs. I'll just wait here, and you bring me four rabbits." He handed Flint eight dollars.

Flint shoved the money inside his shirt pocket. "Well, I'll be!" he whispered as he walked past me. "It does work! People are afraid of signs!"

Flint stayed closer to home, just as he had promised, and the man never returned. But in spite of this, I never felt safe again. I watched for movements in the bushes, for shadows that didn't belong, and I listened for footsteps behind me. I went inside early and locked the house up tight before sundown. I checked the locks on the doors several times before I went to bed, and often I didn't sleep well. I began to realize that I was not safe by myself; a girl alone is in danger. My safety depended on Flint. If he left, what would I do? ☀

CHAPTER FOUR

Broken Dream

The garden was breaking up through the soil. The corn plants were young and only a few inches high when Flint announced it was time for the Green Corn Dance and powwow.

I jumped up and down with excitement on the day of the ceremony. As we drove to the campgrounds, we could see many trucks and crowds of Indians getting ready for the dances to begin. We pushed our way through the crowd to get a better place from which to watch the ceremonies.

Flint was wearing a new western shirt, and I was wearing a buckskin dress and had beads in my hair. Most of the Indians had on traditional tribal clothing to honor the day. The Green Corn Dance was performed to ask the corn to grow tall and give food to the people so they would not go hungry the next winter.

Indians of several tribes lined up facing east across the dance grounds. Silence fell over the crowd, and for several minutes we stood waiting.

Then, like a thunder of drums, fifty screaming Kickapoo warriors came charging over the crest of the hill on galloping horses.

My heart leaped with emotion and tears stung my eyes at the

sight of the young braves on half-wild horses swooping down the hill in a cloud of dust. No wonder Kickapoo warriors had terrorized the early settlers! Even now they were a fearful and wonderful sight! Their wild charge ended in a horse race. The winner would be given the horse of the man who finished last.

As the horses raced across the open plains my eyes looked upon one of the riders, and my heart rode with him. He was young, and his arms looked as strong as oak trees. His long, black hair flew in the wind, and around his neck was a necklace of old Indian trade beads. He was a wonderful rider and had a fast horse, but he didn't win the race. A boy on a gray horse won. But it didn't matter to me, because although my warrior had lost the race, he had won my heart.

All morning I tried to catch glimpses of him in the crowd, and it didn't take Flint long to figure out whom I was watching.

"Do you want to meet Yellow Thunder?" Flint asked, smiling. "I know an uncle who can arrange it."

"How do you know his name?" I repeated it to myself. *Yellow Thunder*. It rang like music in my ears.

He laughed. "He sells horses to the ranch where I work. Aren't you lucky to have me for an uncle!" Flint said and looked very satisfied with himself.

True to his word, Flint introduced me to Yellow Thunder, and my heart pounded so loudly I was sure he could hear it. He smiled at me, and when I looked into his eyes I knew I was in love for the first time. It had hit me suddenly and without

Crying Wind   38

warning. It was like being caught in a rock slide, and my life was changed forever.

Each day after that I waited for Yellow Thunder to call on me. I looked out the window hundreds of times, and each evening I combed my hair and sat in the yard and waited. Surely he would come tonight!

I had great dreams about our life together—secret dreams that I kept hidden in my heart. I was sure that if I loved Yellow Thunder enough he would have to care a little for me in return.

Wrapped up in thoughts of the handsome warrior, I grew more quiet each day. One day he would come. I would be patient, I would wait for him. Each day I watched, each night I waited. Weeks passed, and my feelings for him grew stronger.

Then one night he came! When he rode up the path and tied his horse to the fence I wondered if I was just dreaming again or if it could really be true!

I hurried out of the house to meet him, my eyes shining and my hands trembling.

"Hello, Singing Wind. Is Flint home?" he asked.

I was crushed. He had come to see my uncle, not me, and he hadn't even remembered my name!

He went inside the house, and he and Flint began talking about the price of a horse.

I sat down on the sagging wooden steps with my chin in my hand. *How could he not see the way I feel about him? He must be blind!* I walked out and patted his horse for a few minutes and watched the sunset. Then I headed back to the house.

Their voices drifted through the open door, and I stopped when I heard Flint mention my name.

"Crying Wind looks your way, Yellow Thunder," Flint said.

My face burned in the darkness. Flint should not have told him that!

"Flint, you are my friend, so I will speak the truth to you. You and I are true bloods, but your niece is a half-breed. If she was a pure blood, things might be different, but I don't want any of my sons to be quarter-breeds. The girl I choose will have to be a pure-blood Kickapoo."

"She's a true-blood Indian in her heart, where it counts," Flint argued.

"It's our sacred trust to keep the bloodline pure and preserve our people," said Yellow Thunder.

As I stood there in the shadows of the night, the man I loved stabbed me in the heart and left me mortally wounded, like a rabbit with an arrow through its chest. Love had lost its sweetness and left me crushed and hurt.

Half-breed! That's all I would ever be!

I ran into the woods and wept bitterly. My first love had come and gone without even a touch of hands for a memory.

I heard the sound of hoof beats fading into the distance.

"Good-bye, Yellow Thunder," I sobbed. "I'll never love anyone but you."

Flint came looking for me, and I dried my tears when I heard him approach.

"What are you doing out here?" he asked softly.

"Nothing," I choked.

He was silent. Far away lightning flashed across a purple sky and thunder growled.

"You heard, didn't you?" he asked.

I burst into tears. "I wish I hadn't introduced you to him. Forget him, Crying Wind." He put his hand on my shoulder. "Let's go inside before it rains."

He led me through the darkness toward the house. He didn't speak again until we reached the front door.

A kerosene lantern burned brightly inside the house. I didn't want to step into the light and let Flint see my tear-streaked face, so I pulled away from him and sat down on the steps. "I'll come inside in a few minutes," I said between sobs.

He stood holding the door open and then said quietly, "It hurts, doesn't it?"

"Yeah, it hurts," I whispered.

He went inside, and just before he shut the door behind him he stopped and said, "Be tough, Cry. Always be tough. Then you never get hurt." He blew out the lantern and left me alone in my misery.

"I'll never love anyone again." I wiped away my tears. "Never! Never! Never! I'll be tough!" I vowed and went into the house.

After I had crawled into my bed, I lay awake for hours and listened to the storm come closer. I prayed the hurt in my heart would go away. I didn't know that when you are wounded by someone you love it never heals.

My Love Song

Alone in the dark night I dream of you,
When the sun is high I watch for you.
When I see you, the sky smiles, and my heart pounds
And I am afraid to look at you.
You pass me, and I do not raise my eyes,
But after you are gone I look up and watch the strong muscles
of your back
Until you are gone from sight.
When it is sundown on War Pony Hills,
I long for you and walk in the night.
The wind carries your voice to me.
Oh, Yellow Thunder, hear my love song!
Together we will walk quietly on the rainbow trail.
I will give you sweet water of melted snow to drink,
You will hold your hand over my head to protect me.
On my fingers are rings of turquoise,
On my feet are moccasins with silver buttons.
Will you let me follow your path through the forest?
I wish you loved me as I love you.

My heart is filled with words my lips cannot say,
Inside I have songs I will never sing;
They are songs for you alone, and you do not hear.
When you leave, my heart grows dark and cold;
The sky weeps, and so do I.

Weeks passed, and a grayness settled over my days. Bugs and weeds took over my garden and killed our main food supply.

One night Flint finished supper and pushed his empty plate across the table. "Cry, it didn't work. There's no freedom here. The reservation is worse than the outside world. We're eating wormy vegetables and haven't had any meat in three days. I have one more horse to break, and then I'll be out of a job. We shouldn't have come here."

I didn't answer. If we hadn't come here, I wouldn't have met Yellow Thunder. If I hadn't met him, I wouldn't have to live with this dull ache in my heart. I closed my eyes and once again saw him charging over the crest of the hill with the rising sun behind him, his horse leaping and jumping. Yellow Thunder, with his black hair blowing in the wind and the war cry coming from his lips. Yellow Thunder—

"Crying Wind!"

Flint's voice brought me back to reality, and I began clearing off the table.

"I said this didn't work. We shouldn't have come back here." He paused. "I'm ready to leave. How about you?"

Leave? Never see Yellow Thunder again?

"He's getting married, Cry. He chose a full blood, like he said he would."

I dropped the plates I was holding, and they crashed to the floor. My heart was in more pieces than the broken plates.

"I figure there's nothing here for us. Let's go back where we came from" he said.

"When?" I asked weakly and began picking up the broken glass.

"The sooner the better," he answered.

"Tonight?" I looked up.

He looked at me. "Why not? Get your box packed."

I forgot about the broken dishes and ran to my room. An hour later, all our belongings were in the back of the truck, and Flint started the engine.

Before going to the truck I took one last look around. The moon was coming up over the treetops, and I saw Yellow Thunder's face in it. "Good-bye," I whispered to him and shut the door to the old house. I knew I would never return to the reservation as long as I lived.

We rode in silence, each of us brooding over our broken dream. Flint had failed to find the freedom he was searching for, and I had failed to find love with Yellow Thunder. We drove all night, and early the next morning he left me on the

McPhersons' doorstep with my box of clothes.

I rang the doorbell, and Audrey answered.

"You've come home!" she exclaimed and drew me inside the house.

"I don't have any money and no place to stay and no job," I said.

"You can stay here with us as long as you like" she said, just as I knew she would. She carried my box to the spare bedroom.

"You look very tired, dear. Would you like to lie down awhile?"

"We drove all night to get here," I said.

"What was your hurry?" she asked as she folded back the covers on the bed.

"We were running away," I answered and lay down.

"From what?"

"From a broken dream," I said and fell asleep before she pulled down the shade. ☀

CHAPTER FIVE

My Own Buffalo Head

Audrey and Reverend McPherson weren't the kind of people to say "I told you so," even when they had every right to say it. They didn't ask any questions, and I still hurt too much to tell them about Yellow Thunder. But I felt they somehow knew about him anyway.

I stayed with them a week, and then found a job as a waitress in a coffee shop. They helped me find an apartment and lent me rent money until I got paid. I was right back where I had started, except for one thing: now I knew how lonely I was, and night winds brought dreams of Yellow Thunder.

Flint was seeing Autumn Rose again, and he had started going to church with her. I was sure he would soon surrender his life to God and marry Autumn Rose. Things would work out for him now.

My own life was disappointing. I had thought things were somehow going to be perfect when I became a Christian. I had thought nothing would go wrong and that I would have a special power that would keep me from getting hurt or depressed or lonely. I had expected to have a magic shield around me that would protect me from the world. I had expected all my prayers would be answered YES and that I would be perfect and never make any mistakes. I had even hoped a millionaire would drive up in a white Cadillac and marry me and I would live happily ever after.

It didn't happen that way. The millionaire never showed up, I still made mistakes, and things still went wrong. God didn't answer all my prayers YES, and I was often depressed and lonely. Somehow it wasn't working out the way I had planned. I began to have doubts about my decision. Maybe I was doing something wrong. Maybe I wasn't even really saved. Maybe I wasn't good enough to deserve God's blessings. Maybe God hadn't forgiven me for my sins. Sometimes the depression was so strong I felt as if I were buried in a black coffin. I felt guilty about being depressed. After all, Christians never got depressed, did they? And wasn't I really better off than most people? I was healthy, I had a few friends, I had my whole life ahead of me. I had many reasons to be happy. So why did I feel so miserable?

My ups got higher and my downs got lower, and I was living on mountain peaks or in valleys, with no time in between. I remembered an old folk song that went something like, "From here on up, the hills don't get any higher, but the valleys get deeper and deeper." Was that true? Weren't there any higher hills to climb? Did the valleys get deeper and deeper?

My mind was traveling a dangerous path. I began to reason that life had little to offer and that death offered heaven, and wouldn't going to heaven be better than struggling along on this earth? After all, I was a Christian. I knew about heaven and surely God wouldn't be angry if I came home before he called me. Once again thoughts of suicide crowded into my mind, but I was too ashamed to share my fears with anyone. It had been different before; I hadn't been a Christian. But now there was no excuse for my thinking, because I knew better. I began losing my grip on reality, and I spent hours daydreaming, until the world in my mind was more important to me than the real world around me. I lived in daydreams, where I could make the world what I wanted it to be.

I attended church every time the doors were open, and I read my Bible and I prayed. But I felt separated from God, and there was a big, empty hole in my life.

I knew I was feeling sorry for myself and decided that if I could do something for others, I would forget about myself. I took a job at a nursing home and was sure I could find happiness and contentment serving others. I started with big plans and a heart full of hope. I went to work early and stayed late. But instead of feeling better, I felt worse, because the hopelessness of some of the patients began to find its way into my own life. I knew I wasn't helping them or myself, so after two weeks I quit.

I took a job in a candy store but was fired the second day because I was eating more candy than I was selling. I worked a week in a gift shop and was fired because I told a customer where she could buy the same dishes for half the price. In the next few months I changed jobs nearly every week and moved twice. I was looking for happiness in the wrong places. I thought happiness could be found in a place or a job or another person; I didn't know happiness depended entirely on my relationship with God. God had somehow slipped into second place in my life, and I was running in circles and wondering what I was doing wrong.

It was midnight, and there was a wild banging on my door. I got out of bed and pulled on my robe. It had to be one of my uncles—no one else in the world could make that much noise.

I swung open the door, and in staggered Flint and my Uncle Kansas.

Kansas was a year younger than Flint. His name was Kansas Kid, but we just called him Kansas. He was handsome and he was wild and he felt no law ever made was meant for him.

"Kansas! I'm happy you've come!" I hugged him.

"Even in the middle of the night?" he laughed.

"Especially in the middle of the night!" It was true; I didn't sleep well anymore. When I crawled into my bed I found it was filled with memories that crowded out sleep.

"Where have you been for the last year?" I asked.

"Everywhere!" he laughed. "Wyoming, Montana, Arizona, Mexico. I've been driving trucks, training horses, trapping, and doing fifty different jobs in fifty different towns."

"What brings you back here?" I asked.

"I wanted to see what was left of my poor relations, and

you and Flint are the poorest relations I know." He tugged at my hair. "How about some grub?"

"I can fry some bacon and eggs fast," I said and started to the kitchen.

"No! Eggs and buffalo steaks! Indians don't eat anything but buffalo!" He stomped his moccasined foot and shook his fist.

"I haven't had buffalo meat in years," I said, remembering what a treat it had been.

"What? Crying Wind no longer eats the meat of her ancestors?" Kansas demanded.

Flint joined in. "It's a disgrace! Let's go out and shoot a buffalo for Crying Wind!" And both Flint and Kansas disappeared outside.

They've been drinking, I thought to myself.

In an instant Flint came back inside and handed me three fresh steaks.

"What's this?" I asked.

"Buffalo," he answered.

"No, it's not," I argued.

That was what he was waiting for.

"Hey, Kansas, your niece doesn't believe this is buffalo meat! Prove it to her!"

Kansas came through the door holding the huge head of a freshly killed buffalo.

"A buffalo! It's a real buffalo! Where did you get it?" I exclaimed.

"Don't ask," Flint said. "Never ask where food comes from; just eat and be glad you have it."

Kansas set the buffalo head in my bathtub.

"Good medicine!" he said and patted one of the horns. He led me into the kitchen. "Indians need buffalo to live," he said. "If there were no more buffalo, there would be no more Indians. The Great Spirit gave us the buffalo. They belong to us. We have a right to kill them and eat them."

I fried the buffalo steaks and some eggs and made a pot of coffee.

"Kansas, even you cannot hunt buffalo in the city," I said.

"I found a piece of rope and stuck it in my truck. A buffalo was on the other end of the rope," he laughed.

"Where did you find the rope?"

"In the city zoo," he said and cut off a piece of meat.

"That's impossible! You can't steal a buffalo from the zoo!" I protested.

"A Kickapoo warrior can do anything he wants to do," he retorted.

I poured the coffee and silently prayed, *Forgive us, Lord, for eating this stolen buffalo.*

It was dawn when they decided to leave.

"Wait! You forgot to take the buffalo head with you!" I called after them.

"Don't be silly, Crying Wind. What would I do with a buffalo head? You keep it—it's good medicine," Kansas said.

"Kansas! I can't keep it in my apartment! It will start to smell!"

He stopped and came back inside. "You are getting fussy. How many girls do you know who have their own buffalo head? he scolded.

"Kansas!" I pleaded.

"We need a safe place to keep it until it is dried out." He went after the buffalo head. "Pack some food, and let's go."

"I can't go with you. I have to be at work in an hour," I said.

"You won't spend one day with your uncle? After not seeing me in a whole year? And after I brought you this fine gift?" He held up his head.

"I'll lose my job! I've already had a dozen jobs this year," I explained.

"I've had fifty jobs this year. What difference does it make? You would rather go wait on tables than be out in the great, open spaces looking for a hiding place for Brother Buffalo? he sighed. "You hurt your uncle's heart."

"OK, I'll go." I ran to the kitchen and started throwing food in a sack.

"Don't bring any meat," Kansas called after me. "We have five hundred pounds in the back of the truck. Just bring some bread, some ketchup, and some drinks.

As we sped down the highway we sang songs, laughed, and told lies to each other. Tomorrow I would be looking for a new job, but today was like old times. We would have fun, and we would be Indians again!

We drove a hundred miles away from the city, out to some sandy flats where the nearest ranch house was thirty miles away. There we found a small cave and hid Brother Buffalo's head and hide and pushed rocks over the cave opening.

Kansas threw the last rock into place. "Once we had thousands of buffalo here on this open range. Now we have to risk our lives to steal one back from the government," he said with bitterness.

The three of us felt a wave of sadness because we had missed out on our glorious past. We were three Indians who were born a hundred years too late, and there was nothing we could do about it. We didn't belong to the twentieth century any more than our friend Buffalo did. One day Indians would be extinct too. Maybe the government would keep the last Indian in a zoo.

We ate a lunch of fry bread and buffalo cooked over an open campfire.

Flint pulled a couple of guns out of the truck and he and Kansas did some target practice while I lay down on the warm sand and tried to catch some of the sleep I had missed the night before.

"Cry! Help me! I've been shot!" Kansas staggered over and, clutching his left shoulder, collapsed beside the campfire.

I sat up, blinking my sleepy eyes, and saw something red oozing between his fingers and dripping down his shirt.

"Quick! Do something!" He bent in half and groaned, "Flint shot me! I think I'm dying!"

I grabbed my jacket and held it against his shoulder.

"Flint! How could you! He's your brother!" I screamed at Flint, who stood nearby.

"Let me see where you are hit," I said to Kansas and gently wiped the blood from his shoulder. "I can't find the bullet hole."

I pulled open his shirt and found a perfectly healthy shoulder.

Kansas and Flint burst into hysterical laughter. "We sure fooled you! It was ketchup!" They slapped each other on the back and howled like coyotes. "Cry, you would fall for anything! Can't you tell the difference between blood and ketchup?"

They were still laughing when we climbed into the truck and drove back to town. "I'll never believe a word you say again as long as I live!" I shook my fist at them. "That's what I get for caring about you wild animals! You've fooled me for the last time!"

Kansas moved in with Flint for a while. Luckily, I didn't get fired and still had a job when I returned from saying good-bye to Brother Buffalo.

A couple of weeks later I found Flint waiting for me outside my apartment. "Kansas has been shot," he said.

"Sure he has!" I snapped. "Don't you think you should stop wasting all that ketchup?"

"No, Cry, I mean it. It's no lie. He's really been shot, and he's hurt bad. I came to take you to the hospital to see him."

"Flint, if this is another one of your dumb jokes—"

"Not this time, Cry," he said in a tight voice, and I believed him.

It seemed like a long ride to the hospital, and Flint told me the story on the way. "He told the police it was an accident. He said that he was target practicing and tripped with his guns. He said he lost his gun. He said he drove back to town and tried to get someone to help him, but people thought he was drunk and just ignored him. It wasn't until he fell out of his truck and passed out that someone saw he was bleeding and called the police."

"Is he all right?" I felt sick.

"He was shot through the stomach. It's bad, but he'll make it." He paused. "He—never mind."

"What is it, Flint?"

"Well, I told you the story he wants people to believe. Don't ever repeat what I'm going to tell you now."

"I won't." I moved closer to him.

"Kansas was seeing some girl, and her family didn't like it. They already had some nice boy picked out for her to marry.

Her brothers warned Kansas to stay away from her, but you know him. Well, one of her brothers shot him, and then he got scared and drove Kansas into town and dumped him out on the sidewalk. It's a wonder he didn't bleed to death before they got him to the hospital."

"Why didn't he tell the truth to the police so they could arrest the guy who shot him?"

"It's the girl he's protecting, not her brother. He doesn't want her mixed up in it. She doesn't even know it happened." Flint smiled. "Kansas said he was sure cured of any romantic feelings he had for her!" Then he warned me again, "Remember it was an accident!"

"I understand," I said.

Kansas developed peritonitis and was in critical condition. He drifted back and forth between life and death for days, and I was afraid gangrene would kill him the way it had killed my grandmother.

Flint and I visited him every day, and I constantly prayed for God to spare his life. Finally he began to improve, and I praised God for letting him live.

When Kansas was released from the hospital, he was supposed to stay in bed two more weeks, and the bandages on his wound needed to be changed every day. There was no one else who could take care of him, so he moved in with me. He stayed in my bed, and I moved onto the couch.

He spent a lot of his time sleeping and reading paperback

western novels. He really wasn't any trouble, except when it was time to change his bandage. I would swallow hard and hold my breath and try not to look at the big, bloody, scab with the huge black and blue bruise around it. Each day changing the bandage got easier, and then it didn't bother me anymore.

One day he tossed his book to the foot of the bed and it slid to the floor. "Got any more western books?" he asked.

"Don't you want to read something different? Aren't you tired of reading about people getting shot?" I asked.

He started to laugh but caught himself and put his hand over his wound. "You know, in the old days lots of cowboys got shot a half-dozen times during their lifetimes and then died of old age."

"You have five more times to go. Good luck." I laid some books on the bed—two westerns and two Christian books.

He picked up the two Christian books. "You can put these back."

"You should read them; they're good."

"I've told you ten times, I'm not interested in religion. I wish you'd quit preaching to me. I'm tired of hearing it!" he growled.

"I'll never get another chance to make you sit still and listen to me."

"Look, Crying Wind, I'll agree with you—I know the old way is dead. The Indian gods are false but I don't believe in your God, either. I don't think there is any god of any kind, or this world wouldn't be such a rotten place. I don't believe in anything because there's nothing to believe in. I'm going to have a good time while I'm here and then die, and that's the end of it."

I pointed to his wound. "You call that having a good time?"

He picked up a book and disappeared behind it. I didn't mention religion to him again, and a week later he left. I never saw him again.

Sometimes I would hear about his escapades from Flint. Kansas was arrested for trying to steal a bass drum from a band, and he was caught when, trying to make his getaway in a taxi, he got the drum stuck in the door of the cab. He was put in jail for three days for drunken mischief. He was arrested for trying to steal a buffalo from a private animal park, and he argued that Indians had the right to hunt buffalo as long as the sun shone and as long as the grass grew and that it was written in the treaties. He was fined fifty dollars and released. He was married several times and wrecked a dozen cars. He was racing to death and destruction as if his clothes were on fire, and nothing could stop him.

Then we heard Kansas was shot and killed in a barroom fight in Wyoming. When I heard the news I remembered how he had loved western novels and how he had said that some of the old cowboys had a half-dozen gunshot wounds during their lifetimes. I wondered if he had really been killed because of a fight or if he had planned a suicide and had started the fight himself. If that were true, he couldn't have planned an ending that would have been more like the plot of one of his western novels. "Killed in a gunfight in a saloon in Wyoming."

I missed Kansas. I missed his wildness and the reckless way he lived.

Years later I returned to the sandy plain where Flint and Kansas and I spent the day finding a hiding place for "Good Medicine," as we had named the buffalo. I found the cave and pulled the rocks away from the opening. I had expected to find a skull, but instead I found the buffalo head perfectly preserved. The hair wasn't even dusty, and the hide had turned to hard leather. I pulled it out by its horns and took a closer look. The skin had pulled back from the teeth as it had dried, leaving the buffalo looking as if he were smiling. Kansas would have liked that. Good Medicine, the Smiling Buffalo. I took the head home with me and kept it.

Sometimes my company would be startled to see a three-foot-high head of a buffalo in my living room, but I would just smile and remember Kansas and say, "How many people are lucky enough to own their own buffalo?" And I would pat one of the horns and add, "Especially one that smiles?"

Kansas, I miss you! Why were you in such a hurry to die? ☀

CHAPTER SIX

My Calling

Flint and I sat at the table and let our coffee get cold. "Flint," I said, "our family is getting smaller. Grandmother died, Pascal killed himself, now Kansas is gone. Maybe you should get married and have some children, or soon there won't be anything left of our family."

"I think you're right," he said, and my mouth flew open in surprise.

"I've been thinking it over. I might as well take a wife. I'm tired of living alone. Autumn Rose is a hard worker and pretty. I guess she'll be the one."

"She's a Christian. She won't marry you if you aren't a Christian, too," I reminded him.

"I know. I've been thinking a lot about that, Cry. I think I might try out this new God you are always talking about. He helped you; maybe He'll help me."

It was all I could do to keep from shouting with joy.

"Flint, you'll never be sorry if you decide to believe in Jesus and be saved!"

"Might as well. What have I got to lose?" He shrugged.

He was acting as if he were treating the matter lightly, but I knew Flint never treated anything lightly. He had given it a lot of thought and had come to a decision. He looked embarrassed, and I knew he was waiting for me to say something.

"You'll be glad you chose Jesus. I'm proud of you, and I know you and Autumn Rose will be happy and have many sons. You can believe in God and still be an Indian. Being a Christian makes you more of a man, not less."

He looked relieved. "I guess I might as well get it over with, now that I've made up my mind. I'm going to see Autumn Rose tonight and set the date."

Now I was able to say something to Flint that I had been saving in my heart for months. "God bless you, my uncle!"

I was happy for him but I was sad for myself because I knew our wandering days were over. Flint would have a wife and then children. He couldn't go running wild like the wind anymore.

Uncle Cloud came home for the wedding and stood with Flint as his best man. I looked at the two of them as they stood handsome and proud at the front of the church. The last of my seven uncles; two were dead, one was in prison, and two were missing, and we didn't know if they were dead or alive.

I watched Flint and Autumn Rose as they pledged their love, and I felt a dull ache as I wished it could have been Yellow Thunder and myself being married that day. I closed my eyes and once again saw his face. When I looked up I saw the bride and groom coming down the aisle. I had never seen Flint so happy.

After the wedding Cloud drove me home. On the way, I said, "It made Flint happy to have you here today. He needed his brother beside him. I'm glad you came, too; I didn't think I'd ever see you again."

He smiled. "It's a miracle, Cry, the way you and Flint and I all believed in the old Indian religion and worshiped the old gods, and then within a few months we all heard the gospel for the first time and got saved. It's really a miracle."

I agreed with him and then asked, "Did you know Kansas stayed with me awhile? I tried to share our story with him, but he wouldn't listen. I felt terrible when he was killed." I took a deep breath and tried not to let my voice tremble as I asked Cloud, "Do you think—do you think Kansas went to hell?"

He chewed on his lower lip a minute before he answered. "I don't know, Cry. I don't think there is any way we can know who will be in heaven or hell until we die and get to heaven ourselves. The thief that died on the cross next to Jesus confessed and believed in the last minutes of his life, and Jesus said He would see him in heaven. Maybe Kansas did the same thing."

"I'd like to believe that," I said quietly.

"So would I," he agreed.

"Let's do believe it—maybe it really did happen that way," I said hopefully.

"Maybe," he said and changed the subject.

We began telling each other about all the things that had

happened to us since he had gone to Oregon and left me in Colorado after Grandmother's death.

Then he spoke of his girlfriend. "I wish you could meet her," he said, and his eyes sparkled. "She is so sweet and gentle, like a fawn. She was the one who told me about God. We're getting married in the spring." He stole a quick glance at me to see my reaction.

"I'm happy you found someone. I hope you and Flint both have happy homes and many children."

"And what about you, Crying Wind? Have you found someone?" he asked.

I looked at him and hesitated, unsure whether or not to tell him about Yellow Thunder.

Before I had made up my mind, Cloud said, "Flint told me about Yellow Thunder. I'm sorry, Cry. You'll get over him. There will be someone else some day."

"No," I whispered, "there will never be anyone else."

"Cry, would you like to go hunting? Maybe we could get some fresh meat for you before I go back to Oregon. I have my bow in the back of the truck."

"I'd like that!"

We stopped at the apartment, and I changed my clothes, and we were on our way to the high mountains.

I walked quietly behind Cloud as he moved like a shadow through the thick forest. The smell of pine and damp earth was thick in the cool air. Cloud was the best hunter and trapper I had ever known, but he would never kill an animal for sport. He loved the wild creatures and took only what he needed for food. Cloud crouched near a fallen log and pointed to a small buck grazing on the side of the hill. He pulled his bowstring tight, took careful aim, and let the arrow fly to its mark. The arrow flew silently through the air and found its way to the deer's heart. Cloud walked over to where the deer had fallen and spoke the ancient words, "Forgive me, my brother, my family must eat." He hesitated and looked at me. "I'm a Christian now. Is it wrong to still call the deer my brother?"

"I don't know. I don't see anything wrong with it. I think God meant us to feel close to animals. But—" I added, "but not like we used to in the old days, when we thought some animals were gods."

Cloud nodded, and I knew he remembered the time he had worshiped the eagle and bear gods. He bent over and began skinning the deer.

"Do you need the hide?" I asked.

"No, I don't want it. You can have it." He stood back, and I took his place beside the deer, skinning it with my hands instead of a knife because I wanted the hide for a dress and didn't want any knife marks on it. After I was finished, I rolled up the heavy hide and dragged it to the truck while Cloud struggled with the deer.

After Cloud left for Oregon I felt more alone than ever and spent as much time at the church and at Reverend McPherson's home as I could. I knew that at times I overstayed my welcome and that I came at mealtimes too often, but I didn't know what to do with myself. My hours were long and empty.

Audrey and Reverend McPherson may have groaned when they heard my knock at their door, but they were too kind to let me hear them. They always welcomed me and put an extra plate on the table.

I changed jobs again and worked in a greenhouse, but my thumb was red, not green, and plants seemed to just look at me and curl up and die.

Once again I sat in Reverend McPherson's study and announced I was unemployed.

"Crying Wind, soon you will hold a world record for changing jobs!" he scolded gently. "What are we going to do with you?"

"I'm lonely. Now that Cloud is gone again and Flint is married and Kansas is dead, I feel like the last of the Kickapoos."

"You need a cause, a calling, something you believe in that would add richness and purpose to your life," he said.

"Any ideas?" I asked.

"No, I'm sorry, you'll have find your own calling. But I'll pray about," he promised, and I left.

The following morning I found a job as a cook's helper in an Italian restaurant, and I called Reverend McPherson. "Do you think my life's calling could be making spaghetti?" I asked.

He laughed and said he didn't think so, but he was glad I had a job.

After work that day I was walking home, and as I stood on a street corner waiting for the light to change to green I noticed a scrap of paper in the gutter. It had the word *Navajo* written on it.

I picked it up and brushed it off and read that a Navajo mission in New Mexico needed workers.

I knew this wasn't an accident. God had planned this just for me! He had put that paper in the gutter and had made the light red so I would see it while I waited. I was sure of it!

I went straight to see Audrey and Reverend McPherson.

"How is the spaghetti maker?" Audrey asked.

"I'm going to quit," I said, and ignored their protests as I smoothed out the piece of paper and handed it to them, "I've found my calling. It's God's will for me," I said confidently.

They looked at the paper and handed it back. "What is this?" they asked.

"It says a mission in New Mexico needs workers," I explained to them, as if they couldn't read. "That's me! I'm going there to work!"

"Where did you get this?" Audrey asked.

"I found it in the gutter while I was waiting for the traffic light to change. God put it there for me."

"It could have been there for weeks." Reverend McPherson looked at the dirt on it. "What mission is this? Who supports them? What do they believe?"

"I don't know. I'll write them today and say I'll come."

"Crying Wind, you have to think this over. It could be a cult or who knows what!" Reverend McPherson protested.

I folded up my precious piece of paper and left. I knew it was my calling, but it would take time to convince the McPhersons.

That night I realized what a big change had come over me since I had become a Christian.

Years ago, when we had heard about the five missionaries killed by the Auca Indians, we had laughed. We were glad they had been killed. Those missionaries asked for it; they had it coming! They deserved to die. After all, what the Indians believed was their business. Those missionaries didn't have any right to butt in where they weren't wanted! We were glad the Indians had killed them, and we joked about it. We recalled that our tribe had killed many missionaries and had cut their heads off. We had been proud of that fact.

Now I wanted to work with missionaries to tell Indians about Jesus. Only God could have brought about that kind of change in my heart.

I wrote to the mission that night and explained that I

was a Christian Indian and would come if they wanted me.

I waited on pins and needles until the answer came one week later. The missionaries asked me to come!

I almost ran to the church to show Reverend McPherson and Audrey the answer. "I'm going to work in a mission for Navajo Indians!" I shouted.

"What kind of mission? What is their doctrine? Who are they?" came the questions.

"I don't know." I shrugged. "I said I'd come, and they said OK."

Audrey rubbed her forehead as if it ached, and Reverend McPherson stared at me as if he thought I was losing my mind.

They argued for hours, but my mind was made up. In the end, Reverend McPherson loaned me a dozen books on prayer, doctrine, and devotions to take with me, and Audrey slipped twenty dollars into my pocket.

Once again we were saying good-bye, but it wasn't so painful this time, because I knew God's hand was in it.

I left on the midnight bus and rode five hundred miles to New Mexico. I was full of confidence and happy to have such a wonderful adventure ahead of me.

It wasn't until the bus door swung open and I stepped off and saw the mission truck waiting for me that I panicked. ☀

CHAPTER SEVEN

Among the Navajo

A large man with a friendly smile came up and shook my hand. "Hello and welcome," he said. I froze and my mind went blank. The only words I could remember were words I had heard my uncles say so many times. "Hi, honey!"

The missionary turned scarlet.

I bit my lip. "I'm sorry! I'm so nervous—I don't know why—I'll just get back on the bus and go home—" I stammered.

He began to laugh and picked up my bag and helped me to the truck, which had the name of the mission painted on its side.

Reverend Bell introduced me to his wife Lola, and we began the long, dusty drive to the mission.

The missionaries asked many questions, and my answers were a disappointment to them.

"You are younger than we expected. How old are you, Crying Wind?"

"I don't know."

"What Bible college did you attend?"

"None, but I've read most of the Psalms."

"What education do you have?"

"None worth mentioning."

Reverend Bell went into a fit of choking.

Lola smiled nervously. "How long have you been a Christian?"

"A few months."

Her smile trembled and she simply said, "Oh."

Reverend Bell was once again in control. "What church is sponsoring you?"

"None. I just came on my own."

"But you said in your letter you spoke Navajo," Lola said encouragingly.

"Well, I used to, but I've forgotten a lot. I think I can pick it up again."

Reverend Bell turned red but remained silent.

Luckily we arrived at the mission soon after that. It was a brown adobe building with many rooms and had a chapel beside it. I fell in love with it at first sight. It was old and run down, but to me it was beautiful.

The sun went to bed and covered the sky with his red blanket. I unpacked and put my things away in my small room. Then Reverend Bell and Lola and I walked around the mission grounds.

I felt great peace in my heart, and knew it was God's plan for me to be here. Now it was up to God to convince Reverend Bell and Lola!

For the first time I was dealing with Christian Indians, and it thrilled my heart. The hours were long and the work was hard, and since I had come on my own, without support of a church, I received no pay. Once a week Audrey sent a letter and five dollars for my personal needs. I was working fourteen hours a day every day and getting five dollars a week, and I had never been happier.

I liked Lola and Reverend Bell, and they treated me as one of the family. I helped Lola with the cooking and housework and other chores and taught Bible verses in English and Navajo. Several times a week we would go around the reservation and visit the Navajo families in their hogans.

One day Lola wasn't feeling well and didn't want to travel the eighty miles through the hot desert and bumpy road to visit the settlements, so Reverend Bell and I went together and left Lola at the mission to rest. We had the truck loaded with clothes to give the women and candy for the children.

We had just left the first family, when Reverend Bell decided to cut across country and save ten miles instead of going down the road.

We hadn't gone far when he drove through a pile of tumbleweeds. He found out too late that the tumbleweeds were hiding a deep ditch, and we felt as though the world dropped out from under the truck.

When the dust settled, we climbed out of the truck and looked for damage. We had one flat tire, and a hole was poked in the gas tank. We plugged up the hole the best we could with a stick and changed the tire.

After several tries, Reverend Bell drove the truck back up the steep ditch and we were on our way once again.

We had gone only a few miles when the truck choked, gasped and died. Reverend Bell turned the key several times, trying to start it, but it only groaned.

"We're out of gas," he said. "It's only a couple of miles to Old Mustache Woman's house. We can get help there."

When we got out of the truck the heat hit us like a giant fly swatter and almost knocked us to the ground. It was hard to breathe, and our eyes watered from the glaring white sun. Walking through the sand was slow, we were hot, and our mouths were too dry to talk.

I walked ahead of Reverend Bell, and when I looked back I saw he had dropped far behind me. As I sat down beside the road to wait for him, I noticed a beer can a few feet away. I picked up a pebble and threw it at the can. The pebble hit it with a dull clank. The can was not empty. I reached over and picked it up and shook it vigorously. The can had not been opened and was full of beer. It must have fallen out of some-one's truck.

Reverend Bell walked up beside me. "What have you got there?" he asked, looking at the can in my hand.

"It's full of beer. I found it lying here in the sand." I handed it to him.

He looked at it and said, "I think I'll remove temptation from someone and pour this out in the sand, where it can do no harm." He grabbed the ring and yanked it off. At the same instant he was sprayed by a fountain of hot beer! He was soaked from head to foot and smelled like a brewery.

He looked at me with a red face and beer foam on top of his head.

I burst into shrieks of laughter and sat down on the sand and giggled helplessly. He stomped away across the sand, leaving me behind wiping tears from my eyes and laughing hysterically!

I thought it would be wise to walk behind him. It was better for him to think the hot sun had made the beer explode rather than my shaking the can to see if it was full!

The hot sun had dried out his clothing by the time we reached Mustache Woman's house, but the odor of beer lingered.

The dogs began barking as we approached the hogan. A gray, bent old woman pulled aside the blanket that served as a door, and she stepped outside.

"*Yah'a'teh*," she said.

"*Yah'a'teh*," said Reverend Bell, and he began telling her our reason for being there.

She said her son would be back soon with his truck and he would give us a ride back to the mission. While she spoke she kept sniffing the air and giving Reverend Bell suspicious looks, which he tried to ignore.

As we stood talking beside the hogan I noticed a bucket of water sitting on a stump. My tongue was stuck to the roof of my mouth. I nudged Reverend Bell and nodded toward the bucket of water.

Mustache Woman reached into her pocket and drew out a piece of black chewing tobacco and bit off a chunk with her few remaining teeth. In the next instant I knew how she had gotten her name. Tobacco juice streaked around her mouth and ran down her chin, making her look as if she had a mustache and beard.

She reached over and picked up a metal dipper and filled it with water from the bucket and offered it to me. I looked at her mouth and decided I wasn't as thirsty as I had thought I was. I couldn't bring myself to drink from her dipper.

She offered the dipper of water to Reverend Bell, and he took it and held it in his hands. He looked once again at the tobacco juice running down her chin, and then he looked back at the dipper. Thirst won the battle, and he took the dipper and turned it sideways. He drank awkwardly from exactly where the handle was attached, thinking that by drinking there his mouth would not touch where hers had.

The old woman laughed and slapped her knee and cackled, "Reverend Bell! You drink from the dipper the same way I do!" Then she spat.

Reverend Bell turned pale and sat down in the shade of a mesquite bush to recover.

He wiped his face with his handkerchief and said, "Crying Wind, I wondered why the Lord chose to send you to us, and today I found out. The Lord, in His wisdom, has used you to teach me humility today. When I became a minister I swore liquor and tobacco would never touch these lips. And thanks to you—" he glared at me—"I've been introduced to both vices in an hour!"

The ride back to the mission was silent except for the few times I couldn't hold back a small giggle.

After Reverend Bell recovered from his brush with alcohol and tobacco we had many laughs about our adventure. Whenever anyone mentioned the sin of pride, Reverend Bell would laugh and say, "Turn Crying Wind loose—she can make a person very humble very fast!"

After I had been at the mission one month a second volunteer worker arrived. She was a pretty blond girl with one year of Bible college behind her, and she felt she was being called to be a missionary. I eagerly awaited her arrival, because as much as I liked the Bells, I welcomed having someone near my own age.

Sharon was energetic and eager to win souls. The daily drudgery of kitchen chores and laundry rubbed against her grain. She wanted to be in the field spreading the gospel, not up to her elbows in dirty dishes.

At last her day came. Reverend Bell, Lola, Sharon, and I rode in the truck across the desert to visit a Navajo settlement twenty miles away.

"I'm so excited!" Sharon was bubbling with enthusiasm. "How many do you think will get saved today?"

"Probably none. Saving a soul is as rare as rain in the desert. It takes patience. Last year I saw only five people come to the Lord," Reverend Bell answered.

Sharon was more determined than ever to bring someone to God that day.

We parked the truck and walked into the Navajo camp. A Navajo woman with a half-dozen children clinging to her motioned us into her hogan.

The heat inside made it like an oven, and we had a hard time breathing. The Navajo woman and children crowded into one half of the hogan, and we sat in the other half, forming a circle on the dirt floor. The smell of the children's unwashed bodies hung heavy in the hot summer air.

The Navajo woman served us each fry bread and a cup of stew. Sharon looked at the thick grease floating on top of her stew and whispered, "What do you think is in this?"

"Never ask!" I whispered back and took a bite. "It tastes a little like—" I looked around. "I wonder what happened to that old, gray cat they had?"

Sharon choked on her last mouthful of stew and turned pale.

"I was about to say, it tastes like mutton," I finished.

Sharon pointed at the only decoration inside the hogan. "What's that?" she asked.

It was a long, black horse's tail, which the Navajo woman used as a comb holder. It looked for all the world like a scalp.

"I don't want to talk about it," I whispered, and Sharon's eyes grew wide.

At the same instant the Navajo woman spoke several words and pointed at Sharon.

Reverend Bell said, "Sharon, she just said your hair is like sunshine and she likes it very much."

Sharon put both hands on top of her head, scrambled to her feet, and ran to the mission truck, where she remained behind locked doors until it was time to leave.

As we drove away from the camp she finally stopped holding her hair. "Nobody told me Indians stink!" she said, on the verge of tears. "Those heathens!"

"They only get one quart of water per day per person from their shallow well. They need it to drink, not to waste on washing. They smell like dust and campfire smoke and sagebrush. You smell like toothpaste, deodorant, perfume, hair spray and powder. They think you smell funny," Reverend Bell explained.

Before we reached the mission we ran into a dust storm that left us choking and rubbing our eyes and scratching our itchy skin.

Sharon began scratching her head. Her hair spray had acted as a dust magnet, and her scalp was becoming irritated. The more she scratched, the more she itched.

"What a horrible day!" she groaned as we drove onto the mission grounds. "I feel so dirty! I can't understand what's making my head itch like this!"

"I hope it isn't lice," I said dryly. "You know how dirty those heathens are."

Sharon screamed, "Lice, I've got lice!" and she jumped out of the truck before Reverend Bell shut off the engine. Before we got inside the house she was washing her hair in the shower. A half-hour later she was still in the shower.

"Maybe you should go tell her it was just the dust making her itch," Lola suggested.

"She probably wouldn't believe me. After all, I'm 'one of them,'" I said.

Lola knocked on the bathroom door and finally convinced Sharon to come out.

"I'll never marry a missionary!" Sharon yelled. "I'm going to marry a minister who has a nice, quiet, civilized church in the middle of Los Angeles!"

Two days later she packed and left, just before we were ready to visit another Navajo camp.

I missed her, and I felt guilty after she left. I knew I could have made things easier for her. I really shouldn't have teased her about the horse's tail hanging in the hogan. How was I to know she believed Indians still scalped people? I hoped she would find her minister and that he would have a big city church. She would be a good minister's wife. I was sure she would have some interesting tales to tell her children about the two weeks she spent among the "savages"!

We would rejoice when Indians came to Christ, and we would weep when we saw nearly half of them return to the old ways, going to the medicine man and ancient ceremonies and turning their backs on Jesus.

One day Blue Glass, a woman we considered our most faithful Christian, came to the mission asking for clothes.

"What happened to the clothes we gave you last week?" Lola asked.

Blue Glass looked at the floor and explained that she had washed them and hung them out to dry, and a dust devil had swept through them. Now they had little devils in them, and she was afraid to even take them off the clothesline. She was going to pay the medicine man a sheep to come to take all the clothes down and burn them for her, to protect her from the dust-devil spirits.

Lola sighed and gave her some more clothes. "Do we ever reach them?" she asked tiredly. "Do we ever really reach them?"

Pony Boy Chee was a young warrior who caused more

trouble than anyone in the area. He let air out of the tires of the mission truck, threw rocks at our windows, and threatened to burn the mission down. When he stole a horse belonging to the medicine man, everyone waited anxiously to hear the outcome, because the medicine man put a curse on him. He said that Pony Boy Chee would be burned up like dry grass.

Reverend Bell was aware of the constant battle between demonic power and the power of Christ, and he decided to use that as the topic for his sermon on Sunday. He said that although the evil power of the devil was very real, he didn't really believe the medicine man's curse would come true and that Pony Boy Chee, being the stinker he was, would probably live to a ripe old age.

That same Sunday afternoon, Pony Boy Chee was caught trying to rob a grave on the sacred burial grounds, and he was arrested by the Navajo police. As they were driving him into town to jail, a sudden thunderstorm blew up and rain came down in such heavy sheets the Navajo police were forced to pull the car off the road and wait out the storm.

Pony Boy Chee saw his chance and jumped out of the car and started to run. He hadn't gone a hundred yards when a bolt of lightning struck him and killed him on the spot. The police said his handcuffs must have attracted the lightning. The medicine man just smiled a lot and took advantage of his new power over those who believed his curse on Pony Boy Chee had come true.

I loved working at the mission and was very fond of Lola and Reverend Bell but many things troubled my heart about the way the mission was managed.

When clothes arrived for the Indians, Lola carefully went through each box and barrel and picked out the best of everything for Reverend Bell and herself. I learned that many missionaries did this, even though most poorly paid missionaries earned at least $8,000 a year and the average Indian family of six earned $1,000 a year at that time. Surplus clothes were stored in boxes in an old wooden shed.

"Why can't we just give out all the clothes as soon as they arrive?" I asked.

"The Indians don't appreciate them as much. It's better to dole out a little at a time," they would answer. I could understand that one shouldn't overwhelm a family with excess clothing; but I couldn't understand why Indian families had to freeze while dozens of boxes of good clothing sat in a dirty shed and molded or were eaten by mice and moths. Eventually they had to be burned because they were ruined.

Ladies' groups from many churches sent quilts for the Indians, but once again the missionaries didn't give them away freely. An Indian woman had to earn a quilt by coming to church six Sundays in a row. So her family shivered during the cold nights until she earned her quilt by walking many miles in all kinds of weather to meet her required Sundays. If she came five Sundays and missed the sixth, she had to start all over again. It seemed hopeless, and quilts were stacked up in the storage shed while children slept cold.

"We can't let the Indians use us or take advantage of us," Reverend Bell would scold when I complained about the policies. "And be sure to keep all the doors locked. You know how Indians steal," he would say, forgetting that I, too, was Indian.

There was no record of anything ever being stolen from the mission. Indians, on the whole, do not steal. If an Indian does take anything it is nearly always food or an animal that can be butchered and eaten.

Reverend Bell was not the only one who made such sad mistakes in dealing with the Indians. Nearly every missionary in the area was equally guilty. They were all white people dealing with the red man, whom they didn't understand at all. Nearly half of the missionaries couldn't speak a word of Navajo, and several missionaries were just killing time until the doors opened to a more glamorous mission field in China or India or South America. The Bells had wanted to serve in Africa but had been turned down and had taken the Navajo as second choice. They never got over the disappointment, and it showed in their attitude.

After a year with the Bells I could see the mission system would never change until Indian preachers had their own missions. The white man could never reach the Indian as long as he looked at him as inferior, untrustworthy and childish. The sheds filled with rotting clothes and quilts bothered me, and my heart broke over the way the missionaries treated the Indians.

I didn't want to leave the mission, because I loved the Indian Christians, but I was too restless to stay, and I knew it was time to move on. I had grown in my Christian life; it had been good for me to be in Christian surroundings for a year. I would always remember these days as happy times, and I remained friends with Reverend Bell and Lola in spite of our differences over mission policies.

My last night at the mission I stood motionless and looked out across the desert at the red sun sinking into the sand. Now it was only a scarlet sliver, and in another second it would be gone. I felt so lonely I wanted to cry. I could hear Lola and Reverend Bell talking in the house, man-and-wife talk about had she remembered to pay the light bill? And did he notice the cat was going to have kittens? Small, unimportant things, but things that weave two lives together.

Would I ever have anyone to share small talk with? I doubted it. What did I have to offer anyone? My family called me Double Ugly because I was twice as ugly as anyone else. No man would marry a girl called Double Ugly. I wished that somehow I could become beautiful. I kept waiting to "bloom" like other girls did, but instead of blooming I seemed to be wilting on the vine. I wasn't going to get any better looking; there was no Cinderella story for me. I cringed when I looked into the mirror. If only I had one good feature I could make the most of—but I didn't, and my uncles had been right, I was Double Ugly.

"God—"

I almost asked "Why didn't you make me pretty?" But there wasn't much point to that, so I just said, "Don't let me want things I can't have. I know I'll never have a home or a husband or a family, so teach me not to want them, and show me how to be satisfied with only You."

I felt guilty as I walked back up the dusty trail to the mission for the last time. God should be enough for anyone. Why did I want more? After all, it wasn't so long ago that I had nothing. Was I just greedy? Would anything ever satisfy me? ☀

CHAPTER EIGHT

Lonely

I t was a joyful homecoming when I returned to Audrey and Reverend McPherson. We talked for hours and tried to catch up on a whole year in one day. Once again, I stayed at their home until I could find a job and an apartment.

I looked up my Uncle Flint and found he had a baby son. Cloud also was married and had a baby daughter. They both seemed content with their new lives, and they were both becoming dedicated Christians.

A home, a wife and a baby had put a smile on Flint's face. He was working hard at a steady job. He was at peace with God, himself, and the world at last.

I took a job selling stationary and cards. It was easy work, and I liked the people I worked with. I made a new friend named Daisy, who was also a Christian, and we spent a lot of time laughing and sharing and praying together.

I felt as if everyone in the world were married except me. I read books on how to be single and happy, books on living alone, and even books on how to catch a husband, but nothing helped.

I spent hours talking to Reverend McPherson, and every conversation sounded the same.

"I'm lonely," I would begin.

"I know," he would answer.

"I want to get married," I continued.

He smiled. "Just getting married won't cure loneliness. Some of the loneliest people I know are married."

"Anything would be better than this," I shrugged.

"No, you're wrong. You could be a lot worse off. Believe me, a dozen people come to my office every week who are trapped in unhappy marriages and would give anything to be single again."

I nodded. I knew he was right. I knew many unhappy married women.

"You're young. It's a natural instinct to seek out a mate; you're hearing the 'call of the wild.' Be patient. If you make a mistake now, it could ruin the rest of your life."

"I don't suppose you know any half-breed who is looking for a squaw to keep his teepee warm?" I meant it as a joke, but it came out flat, and he didn't smile.

"Do you want to marry a—a man who is half Indian and half white?" He always refused to use the term *half-breed*.

"I don't know who else would have me. A full-blood Indian won't marry me."

"You wouldn't really want to go back and live on the reservation, would you?"

"No," I was quick to answer. There was too much poverty and hunger there. I would never go back. I didn't want to live in a one-room shack with a dirt floor. I wanted a real house, with electricity and water.

"You must marry a Christian man. Be sure he is a Christian before you marry him, because there's very little chance he'll change his ways after you're married."

"I've got to find him first," I said.

"Don't be in a hurry. He might be right around the next corner." He paused. "Or maybe God wants you to remain single."

"He must, or He wouldn't have made me look this way!" I complained.

"Crying Wind, you aren't an old maid! You are still very young. You have time to look around and make sure you get the right man. Let God guide you."

"That's easy to say. You aren't alone; you have Audrey."

"Yes, that's true. Sometimes it's too easy to give advice." He was quiet awhile and then he said, "Just don't get hurt." And the name *Yellow Thunder* hung unspoken in the air.

I walked back to my apartment, shut the door behind me, and stood in the darkness. Loneliness like winter frost filled every part of my body and left me cold and shivering.

It would soon be Valentine's Day. How I hated Valentine's Day! It was a screaming reminder that I was alone. I had never had a Valentine and probably would never get one.

I placed the Valentines on the card rack. Stupid cards! I picked one up and started to place it in the display rack and then hesitated. It was such a beautiful card. It had a huge, red heart on it and said, "For you, darling, all my love, all my life." I held it in my hands and studied it, reading the verse over and over. On an impulse I put it in my purse and paid for it when Daisy wasn't watching.

That night I placed it on my table and looked at it as I ate my dinner. How I wished I would get a real Valentine someday. What a difference a silly paper with a heart on it could make!

Daisy dropped in to visit, and soon she noticed the Valentine sitting on the table. She picked it up.

"Oh, Crying Wind, it's so pretty! Who is it from?" She opened the card. "It's not signed!"

I held my breath.

"A secret admirer!" she gasped. "How exciting! Do you know who it is?" She put the card back on the table.

I wanted to let the matter drop, but Daisy was too good a friend to deceive.

"I bought it for myself," I confessed.

"Me and my big mouth," she apologized.

After she left I took the Valentine, looked at it one more time, and threw it into the trash. I hated Valentine's Day!

The months dragged by. I thought of only one day at a time and never allowed myself to think of the future. I never missed church, but I had lost some of the joy I had known when I had first found God.

The skies always looked stormy, and there was always a gray wind blowing. There was no color in my world. ❈

CHAPTER NINE

Gray Eyes

The store was being remodeled and we were given three days off. I was planning to sleep late and do a lot of reading, but the phone rang early and woke me up from a sound sleep. It was Daisy calling about a picnic.

"I don't want to go. I'm too tired," I yawned. "I'll go next time."

"No, we're counting on you. You'll wake up as soon as we get up in the cool mountain air. We'll be by to get you in fifteen minutes. Be ready." She hung up.

I hung up the phone and snuggled back down in bed. I could go back to sleep, and when she came I would ignore her. My eyes blinked back open. I couldn't ignore Daisy; she would bang the door down until I answered. I might as well get up. I would go this time, but never again. I felt irritable. I was tired. The last thing I wanted to do was go on a picnic in the mountains. I pulled on an old pair of patched jeans and an old, faded shirt that had belonged to one of my uncles. I barely got a brush through my hair before I heard a horn honk outside. I practically staggered out to the car and flopped into the back seat beside two other girls.

"I'm sleepy," I mumbled. Daisy and her uncle and the other girls laughed and joked while I looked out the window and wished I were back in bed.

"My Uncle Dan thought he'd come along and do some fishing while we were getting the food ready," Daisy said over her shoulder.

I shivered. A fisherman. The thought of fish made my skin crawl. To my people, fish were unclean and had the spirits of evil women in them. My people would never eat fish! This just wasn't my day.

After traveling over winding roads for an hour, we reached the high mountain pass, and Daisy said, "This is it! Everybody out." Everyone grabbed food and blankets, and Daisy's Uncle Dan grabbed his fishing pole and headed for the trout stream nearby.

I spread out a blanket for our table and helped put the food out.

It wasn't long before Daisy and her friends were standing on the rocks beside Dan and offering him suggestions on his fishing technique. I watched from a distance for awhile but became bored sitting by myself, so I headed down to the trout stream to join the others.

There was a lot of giggling and silliness as the girls teased Dan, and he took it good-naturedly. I found myself laughing at them and was beginning to be glad I had come along.

"Why don't you guys go help that fisherman over there

and leave me alone so I can get down to some serious fishing?" he said, trying to get rid of us.

It was the first time I had noticed that there was another fisherman downstream. He was too far away for me to see him clearly, but I could tell he was young and tall and strong looking.

Daisy looked downstream. "We could go down and ask if he's caught anything and what he's using for bait." And with that she and the other girls headed through the willows and across the rocks toward the other fisherman.

I sat down on a rock and leaned against a tree and watched the water rush by.

Dan laid down his pole and said something about having to go back to the car for more bait, and I was left alone.

I looked at the fishing pole lying beside me. I had never been fishing. After all, why would I want to catch something I would never eat? No, fish were dirty and unfit to eat. Even though I was a Christian now and knew there were no evil spirits in fish, I still couldn't bring myself to eat one of them.

I nudged the fishing pole with my foot. What an odd thing, a string and a hook on a stick. It didn't look hard to use. I wondered why people made such a fuss about it.

I looked up toward the car. Dan was digging around in the trunk, with his back to me. The girls were nowhere in sight. On a sudden impulse I picked up the pole and held it in my hands. I stood up and dipped the hook into the water.

Wouldn't it be funny if I caught a big fish! I smiled to myself. That would be a good joke on everybody! I would have to get the hook out in deeper water as Dan had. *Let's see, you push this little round thing, and then you toss the pole backward and let it go, and then the hook lands far out into the water.*

Something was wrong! The hook hadn't gone out into the water! I turned around and looked in back of me. I had flipped the hook up into the trees, and it was tangled around a small limb. I jerked it a couple of times, and the pole bent. I looked toward the car. Dan was sitting on the blanket and drinking a cup of coffee. He didn't see me. I pulled on the pole again. The string wouldn't budge! Panic set in. Why couldn't I leave well enough alone! Now I had probably ruined Dan's fishing machine and made a fool of myself. I wondered if I could climb up the tree and get it untangled. No, this wasn't a climbing tree. What in the world was I going to do? I stood there looking up into the tree and didn't hear footsteps behind me.

"There aren't any fish up there," a man's voice said.

The pole slipped from my hand. I whirled around and found myself looking into two gray eyes set in a tough-looking face.

He reached up and untangled the fishing line from the branch and turned the little handle until it was neatly wound up again. He handed the pole to me, and I let out a sigh of relief and laid it back where Dan had left it.

I could feel the gray eyes watching me, and I wished he would go away. Just then I heard Daisy and the other girls pushing their way through the bushes. Daisy appeared first, picking leaves out of her hair.

"Oh, I see you've met Don," she said. "We've invited him to have lunch with us." Daisy walked past us with the other girls close behind her. "Did he tell you he's from Alaska? He's just here on vacation," she said and started up the path toward the picnic.

I hurried after her and wondered if Gray Eyes was going to tell everyone he had rescued me, but he didn't mention it.

Uncle Dan and the fisherman and the girls talked easily about the mountains and fishing, but mostly the girls asked him questions about Alaska. It was easy to see he loved the wilderness of his northern home.

I sat on a corner of the blanket and tried to eat lunch, but every time I looked up from my plate, old Gray Eyes was watching me. I became too nervous to even swallow my food.

After we had cleaned up the food and dishes, Dan suggested we all walk up the hill and look at the waterfall. I fussed over folding up the blanket until I saw they all were well on their way up the hill. Then I followed far behind.

I didn't try to catch up with the others until they had reached the waterfall. They were talking about crossing the stream and climbing to the top of the cliff. There was a three-foot jump across the fast-moving water. Dan was the first to go, and he made it easily. Daisy was next, and she nearly lost her footing and had to scramble a bit to get on solid ground. The two girls jumped across to the other side, and Gray Eyes simply stepped across with his long legs. Now everyone turned and waited for me to follow. I stepped up to the edge of the rocks and looked down at the swirling water. I wasn't sure I wanted to cross the stream.

"Come on, Cry!" Daisy urged.

The Alaskan leaned out over the water and held out his hand toward me. "Here, take my hand. I'll help you across," he said.

I hesitated. I didn't want to take his hand, but I was afraid I was going to fall into the water if I didn't.

"Trust me. I won't let you fall," said the Alaskan.

I took a deep breath and held out my hand. Strong fingers curled around mine and pulled me across the water, but when I was safely on the other side they didn't let go. I started to pull away, but the grip was firm, though gentle, and Gray Eyes led me up the path to the top of the cliff. Only when we reached the top did he allow my hand to slip out of his.

Daisy and the girls were picking wild flowers, and Dan was sitting on a rock to catch his breath.

The Alaskan reached down and picked a columbine and held it for a minute.

"Can you talk?" he asked.

I nodded my head yes.

He smiled and handed me the flower.

"It's pretty," I said.

"So are you," he said softly.

I looked at him to see if he was making a joke, but he was not laughing. My heart sank to my toes and then climbed back up again. I backed away and walked over to stand beside Daisy for protection. When I looked back, he was talking to Dan and seemed to have forgotten about me.

Why couldn't he go back to his fishing and leave us alone. After all, it was our picnic, not his!

We took a different trail back to the car, and I stayed as far away from the Alaskan as I could. It wasn't until we were starting to get into the car that he caught up with me.

"Do you have a boyfriend?" he asked.

I shook my head no.

"Can I see you again?" he asked.

I looked around. Everyone was watching us, and I could feel my face getting red.

"Where do you live?" he asked.

Dan started the car.

Daisy couldn't stand the suspense and said, "Since you are new here, why don't you come to church Sunday? We'd be glad to have you. It's the little brick church on Thirtieth Street." Then she added, "Crying Wind never misses a service," and she giggled.

The Alaskan smiled at her. "Thanks. I'll see you Sunday."

I refused to look at him as we drove away. Instead I looked down at the wilting columbine that I still held in my hand.

Occasionally the girls would nudge each other with their elbows and giggle and say that Dan hadn't caught any fish but it looked like Crying Wind had caught a man. I was glad when they left me at the door of my apartment.

Later, when I was alone, I gently placed the flower between the pages of a book. I would remember the day when a stranger had called Double Ugly pretty.

Sunday morning as I walked to church I wondered if Gray Eyes would show up. I found myself wishing he wouldn't. He made me uncomfortable. I didn't see him when I entered the church, and I felt relieved. Well, that was that; I'd never see him again.

I had hardly sat down when someone sat down beside me, and I looked up into the face of the Alaskan. My hands trembled as I held the hymnbook, and I stole quick glances at the man beside me. His face was hard and tough looking, and his jaw was square and firm. With his blonde hair and gray eyes, he really was a "pale face." It was only when he smiled that his gray eyes twinkled and gave way to the warmth inside. He was tall and had broad shoulders. His hands were strong and covered with scars and calluses from years of hard work.

For the first time since I had started coming to this church I didn't hear the sermon, because my thoughts were on the stranger beside me.

As soon as the last *amen* was said we stood up to leave, and several people came over to meet "the man who sat beside Crying Wind." While he was busy talking to them I slipped out the other side of the pew and stood beside Audrey.

"Is he your boyfriend?" she asked with a smile.

"I don't know him; he's a friend of Daisy's" I shrugged.

"It's strange he didn't sit beside Daisy," she said. "Why don't you come and have lunch with us? You can bring your friend if you want to. We'd be happy to have him." She patted my arm and began shaking hands with some of the people.

Gray Eyes was beside me again. "Can I take you out to lunch?"

"No, I'm eating with someone. Thanks anyway."

He looked disappointed. "Can I see you later today?"

"I don't know when I'll be home," I said.

"That's all right, I don't mind waiting. Where do you live?"

I looked around for someone to come to my rescue, but everyone was visiting. I gave him my address and hurried to where Audrey was waiting for me.

During lunch Audrey and Reverend McPherson had many questions about "the man who followed Crying Wind to church."

"I don't know him at all," I tried to explain. "He's a stranger here, and I doubt I'll ever see him again."

"Oh, I'm sure we'll see him again," Audrey laughed.

I was glad when the conversation turned to other things. ☀

CHAPTER TEN

Tears and Fears

I'd been home nearly an hour and was painting a picture of a sunset when there was a knock on my door. When I opened it, I was once again face to face with Gray Eyes.

"Hi. I heard a man was supposed to bring flowers and candy when he came courting." He smiled and handed me a penny sucker and some sad-looking dandelions. "I wanted to bring you something, but I couldn't find a store open."

"I didn't hear your car," I said.

"It needed some work done on it, so I left it at a garage and walked here from Red Rocks Park."

"That's five miles," I said.

"It didn't seem very far. Besides, I have the feeling I came two thousand miles to meet you." He followed me inside.

We spent the afternoon working on a jigsaw puzzle I had started earlier. I couldn't think of a single thing to talk about, and whenever he tried to break the long silences by asking me a question, I would answer either yes or no, and again we would sit in silence.

He slipped the last piece of puzzle into place and stood up and stretched. "I have to go pick up my car now. Would you like to go out tonight?"

I hesitated, wondering what in the world we could talk about on a date. Besides, I didn't own any "dress up" clothes or even a pair of shoes—only moccasins, which were old and worn.

"No, I guess not," I said.

"We could go anywhere you would like to," he said.

I stood there looking at the floor. "I can't think of anyplace."

"I'll come back for you in a couple of hours. We'll go out to dinner," Then he left.

I shut the door and said to myself, *I didn't say I would go out with you.*

After dinner Don walked me to my door, and while I fumbled in my purse for my key he said, "I'm going to marry you someday. I only have a few days left here, and then I'll have to go back to Alaska. But someday I'll come back and marry you."

I dropped my purse, spilling everything in it. "You are making a joke," I said.

"No." He shoved my things back into my purse and handed it to me. "No, it's not a joke. I think we were meant for each other. I think our meeting was arranged, and I knew the minute I saw you that you were the one for me." He grabbed me and kissed me. "I love you, Crying Wind."

As soon as I got my breath back I said, "I can't marry anyone who doesn't belong to my church."

"I'll join."

"You have to be a Christian," I argued.

"I am a Christian," he said.

"Why would you want to marry me?" I asked.

"Because I love you. I'll never be rich. I have to work with my hands, but I can give you a house and food and clothes, and I'll take care you. I'll never lie to you, and I'll take you to church every Sunday."

"It's too fast. I can't think so fast," I said, trying to get my key into the lock. I was shaking so badly I kept missing.

"I don't have time to do things the right way. I can't court you and bring you presents. I'll have to court you after we're married. Look, I know you don't feel much for me now, but someday you will." He waited for me to speak.

"I'll think about it," I said and quickly slipped inside and shut the door.

I couldn't believe it! A man had asked me to marry him! He didn't care that I was a skinny, ugly half-breed!

I didn't sleep at all that night. Of course, it was silly to think about marrying a stranger. I didn't know anything about him. Besides, he wasn't the kind of man I wanted. I wanted to marry Yellow Thunder, but he didn't want me. What if this was my only chance to get married? What if I didn't marry this Don Stafford and I was an old maid and lived alone all my life? I couldn't be too choosy; after all, who did I think I was? I wasn't pretty or smart or rich. What did I have to offer? True, Reverend McPherson said I was worth more than a star, but I couldn't picture myself telling any man he was lucky to marry me because in God's sight I was worth more than a star!

Early the next morning Reverend McPherson called to tell me that my friend, Don Stafford, had seen him and asked to become a member of our church and that he would join on Sunday morning. I was too stunned to say anything.

Later that day the Alaskan came to see me. He brought a silver locket engraved, "All My Love, Don."

"Did you think about it?" he asked.

"Yes."

"Well?"

"I don't know," I answered.

"I understand. For all you know, I could be Blue Beard or Jack the Ripper."

"Who?"

"Never mind," he said.

"Thank you for the locket." I put it on.

"I bought something else—just in case." He handed me a small box.

I opened it and found two gold wedding bands. Why did white people think gold was pretty? To me, silver and turquoise would have been far more beautiful.

I felt tired. Tired of working, tired of being alone, tired of making decisions, tired of wondering about my future. "If you want me, I'll marry you." I sighed. What did I have to lose?

He grabbed me and picked me up so that my feet dangled at least a foot off the floor. I was sure my ribs would snap if he hugged me any tighter, and the only thought that raced through my mind was, *What have I done?*

That night I met Reverend McPherson in his office. "Don asked me to marry him," I said.

"What was your answer?" he asked.

"I said I would." I felt embarrassed.

"Do you love him?"

The silence was so heavy I could feel it. "I'm tired. I don't want to be alone anymore," I said almost in a whisper.

"I want you to be happy. Do you think you'll be happy with Don?" he asked.

"I don't know. He seems to be all right, and he doesn't think I'm too ugly to marry. I don't think I'll ever get another chance to get married."

"Did you pray about this and ask God's will for you?"

"I prayed, but I didn't hear any answer," I admitted. I was silent and looked at the floor.

"Marriage is difficult even when two people love each other," Reverend McPherson said. "But it's the love that holds it together during the hard times. Without love— well—" He made a hopeless gesture with his hands.

"But he must want me, or he wouldn't have asked me to marry him. He could do a lot better than me, but I'm the one he chose. It's the first time anyone ever wanted me. Besides, what have I got to lose?" I argued.

Reverend McPherson groaned and shut his eyes. "Crying

Wind! If you only knew! I can't tell you the heartbroken people who come here from unhappy homes."

"But I'm lonely!" I pleaded.

"But you might get married and still be lonely."

"Look, maybe this love business is overrated. Maybe people expect too much from love and they get disappointed. Maybe when you get married you shouldn't expect anything at all; then you won't be disappointed," I reasoned.

"What do you think your life will be like with Don?" he asked.

"I don't know. I'll keep his house and cook, and he'll provide food and shelter. It's a good deal."

"What about children?" he asked bluntly.

I blushed. "I don't want any."

"What does Don want?" he asked.

"I don't know. We didn't talk about it."

"Crying Wind! What are you doing with your life?" he demanded.

"My life hasn't been worth much so far. Maybe it will get better. All I know is that I don't want to be alone."

"But you aren't alone!" he said. "God loves you, we love you, you have friends in the church—"

"I know that, but every night I go home to an empty room, eat supper by myself, and spend my evening reading a book. I know God loves me, but I want someone to talk to and be with. I want to get married," I said.

"That's it, isn't it. You didn't say 'I want to marry Don,' you just said, 'I want to get married.'" He sighed.

"Don asked me, and nobody else has, so he's the one I'll marry," I said stubbornly.

"For the rest of your life, till death do you part?" he asked.

I refused to answer.

"Marriage isn't one of your jobs that you can quit after a week if you don't like it," he warned.

"I don't want to be alone," I repeated.

He rubbed his eyes as if he felt very tired. "I can see your mind is made up. I can't tell you how to live your life. I wish you would wait awhile, but if you won't, I would be proud to perform the marriage ceremony." He held my hand, "God bless you, Crying Wind, and God help you!"

I wrote to Cloud and told him I was getting married and that I would write again after I knew where I was going to live.

Next I told Flint.

"You're what?" he asked.

"I said I'm getting married."

He burst out laughing. "Are you serious?"

"Yes. I'm getting married in a few days." I swallowed hard and waited for the explosion I knew was coming.

"Who is it? You aren't even dating anyone!" he laughed.

"I met him a few days ago," I said.

"Who is he? Where is he from? What tribe does he belong to?" Flint asked.

"His name is Don Stafford. He's from Alaska." I took a deep breath. "He's white."

"He's white? You want to marry a white man? Are you crazy?" he yelled.

"He wants to marry me, and I said OK. He joined my church—" my voice trailed off.

"You know what they say about mixed marriages! Will your Mr. Stafford like being called a squaw man? You'll be called worse things than that. It will never work!" he said flatly.

"I've been called names all my life. You know that. Besides, I'm a half-breed, so that makes me half-white. Indian men don't want me. What do you expect me to do, wait for a half-breed to come along?"

"Your own mother was Indian and your father was a white man, and their marriage didn't last a month. That should prove something to you!"

"They weren't Christians. Don and I are both Christians," I argued.

"You're making a terrible mistake!" He paced the floor. "Why are you doing it?"

"You should understand better than anyone, Flint. I'm lonely," I said simply.

"You're selling yourself!" he shouted.

"I'm getting married!" I shouted back.

"Not for love! You're not getting married for love!" he yelled more.

"What do I know about love? Who has ever loved me?" I answered.

"You'll be sorry! He'll leave you in a month for a white woman. You'll be left with a baby and no place to go, and you'll end up like your mother."

I didn't want to argue anymore. "Please come to my wedding, Flint."

"No!" he growled.

"I came to yours," I said.

"We married for love. It wasn't a business deal!" he snapped.

"Try to understand—"

"I do understand. You sold out!" He lowered his voice. "Why does he want to marry you?"

"I don't know," I answered truthfully.

"You'd better think about this. What is he after?"

I braced myself for the same lecture I had heard all my life.

"You're hard to look at, Cry. You have a big nose and crooked teeth, your ears stick out, and you're too skinny to have a figure. You aren't even a good cook. A man would have to be crazy to want you!"

"Maybe I'm marrying a crazy man." I'd had enough. "Look, Flint, he said he'd marry me, and, like you said, I can't be choosy. If he only keeps me a month, then at least I'll know somebody wanted me for a month. If I end up with a baby, then I won't be alone anymore. I have nothing to lose."

I left feeling worse than when I had come. Once again thanks to Flint, I was aware of every fault I had, and I wondered, *Why would the Alaskan want to marry me?*

The next few days flew by. We had just ended our fifth date, and Don walked me to the door of my apartment.

"Well, tomorrow is the day," I said. "If you still want to go through with it."

He smiled. "I love you," he said.

I knew I was supposed to say "I love you" back, but I couldn't, so I said "Thank you," and shook his hand. "I'll see you at the church tomorrow." And with that I said good night to the man who was to be my husband the next day.

It was a cold, windy day. I woke up and felt fear spread from my heart down to my fingers, which were shaking so badly I couldn't hold a cup of coffee without spilling it.

Today is my wedding day. Today I'm going to marry Don Stafford from Alaska, I said to myself.

"Oh, no I'm not!" I answered and walked outside slamming the door behind me.

I went to a nearby riding stable and rented a horse.

"How long will you be gone?" the stable owner asked.

My wedding was set for two o'clock. "I'll be back at four o'clock," I said. I kicked the horse in his sides and galloped off toward the mountains.

The horse was fat and slow, but at least it was a horse, and riding beat walking any time.

A good ride always lifted my spirits, but today the farther I rode, the worse I felt. I kept seeing Mr. Stafford standing there in the church and waiting for me to show up; people watching the door, waiting for me—

No. No, I bet Mr. Stafford wasn't going to show up, either. He wasn't really going to marry me; it had been a joke. I smiled. It would be funny. Wouldn't everyone be surprised when neither the bride nor the groom showed up for the wedding? That would sure be a first for Reverend McPherson! I wished I could see the expression on his face when he had to explain to the people that there would be no wedding because the bride and groom had both changed their minds!

But what if the Alaskan did show up? What if he was there now, waiting for me? How embarrassing for him, how humiliating! How cruel of me!

My heart felt sick. I would have to go back. I had said I would marry him; I would have to do it.

I turned the horse around and headed toward the stable. The air was growing colder, and my hands were stiff and clumsy as I guided the horse back down the trail.

It was ten minutes before two o'clock when I sneaked in the back door of the church and walked into the kitchen, where Sally and Audrey were putting out punch and plates.

Sally looked up. "Where have you been? You aren't even dressed! You have hay in your hair!" She flew around the edge of the table and grabbed my hand, and she and Audrey dragged me off to a small room where a borrowed wedding dress was waiting.

"Did he show up?" I asked. "Is Mr. Stafford here?"

"Of course he's here! He's been here over an hour!" Audrey slipped the white lace dress over my head while Sally untied my moccasins and slid on some white shoes. "Where have you been?"

"I was horseback riding," I said.

"Horseback riding on your wedding day?" Sally looked up.

"I didn't think he would show up," I shrugged.

"Oh, for heaven's sake!" Audrey groaned. In a matter of minutes they had me dressed, the hay combed out of my hair, and a veil stuck on my head and they were pushing me out the door.

They each gave me a quick "God bless you!" and a hug and disappeared into the sanctuary.

I looked over to the exit door. *Maybe I could just walk out that door and go home and—*

"Are you ready?" Reverend McPherson's voice made me jump.

"I guess so. Did any of my uncles come?"

"No," he said.

"I didn't think they would." I shrugged.

"You look beautiful. May I give the bride away?" He smiled and took my arm.

The music started, and we entered the sanctuary. When we stepped inside I saw all my friends from the church, and a lump came to my throat and tears stung my eyes. Up in front the candles were flickering on the altar, and there stood the Alaskan, watching me and smiling.

I was petrified throughout the ceremony and reception and moved like a robot, with a frozen smile on my face.

In less than an hour we were ready to begin our lives as man and wife.

There was a bad moment when it was time to sign the marriage certificate.

"I don't want to change my name. If I'm Mrs. Don Stafford, what happens to Crying Wind?" I asked.

"You aren't changing your name, you're adding a name. It only means you belong to somebody. Now you are Crying Wind Stafford." Reverend McPherson handed me the pen and I signed.

The car door slammed shut behind me and everyone stood around the car waving and throwing rice. Audrey and Sally were crying, and Reverend McPherson looked worried. As the car pulled away, I realized again that I was going away with a stranger.

I glanced over at him. He didn't take his eyes off the road, but he said, "It's going to be all right. I promise you won't be sorry." He drove about a block and then reached into his pocket and pullet out an envelope and handed it to me.

"There's a hundred-dollar bill in there. Reverend McPherson gave it to me when we left and said it was from your friends at the church. You keep it; it's yours. Call it escape money, and if you are ever unhappy, you can take the money and come back to your friends."

I reached over and took the money and hid it in my purse. I felt better. *Escape money.* I liked that. Now I could leave any time I wanted to.

And so began my life as Mrs. Don Stafford. I was married to a quiet stranger I had known only a few days. I went to my marriage bed with tears in my eyes, fear in my heart, and the knowledge that I had married a man I didn't love while I still carried memories of Yellow Thunder in my heart. ☀

CHAPTER ELEVEN

A Period of Adjustment

We were on our way. Miles flew under the wheels and were tossed away by the rear tires. A hundred miles, five hundred miles. In a few days we would be in Alaska, thousands of miles from my home and friends.

Would we live in an igloo? Did it snow all year? What if he decided he didn't like me and threw me out? I looked over at him. He was deep in his own thoughts. Was he sorry he had married me?

We stopped to eat, and he looked at the menu. "What do you want?" he asked.

"Nothing. I'm not hungry," I said. I was too frightened to eat or drink. I felt like a wild animal that had suddenly been thrown into a cage.

We crossed the American-Canadian border, and as I saw the American flag fade into the distance I was sure I would never see my home again. I was going to the end of the world.

I had eaten only a few bites of food since we had been married, but by the time we reached the Yukon, hunger won over everything else, and I began eating like a lumberjack—much to my groom's relief. The Yukon was the most rugged, beautiful country I had ever seen. We would drive for hours without seeing another car or house. The wildlife was thick, and we saw moose, fox and deer. Beside one lake we counted over a hundred bald eagles diving into the water to catch the small fish. Once we stopped to explore a long-deserted Royal Canadian Mounted Police camp, and I saw a three-legged bear. Don grabbed me and we ran to the car while he mumbled something about a three-legged bear still being faster than a two-legged girl and how was he going to explain to Reverend McPherson that he had let a bear eat me!

It was late and we were both tired and hungry when we stopped at a small café one evening for dinner. We sat down in a booth and a waitress came to our table with one menu, which she handed to Don.

"I'm sorry, sir. We won't serve her here," she said.

Don looked up from the menu. "What do you mean?"

The girl jerked her thumb toward me and repeated. "We won't serve Indians. She'll have to leave." She pointed to a sign on the window. "NO INDIANS ALLOWED."

Don's eyes were like cold steel as he handed the menu back to the waitress. He reached over and took my hand, and we left.

We drove in silence for several miles. Then I decided I'd better say something.

"It doesn't really matter. Let's just forget it."

"They're stupid!" Don spoke louder than he had to.

"I know. Shall we go back and scalp them?" I asked.

A smile broke the hardness of his face. "I'm sorry, Cry."

"It's harder for you. I've lived with it all my life," I said.

"Does that mean you are used to being treated like that?" he asked.

"No," I answered quietly. "No, you never get used to it; you just live with it."

Don had his first taste of what it was like to be a "squaw man," and it had made him angry. I wondered if he would be able to take it, or if he would decide it was too hard and leave me for a yellow-haired woman.

We arrived in Alaska late one evening. The only room we could find was above a bar, and it cost fifty-two dollars for the night. The noise and brawling sounds filtered into our room as badly as the smell of whiskey and smoke. We both looked at the small, dirty room and then at each other.

"It's too cold to sleep in the car. This is the only room left," he explained. "I just hope those drunken Indians don't keep us awake all night—" His face turned red and he closed his eyes tightly. "I didn't mean that! I'm sorry1 I wasn't picking on the Indians, I just meant that I hoped those people downstairs would settle down pretty soon and we could get some rest."

"It's all right," I said.

"I'll go see if I can get us some food. Be sure you lock the door, and don't open it until I tell you it's me."

"Don't let any Indians scalp you," I warned and locked the door behind him.

It was nearly an hour before I heard his knock.

"They didn't have any food downstairs so I had to walk to another place down the block, and it took them so long to cook it." He unwrapped some greasy hamburgers. "The Indians downstairs had a bear in the bar that one of them had killed today." He handed me a hamburger. "It isn't going to be like this, Cry. It isn't going to be dirty rooms and cold food for you. Don't judge our married life by tonight."

I suddenly felt sorry for him. He was trying so hard. It hadn't occurred to me until that minute that maybe he was scared to death, too. I had thought of him as older than myself because he had been so many places and done so many things. But now I realized that in spite of his adventurous life, he wasn't much older than I was.

He told me how he had left home when he was a teenager and had driven to Alaska, where he had worked as a fisherman on a crab boat. Then he had worked in the oil fields, where it was sixty-five degrees below zero. He told me of the years he had spent working in the cold wilderness, and I began to realize that he was lonely, too. He was so lonely that he didn't even know I was ugly.

"Marriage is a period of adjustment that lasts all of your lives," Reverend McPherson had said to us. He had given us a lot of advice, but when he had used the word adjustment he had just shown us the tip of the iceberg. As if it weren't enough of a difference that Don was a man and I was a woman, he was white and I was Indian, and we were from two different cultures—he was living in a modern, complicated world, and I still had one foot in the Stone Age.

The long trip had given me a terrible headache.

"Why don't you take something for it?" Don asked.

"I don't have anything here with me," I said, holding a cold washcloth over my eyes.

"I can go get you something. What did you use for a headache back on the reservation?" he asked.

"I put rattlesnake rattlers in my headband."

"You what?"

"That was the best cure. But if you couldn't find a rattlesnake then you could eat wild rose petals."

"I'll buy a bottle of aspirin," he said.

"Do you really think that will work?" I peeked out from under the washcloth.

"A lot of people use aspirins for headaches," he answered.

"Well, all right, I guess that will do until we can find a rattlesnake," I agreed.

That was only the beginning.

As soon as we arrived in Anchorage he rented a small cabin and bought supplies. He only had a few days before he would fly hundreds of miles away back to his job on an oil platform. He would be gone ten days and then home five days.

I had mixed emotions about my new home. Living in the middle of Alaska was not what I had planned for my life, but it was what I had agreed to.

"Lord, help me!" I prayed. ☀

CHAPTER TWELVE

Indian Ways

I cooked our first dinner—meat, potatoes, onions, corn, and fry bread—and set it on the table.

Don smiled at me and took a bite and chewed it a very long time. He started to take a second bite but instead he excused himself and left the room. In a few minutes he came back into the kitchen. He still had a smile on his face, but he was white as a sheet.

"It's my cooking, isn't it? You can't eat my food," I accused, half-angry, half-ashamed. "I should have known a white man couldn't eat Indian food!"

"No, it's not that. It's just, well, I've never eaten an entire meal that has been cooked in one skillet all at the same time. It tastes—unusual," he explained.

"You hate my cooking," I sulked.

"No, really, it's fine. I'll get used to it." He sat back down and looked at the food floating across his plate in yellow grease. "Maybe if you used a little less grease? My potatoes keep slipping off my plate."

"Grease is good for you; it keeps bears away."

"There aren't any bears here," he said.

"See! It works!" I snapped.

"Don't you have any recipes?" he asked timidly.

I lit up. "Yes! I have a very good recipe."

"Good!" He was encouraged. "What do you need?"

"First you mix one quart of raw alcohol; one pound of rank black chewing tobacco; one bottle of Jamaica ginger; one handful of red peppers; one quart of black molasses; and one quart of water; and then you boil it until all the strength is drawn from the tobacco and peppers, and you drain it and it's finished," I said proudly.

"What in the world does that make?" he asked.

"Kickapoo Trade Whiskey!" I answered eagerly.

"Is that the only recipe you know?" he asked.

"Yes." I had the feeling it was the wrong one.

"I'll buy you a cookbook." He shook his head. "That stuff probably killed more Kickapoos than all the wars in history."

"My uncles drank gallons of it. It didn't hurt them," I said, and watched potatoes float across my plate in a river of grease.

"Your uncles must have cast-iron stomachs," he observed and scraped the food off our plates. He dug out three skillets and cooked eggs in one, bacon in another and potatoes in the third. Soon we were eating a delicious meal. I had married a good cook. He did everything so well for himself, I wondered why he had married me.

After dinner I kicked the front door open, as I always had, and threw out the leftovers.

"Honey, you can't do that," Don said.

"Do what?"

"You can't throw garbage out the front door. It looks bad."

"What am I supposed to do with it? Back on the reservation we always threw it out the front door."

"But it's different now. Put it in the garbage disposal."

"What's that?"

He led me to the sink and shoved some food down the drain.

"So that's why the sink looks funny on one side." With a spoon, I shoved the rest of the garbage into the hole in the sink and turned on the switch. The spoon was yanked out of my hand and disappeared down the drain with a terrible, loud, grinding sound.

Don reached over and flipped off the switch and pulled out a mangled spoon.

I looked at the spoon. "Seems to make more sense to throw garbage out the front door than to bend up all your spoons," I said and left the kitchen.

The first night in our new home I sprinkled a generous supply of cornmeal on the doorstep to insure that we would always have enough food to eat. Let people throw rice if they wanted to, but I would depend on cornmeal on the doorstep.

I had always been so quiet, so silent—seldom speaking, and moving through life like a shadow, remaining invisible and unnoticed in the background. I had been trained in the old way, a reminder of the days when silence meant survival. Silence kept you hidden from your enemies; silence helped you stalk a deer or trap a rabbit. Noise frightened away game, and you went hungry. Noise could get you killed. Now it was different. I had to learn to talk, to make unnecessary noise, to speak when there was nothing to say, to "make conversation."

It was hard to think of things to say to this stranger who knew nothing of life on the reservation or what it meant to be an Indian.

When Don would complain that I was too quiet I would answer, "We don't have anything in common to talk about."

I was surprised when Don suddenly seemed to know a great deal about Indian cultures. Every evening during dinner he would have something to say about one of the tribes or one of the great chiefs.

"I didn't know you knew so much about Indians," I said one evening after he had finished talking about Geronimo.

"Oh, yes, I've always been interested in Indians." He paused. "You were wrong, you know; you and I really do have a lot in common."

Something in his look was odd, but I couldn't put my finger on it.

It wasn't until late one evening that his little secret came out by accident. I was cold, and I remembered I had left my sweater in the car and went after it. As I reached into the back seat to get it, I saw the corner of a book sticking out from under the seat. I couldn't remember leaving a book in the car, but I knew it had to be mine, because Don never read books.

I pulled it out and found there were not one but three books stuffed under the seat. I read the titles.

The A to Z of American Indians—Apaches to Zunis, Battle of the Little Bighorn, The Red Man—The Noble Savage.

I started to giggle. Thinking they would help him understand me, Don was secretly reading these books. When I looked at the title *The Noble Savage* I burst into laughter.

He had underlined parts of the books and memorized them almost word for word. I could remember his dinner conversations and could see they were straight from the books. I wondered how many hours he had spent sitting in the car, trying to read these dull, outdated books, as slowly as he read.

I stopped laughing. It wasn't really very funny at all. He was trying so hard to understand me. I was touched by how much he cared. Maybe I should try harder, too. I slid the books back into their hiding place under the seat and went inside. It would remain his secret.

Nightmares. Every night. Horrible dreams that made me wake up screaming, with my heart pounding so hard it shook my whole body. I had thought that after I became a Christian the nightmares would stop, my mind would no longer be troubled, and I would sleep peacefully; but the dreams had continued, and each night I dreaded going to bed. I knew that in the middle of the night my dreams would haunt me, and I would wake up frightened half to death.

One dream I had often was about Twice Blind, the medicine man whose family had cut his legs off when he died so that he wouldn't walk back from the grave and kill them. I dreamed over and over that he was crawling on his bloody stumps out of his grave.

In other dreams I was a child back in school again, with a hard-looking teacher punishing me for everything I did because it was wrong in her eyes. When the school day ended, gangs of children would chase me home, shouting names and throwing rocks. When I woke up and realized I was not a child and would never have to go back to school again, I would thank God. I was grown up now; I never had to go to school again. No one would chase me home and throw rocks at me; no more teachers would frighten me until I was sick to my stomach. No, I was safe from school.

Some nightmares were so bad I couldn't repeat them even to Don. I would wake up screaming and weak with fear. Too afraid to go back to sleep, I would get out of bed and sit in a chair and keep all the lights on the rest of the night.

It was time for our first separation; Don was flying away to work.

"I'll be back in ten days," he said, holding on to me at the airport. "It will go faster than you think. If you need anything, call the number I gave you, and my friend will help you." He kissed me good-bye and picked up his suitcase and climbed into the plane. In a few minutes the small plane was out of sight.

He's gone! He'll never come back! I'm alone here in a foreign country! I cried all the way home. Flint had been right; I'd been abandoned, just as he said I would.

I moped around for days and passed the long hours by reading books. Exactly ten days later Don burst through the door in a swirl of snow. "I'm home!" he shouted.

I ran to him and threw my arms around his neck. "You came back! You came back!" I couldn't believe it.

"I told you I'd be back in ten days. Why would I marry you and bring you all the way up here just to leave you? Won't you ever learn to trust me?"

The five days together slipped away fast, and it was soon time for him to leave again. Time was heavy on my hands when Don was gone and flew by quickly when he was in town. After each ten-day absence he would return, and each time I would wonder how many more times he would return before he left for good. I'd been abandoned too many times in my life not to expect it to happen again.

When I had lived alone there had been no sounds except

my own. Now there were sounds in the house as he wound the alarm clock in the bedroom or emptied change from his pockets and put it on the dresser. Sounds of doors opening and closing, dishes rattling. Sounds of life. There was silence when he was gone, but it wasn't the deep, lonely silence I had known before, because I knew that when he returned the house would again have life in it.

NIGHT MUSIC

The night is still,
Except for the sound of love beside me,
A warm, familiar sound
That tells me I am not alone.
The burdens of the day are hidden by the darkness;
I drift far above the earth on a soft, white cloud,
Taking only the echo of your presence with me.
The night is still,
Except for the sound of my husband snoring,
A warm, familiar sound
That tells me I am not alone.

"You haven't asked for anything since we've been married," Don said one day. "You need some things. Wouldn't you like to go shopping and buy some new clothes or something?"

"Well—" I hesitated—"I would like a new dress."

"Great! How much money do you need?" He dug out his wallet.

"Oh, I was going to make it myself," I said.

"All right, what do you need? I'll get it for you."

"Well, I need two elk skins and ten pounds of beads," I answered.

"What?"

"I want to make a new buckskin ceremonial dress," I explained.

He was silent for a moment and then his face lit up.

"There's a fur trader down by Boot Legger's Cove. Let's see if he has some skins."

A short time later I had some deerskins and ten pounds of beads and six rabbit skins that I had admired.

The next time Don returned from work the dress was nearly finished.

"What are you going to do with the rabbit skins?" he asked.

"I drew on them with ink," I said and pulled my surprise out to show him. He looked at my ink drawings of moose, caribou, and deer on the skins.

"They are a gift for you," I said shyly.

"They are really good! I like them." He studied them awhile. "Would you like to make some to sell?"

"No one would buy my paintings. I'm not an artist," I said.

"Let's buy ten skins, and I'll get you some paints and brushes. You make more pictures like these, and I'll sell them to the gift shops."

I laughed at him but painted the ten skins. He sold them

to a gift shop the next day for seven dollars each and came home with an order for forty more pictures.

"This is your money," he said as he handed it to me. "You can make a lot of money with your paintings if you want to. Use the money for anything you want, but don't buy food or pay bills with it. I promised to support you, and I will. But if you enjoy painting and want to use the money to buy gifts for your friends or give it to your church, it's all right with me."

I nodded, too excited to speak. People were buying my paintings! During the next year Don sold over five hundred of my sketches and paintings, most of them on rabbit skins. I became so used to painting wild animals, I could paint thirty pictures in a day. Don had talked every gift shop within a hundred miles into carrying my pictures.

One day he said, "I think you should have your own checking account and keep your money from your paintings in it. Fill out this form and put your social security number on it and sign it Mrs. Don Stafford."

"Why can't I be Crying Wind?" I asked.

"People will think we aren't married," he answered.

I compromised and wrote, "Crying Wind Stafford."

Don sighed. "Now fill in your social security number."

"I don't have a number, only a name," I said.

"Everyone has a social security number," he insisted.

"Not me."

"You've had a lot of jobs—you had to have a number!"

"No, I just said I forgot it, and since I didn't work anywhere more than a few weeks nobody bothered me about it," I explained.

"We'll get you a number."

"I don't want a number! I'm Crying Wind. I have a name; I don't want a number. Numbers are bad luck. If you let the government give you a number, they can find you," I insisted.

"What's wrong with that?" he asked.

"Indians should never let the government find them," I said.

"Why not?"

"They might decide to exterminate all the Indians."

"That's ridiculous!" Don laughed.

"They tried it a hundred years ago. It could happen again," I argued. "Look what happened to the Jews in Germany!"

"You are an Indian living in the United States. I'll get a social security number for you." Then he laughed. "If the government comes looking for you, I'll hide you in the attic!"

"Sure, that's what you say now!" I said, frowning.

A short time later he showed up with an envelope with two social security cards in it. He took one out and put it inside the box where he kept his important papers and handed me the other card.

As Don left the room, I looked at the card. I was no longer Crying Wind. I was number 522-54-2700. Now the government had me in their number machine. Now they could find me, and Don had probably lied about hiding me in the attic! I took the card and tore it into many small pieces and threw it into the wastebasket. There! Now I was Crying Wind again!

Don came back into the room. "By the way, you'll have to get an Alaskan driver's license. Let me have a look at the one you have now."

I dug out my driver's license and showed it to him.

"This says it belongs to Rose Begay Tsosie," he said.

"Yes, I know," I said, nodding.

"Where is your own driver's license?"

"That *is* mine. I bought it at the pawnshop."

"You can't get a driver's license at a pawnshop!" he laughed.

"Of course you can. On the reservation you can pawn your driver's license for fifty cents. That is enough to buy one drink at the saloon. Then if you can't get it back out of pawn, the pawnbroker sells it for two dollars."

"You can't do that!" Don exclaimed.

"Sure you can. All Indians look alike to the police—black hair, brown eyes, dark skin. All you have to do is buy one that reads close to your age and weight."

"You can't do that!" Don repeated. "That's illegal! Are you telling me that half the Indians in America are driving around using a license they bought in a pawnshop for two dollars?"

I shrugged.

Don went off mumbling to himself, and I put Rose Begay

Tsosie's license back into my purse. I had never seen anyone so concerned about laws and rules.

After several heated discussions, Don took me down to the police station, where I got a legal driver's license.

"I don't see what difference it makes. I drive the same way whether I use this one or the one I bought in a pawnshop," I complained.

Don shook his head and sighed, "A man needs nerves of steel to be married to an Indian!" ☀

CHAPTER THIRTEEN

The New Me and My Husband

I t was the middle of the night when something woke me. When Don was gone I slept lightly and heard every little sound, and I knew something was wrong. I lay listening in the darkness for a few seconds, but when I didn't hear anything I concluded I must have been dreaming and decided to go back to sleep. I pulled the covers up around my shoulders and turned over in bed—and found myself face to face with a strange man!

I screamed and sent the blankets flying in all directions and was out of bed and running across the room in a split second. I started throwing everything I could find.

The red-bearded stranger sat up in bed and rubbed his eyes.

"What on earth is wrong with you, Cry?" It was Don's voice but it was coming out of someone else's face.

I took a couple of steps closer.

"I got a chance to come to town a day early but it was so late I decided not to wake you. I didn't mean to scare you," he apologized.

"What happened to your face?" I couldn't believe this hairy man was my husband.

"Oh, us guys decided to grow beards," he laughed. "Do you like it?"

"You have hair all over your face! You scared me to death!" I put down the bookend I was holding. "You aren't supposed to change your face when I'm not looking!"

I put the blanket back on the bed and found my pillow across the room, where I had thrown it in the confusion, and I settled back down for the night. Indian men don't have hair on their faces; if you marry an Indian you know he will always look the same—he isn't going to grow a beard or get bald.

"The next thing I know he'll be bald," I grumbled under my breath.

"What's that?" Don asked sleepily.

"Nothing." I answered and reached over with one finger and touched the red beard. "Good night, fur face."

The next morning as I was getting dressed I took a good look at myself in the mirror. I looked as if I had just come off the reservation.

I decided that since I had a new life now, I should look different. I should conform to the way other women dressed so I wouldn't embarrass my husband.

I went shopping and bought a street-length dress, but after wearing long dresses all my life I felt half-naked with my legs hanging out. Besides, they were cold. The panty hose the clerk had sold me did everything but keep my legs warm. They sneaked up and they sneaked down and they moved around more than I did.

PANTY HOSE

Are you some strange jungle beast
Whose savage nature has been released?
Writhing and crawling all around,
Then sneaking up without a sound—
Panty hose, I beg you, please,
Don't twist and sag around my knees!

Next came the beauty parlor. I took a deep breath and walked through the door, and as soon as the women saw my long hair they all began sharpening their scissors. I put my hands over my hair and explained over and over that I didn't want it cut, trimmed, shaped, or touched with scissors. I only wanted it curled up and fixed to make me look different. They reluctantly put away their scissors and began working on it. After three hours of shampoo, curlers, and melting my ears under a dryer, they turned me out of the beauty shop. My hair was piled up so high that I felt as if I had a pumpkin on my head. In addition to my new hairdo, I had a new face; they had put makeup, eye shadow, eye liner, mascara, eyebrow pencil, and lipstick on me. I was convinced that now I looked just like everyone else, and I knew Don would be thrilled with the "new me."

He was not thrilled. He walked through the door, looked at me, and asked, "Did it take long to do that to yourself?"

"It took all day. Do you like the way I look?"

He didn't have to think twice for an answer. "No, I liked you the way you were."

"I wanted to look nice. I wanted to look like everyone else so you wouldn't be ashamed of me."

"I'm never ashamed of you, and one of the reasons I married you was because you weren't like everyone else. You were different. I liked you for being different. Don't try to be something you're not. Be yourself."

I felt foolish. I had spent a lot of time and money just to end up looking silly. Tears began to trickle down my face, leaving black streaks of mascara.

Don touched my hair, which was stiff from hair spray.

"Why don't you go see if you can find my wife under there someplace, and if you can, tell her I'll take her out to dinner."

I stood in the shower and washed the new me away. A half-hour later I returned to the living room—long dress, no makeup and hair in braids.

Don gave one of my braids a tug. "Now *that's* my wife!"

I reached up and touched his face. His beard was gone; he had shaved it off.

"Let's go eat," he said and smiled.

To celebrate the old me, Don took me to a seafood restaurant. When I looked at the menu my stomach turned over. I didn't think I could make myself eat anything that didn't walk across the land on four legs or fly on two wings. Something that wiggled through the water just didn't seem fit to eat.

Don ordered salmon steaks and waited for me to order. I asked for a tuna sandwich, which didn't sound as bad as some of the things they offered. When it came to the table, I picked up one half in my hands, prayed I wouldn't get sick, and then felt my throat close up tight. I quickly shoved the sandwich into my coat pocket and waited for my chance to get rid of the other half. As soon as I was sure Don wasn't watching, I shoved the other half of the tuna sandwich into my other coat pocket.

"See, dear, eating fish doesn't hurt you. It's just a case of mind over matter."

Sure, I thought to myself, *if you don't mind squashed tuna sandwiches in your pockets, it doesn't matter.*

On the drive home the car heater was on, and the warm air spread the odor of tuna fish through the car.

Don kept sniffing the air. "I could swear I smell fish!"

"It must be your imagination," I said and wished he would hurry home.

After we arrived home I hurried into the kitchen and began digging out the tuna and stuffing it into the garbage disposal, trying to get my pockets cleaned out before Don came inside.

A few minutes later he came in and found me sitting on the couch and watching TV.

"I'm sorry," he said.

"What for?" I asked.

"For trying to force you to eat fish. There's no reason in the world why you should have to eat fish," he said.

"All right, we'll forget it." I let out a sigh of relief.

"I'll take your coat to the cleaner tomorrow," he offered.

I sank down farther on the couch and kept my eyes on the TV set.

"As long as we're on the subject of food—do you think we could sometimes have a vegetable other than corn?"

"Corn is best. Indians have eaten corn since the beginning."

"I like corn, but we've had it every meal since we've been married. Maybe we could try some different things sometimes."

I nodded. For the next month we had peas at every meal, and following that we went back to corn.

"Honey, these pants are too long. Do you think you could take up about an inch in the cuff? I'm in a sort of a hurry, I wanted to wear them today," Don said.

I took the pants and hurried to the next room. I knew that it would take me a long time to stitch up the cuffs by hand, but I hadn't yet mastered the sewing machine Don had bought me. I decided to compromise. I rolled up the cuffs and grabbed the stapler out of Don's desk and quickly stapled the cuffs into place.

I handed his pants back to him. He looked at them and put them on without saying a word and left.

Later that night I awoke and discovered he was not in bed. I got up and followed the trail of light coming from the bathroom.

He was sitting on the edge of the bathtub sewing on the cuffs of his pants. I sneaked back to bed. I vowed I would not use the stapler anymore. ☀

CHAPTER FOURTEEN

Christmas in Alaska

W hat was Christmas like for you when you were a kid?" Don asked.

"We didn't celebrate Christmas. We didn't believe in God," I answered.

"Lots of people celebrate Christmas who don't believe in God," Don said. "You mean you didn't do anything at all about Christmas?"

"No—oh, I remember once a girl friend of one of my uncles gave me a present. It was a little bottle of hand lotion. I'd never had anything like that before. It seemed like such a grown-up gift, and I was so proud of it, that I decided not to use it so it would last forever."

"Did it last forever?" he asked.

"No. That night I hid it under my bed and it froze. The next morning when I woke up and looked for my wonderful treasure, there was nothing left but broken glass and frozen hand-lotion. I didn't even get to use one drop," I sighed. "What were your Christmases like when you were a little boy?"

"Awful. My folks were too cheap to buy my sister or me any presents. One year I hung up my stocking for Santa Claus to fill. I wanted a baseball more than anything in the world, and when I saw something big and round in the toe of my stocking on Christmas morning, I thought I'd gotten my baseball. But it was an orange. I hate oranges to this day." He was quiet a moment. "If my folks had been too poor to buy gifts, I could have understood. But even if you're poor, you can still make toys for your kids. I was just cheap labor to them. I worked harder than any hired hand ever did on that ranch. I earned my own living from the time I was ten years old, and as soon as I was old enough to drive I saved money to buy an old pickup truck and I ran away from home and headed for Alaska. It was as far away from Texas as I could get."

"What happened to your family?" I asked.

"I guess they are still on the ranch. My sister got married as soon as she could, to get away from home," he said.

"Do you think you'll ever see them again?"

"No. Cry, my folks are—" he sighed. "They are bad medicine. My dad drinks, and my mother is—well, she's real bad. My sister and I got away from them as soon as we could. I think of myself as an orphan because I never had real parents. I wasn't a son, I was free labor. You'd do me a favor by never talking about my childhood or my family again. I'd like to forget everything that ever happened to me before I met you. You're the only good thing that ever happened to me."

It was our first Christmas together, and I wanted it to be special. For the first time in my life I had someone of my very own to give a present to.

I started decorating too early, but I was too excited to wait any longer. Our Christmas tree was up and decorated on the last day of November.

I shopped for hours to find a special gift for my husband, but nothing seemed right, until one day I was looking at men's shirts and I found the answer. I would make him a Cherokee chief shirt! I bought a pale blue shirt and yards of brightly colored ribbon. At home I sewed the ribbons onto the shirt with tiny stitches. I slipped it on and twirled around. The red, yellow, blue and green ribbons flew out around me in a rainbow of color. He would love it! A chief's shirt! I was sure he had never had one before, and I proudly wrapped it and placed it gently under our tree.

Don placed his gifts under the tree, too, and I shook, pinched and squeezed each of them until the Christmas paper was wrinkled and the bows were loose.

He scolded me and threatened to hide them if I didn't leave them alone, but I couldn't walk past the gifts without giving one of them a jab with my finger.

"You should let me open them now. What if something happened and I died before Christmas? I would never know what you gave me!"

But Don would only laugh and add more tape to the gifts.

On Christmas Eve we sat in the dark, watching the lights twinkle on the tree and listening to Christmas carols from the stereo.

In my heart was great loneliness and longing for my friends back home. An occasional tear trickled down my cheeks. When the stereo played "I'll Be Home for Christmas" the trickle turned into a river, and I buried my face in my hands and cried.

Don knew what was wrong without asking and left me alone with my attack of homesickness.

I was just getting down to some real crying when I felt the house tremble. My tears were quickly forgotten and my heart froze.

"What's that!" I whispered.

"It's just a little earth tremor," Don said.

The house shook again and the dishes rattled in the cupboard and a window cracked.

"It's an earthquake!" I shouted. I grabbed one of my presents and leaped into the middle of our bed. "We're going to be killed! I told you something would happen! Give me my presents now!"

The house gave a hard shake and the Christmas tree lights went out. I was left standing in the middle of the bed with a half-opened gift in my hands. There was a deep silence as we waited to see if there were going to be any more tremors or if the ground was going to open up and swallow us alive.

The light flickered back on, and Don switched on a few lamps. He pulled the half-opened gift out of my hands and started to put it back under the tree.

"Good grief! What on earth?" he exclaimed and I followed him over to the tree.

Standing in a pile of pine needles was a scraggly stick with lights and baubles draped on it. I had put my tree up too early, and it had dried out. The earthquake had shaken every needle off the tree. We now had the ugliest Christmas tree in the whole world! Homesickness was forgotten as we burst into laughter.

We decided to open our gifts instead of waiting until morning. Don handed me three packages, and I ripped them open eagerly. Inside the first one was a silver cross on a chain, and I put it around my neck before I opened the other two. The second package held a tiny whale he had carved from wood, and the last gift was a fuzzy pink robe.

"Thank you. They are wonderful gifts!" I said holding the whale he had carved and pulling on the pretty, warm robe. "I like them all very much. Now you must open your gift!" I handed him his present and waited eagerly as he opened it.

"What a nice—" He held it up and let the colored ribbons dangle down the front and back of the shirt. "It's very nice— What is it?"

"It's a Cherokee chief's shirt!" I said and helped him put it on.

He looked in the mirror. "I'm not a Cherokee chief," he said.

"You don't like it, do you?" I was disappointed. "I keep forgetting you aren't an Indian. I should have bought you a present for a white man."

"I like it, really I do. It's just that I've never had a shirt like this before, and I was surprised. It's real nice," he said, and started to take it off. Then he looked at my face and put it back on. "It's such a nice shirt I was going to save it for good, but I like it so much I think I'll wear it right now, for Christmas Eve." He looked at himself in the mirror again.

"I can cut the ribbons off," I offered.

"No, you went to a lot of work to sew them on. You leave it the way it is. I'm probably the only man in Alaska with a chief's shirt. In fact, I'd bet on it." He smiled. "Merry Christmas, Crying Wind. I love you."

"Merry Christmas," I answered. I wondered if I should say "I love you" back to him, but I didn't think I could ever make my tongue say those words as long as I lived.

We took one last look at our pitiful tree and went to bed. Around my neck I wore the silver cross, and I slid the little whale under my pillow.

It was the best Christmas I had ever had. ☀

CHAPTER FIFTEEN

A Friend Goes Home

We didn't have any close neighbors, and it was hard for me to make new friends, so I clung desperately to my old friends back in Colorado. Writing letters became a part of my daily routine, and I waited anxiously for their answers. A letter from a friend at church made my new life a little less lonely, a little less frightening. I saved every letter I received and read them again on the days I didn't get any mail.

I waited eagerly for the mailman to come each day and was upset if he was late. My days became "good" days if I received a lot of mail and "bad" days if the mailbox was empty.

A LETTER FROM HOME

The mailman has come! I ran through the snow,
My feet were numb, it was twenty below.
A letter from you, though it didn't say much—
Just a line or two to keep in touch.
You spoke of spring and the early flowers.
And how you'd watched the robins for hours and hours.
The snow was gone and the grass was green,

You'd been working hard and the house was clean.
Things back home were just the same,
There wasn't much news, but you couldn't complain.
A couple of old friends had asked about me
The other day when they stopped by for tea.
Well, you had to close, it was time to go,
But you'd write again in a week or so.
My frozen fingers clutched the letter you wrote,
As I stood by the mailbox without my coat.
But I didn't notice the cold or the storm.
Because for a few minutes I'd been
back home, safe and warm.

But one day I received a letter that broke my heart. It was a cold, bitter January. I was chilled to the bone, and nothing could keep me warm. I wore extra clothes and hovered around the stove trying to keep away the chill. I remembered how freezing cold it had been in the tar-paper house back on the reservation. Sometimes I felt as if I had been cold all my life. How I longed for a blazing yellow sun to burn life back into my shivering body.

It came in the morning mail—a letter from Sally saying Audrey had died. My eyes flooded with tears, and my hands shook so badly I could hardly read the rest of the letter. Audrey and Reverend McPherson had finished dinner and had gone in to watch television. In an instant, she was gone.

She had died so peacefully, so quietly, that Reverend McPherson, who was sitting next to her, didn't even know she had been called home. He had asked her a question, and when she didn't answer he looked over at her and thought she had fallen asleep. When he tried to wake her, he found she was dead.

My heart cried out in agony. *Audrey! My friend, gone!* I wept for hours and shivered from an inner cold that came from losing a friend. Audrey's death left me in a black hole of depression. I missed her terribly and didn't understand why she had to die when she was so good and so many people needed her.

I was angry with God for letting someone I loved die. I knew I should be happy for Audrey; she was now standing in the presence of the almighty God, and her joy was full. But I was too grief stricken to feel anything but my own loss.

It wasn't until Reverend McPherson wrote to me that I was able to accept her death as God's perfect will. Through his own grief and loneliness, Reverend McPherson wrote of his great, loving Savior who had called Audrey home. He knew there would be only a short separation before they would be reunited someday in heaven. His faith took the sting out of death for me and I realized that death is not final for a Christian—it is only a step into eternal life! ☀

CHAPTER SIXTEEN

Seeing the Pacific

The snow brushed against the windows with a whispering, haunting sound. Don came inside in a flurry of snow, brushing it off his parka and letting it fall to the floor.

"I'll be gone longer this time," he said. He had told me that several times before.

"I know. I'll be all right," I repeated.

He was flying hundreds of miles north, beyond the Arctic Circle, to work on an oil rig.

"I'll be fine. I just wish the sun would come back. It's so hard to live in the darkness." I walked over to the window and looked out into the Alaskan winter night that would last for months. Months of darkness, months of waiting for the sun to come back again.

"What do you see, Crying Wind?" Don asked.

"Nothing," I answered. How could I tell him I saw faraway mountains and dense forests? Indians racing across rolling prairies on wild-eyed ponies under the hot summer sun? How could I tell him I saw herds of thundering buffalo in the clouds? His gray eyes could never see the things my brown eyes saw. His ears would never hear the ancient drums beating in my heart.

He was gone again and it might be weeks before he would return. I curled up in the warm cabin with a dozen books and shut out the world.

Three days later the wind was howling like a hungry wolf and it blew the crystal snow against the windows so hard that it sounded like pebbles hitting the glass. All morning the snow piled higher and by noon I knew there would be no letup. If the storm lasted much longer I would be snowed in, and there wasn't any food left in the cabin. It had been a mistake to let the supplies run so low; now I would have to go out in the storm to get food.

I pulled on my leather jacket and tied a scarf around my head. I stepped outside into a blinding white world. The flakes were falling so fast and thick it was hard to see more than a few feet ahead, and I prayed I would not lose my way.

In spite of the deep snow, it didn't take long to walk the two miles to the trading post. I knew I was buying too many groceries, but I was hungry, and would need food for several days. When I lifted the two large grocery sacks, I staggered under their weight.

Although it wasn't long past noon, it was already growing dark. As I hurried on my way home, the sacks felt heavier with each step. At the end of the first mile I was so overheated and tired that I stopped and set the groceries in the snow. I took off my coat and threw it down and sat on it until I could get my second wind. I cooled off quickly and put my coat back on. Then I picked up the sacks and walked toward home.

I was gasping for breath when I staggered through the cabin door. I dumped the groceries on the table. My lungs ached and my throat felt funny. I tried to put away my supplies, but I was too weak, so I only set the milk and meat outside in the little igloo we had made. Then I heated a can of soup and took a few sips, but my throat was too sore to swallow, so I went to bed.

When I woke up late the next day, I had an uneasy feeling that I had something more serious than a cold. My chest felt as if a giant buffalo were standing on my lungs, and I could manage only short, shallow breaths. I lay in bed and watched the snow drift up against the window until it piled higher than the top of the window and I could no longer see out at all.

I was too weak to get out of bed, and sitting up made me dizzy. I was on fire with fever, and each breath I took sounded like a death rattle. I dozed off and on, grateful when I could sleep and be unaware of the pain in my chest.

After midnight the next day the wind stopped blowing as suddenly as if someone had shut a door. The furnace quit, and I was without heat. I tried to pray, but my mind wandered so badly I could say only a few words at a time before I would float back into my past, back to the days when I was a child playing in the warm, yellow sun. I thought of my mother, a small delicate woman with sad eyes. Then my mind would come back to the present.

I felt as if knives were stabbing my lungs, and I coughed blood.

"I'm dying," I said in a voice so hoarse I couldn't believe it was my own. "I'm dying here in a cold, dark place far from home."

Home. Home, where it was warm and where friends smiled at you.

Then, raising myself on an elbow, I cried out a name I hadn't spoken aloud in years. "Mother," I sobbed, "Mother! I want my mother!" Once again I was a tiny child needing comfort, needing help, afraid and cold and hungry and sick. All the years apart didn't matter now; nothing was important. I just wanted her here with me.

I fell back on the bed. "If I live through this, I'm going to find her," I whispered. "I want to see my mother."

Some machinery broke down and they sent the men home a week early. When Don arrived he found me huddled in bed under coats and blankets. I was shivering and spitting blood.

He took me to the clinic, and I could hear a doctor talking to Don.

"She would do better in a warm, dry climate. Like so many

Indians, she has weak lungs caused from cold, drafty houses and a poor diet when she was young. She's lucky you came home when you did."

I closed my eyes and thanked God for sparing my life. I was sure it was no accident that the oil rig had broken down and that Don had come home early.

I recovered in a few days, but I had a racking cough that lasted for months.

When I was feeling better, Don took me on a tour of Alaska. We visited tiny trading posts along our way and watched herds of caribou migrating and the great, ugly moose feeding in the marshy valleys. Of all the places we visited, I liked Homer best. The docks, with dozens of fishing boats, looked like pictures in a book. Don showed me one boat that he had worked on when he was fishing for king crab. I made sketches and wrote poetry along the way, and we spent hours beach-combing and watching the waves roll in. I was struck with the vastness of the great water, the Pacific Ocean.

"Crying Wind has seen the Pacific Ocean!" I yelled, and splashed in the icy water.

"And the Pacific Ocean has seen Crying Wind!" Don yelled.

"It's not impressed!" I laughed.

Those days of freedom and rest did a lot to restore my health, and I was feeling much stronger when we returned to our cabin.

HOMESICK

The aching loneliness I feel inside,
For those of you who live "outside,"
Can't be hidden under a blanket of white,
Nor swept away by the northern lights.

The mountains, glorious though they may be,
Are only a barrier between you and me;
I remain a captive in this frozen land,
Held here by the icy grip of its hand.

In summer warmth the forget-me-not grows,
And quickly dies as the autumn wind blows,
And my lonely heartache starts anew,
Another long winter here—without you.

THE WEATHERMAN

"Oh, the winters aren't bad here,
It only lasts ten months they say;
We had a dandy summer last year,
I think it was on a Thursday."
"Yeah, that's right because Friday was fall.
Can't complain though,
Some years we don't have any summer at all!"

THE ICE WORM TURNETH

Alaska, your heart is frozen,
You have no compassion for man;
You hide behind ice and eternal cold
As you jealously hoard your land.

You're the Great Land!
The land of moose and beaver,
The land of whales and caribou,
The land of cabin fever.

You are an unforgiving land,
But, Oh! Would I leave you if I could?
You bet your sweet life I would!

TOTEM POLE

A blind old totem stood alone,
And quaked with inward fear,
Afraid of being all alone,
Never seeing other totems near.
His eyes stared only straight ahead,
He forgot his friends nearby.
He flung out his arms in hopelessness
And uttered forlorn cries.

His tears ran streaming down his cheeks,
The years passed swiftly on,
The rain and snow took their toll,
Leaving his face sad and long.
He was never alone, because close at hand,
Others like him stood;
But he never knew,
Because just like them,
His eyes were carved from wood.
Many times we don't see friends,
As close as they may be;
Perhaps we are just as blind
As the totem who could not see.

CHAPTER SEVENTEEN

Stay Awhile

Don had a high school education, but he could hardly read or write. When he read, it took him a long time to struggle through a simple paragraph, and when he wrote, his handwriting and spelling were so bad they were nearly impossible to make out.

"I don't understand how you can have so little education and can read and write so well, and I wasted twelve years in school and almost have to sign my name with an X!" Don laughed.

"Grandmother taught me to read paperback novels when I was five years old. I was raised on western novels and Agatha Christie murder mysteries. By the time I was eight years old I knew fifty ways to poison someone. I've read at least three books a week for years—that makes a lot of reading. Maybe public education is a handicap," I said.

"Would you like to go back to school and get a diploma?" Don asked while he stacked up my latest pile of books.

My heart froze and I felt sick. I sank down into a chair.

"Go back to school?" Into my mind came pictures of people throwing rocks and teachers laughing at me. "No! I would never go back to school!"

Don went on, "I saw an advertisement today saying that the university is offering correspondence courses in several different subjects. I thought you might like to take one."

"You are ashamed of me because I'm uneducated!" I accused.

"No, that's not true. I just think you can be more than you are, that's all. You have a good mind. You read more books in a week than I'll read in a lifetime. I just thought you might like to study and learn more." He tossed a booklet on the table. "Look at this, then decide, OK?"

I picked up the booklet and flipped through it. There were twenty-five courses offered. I didn't even know what most of them were about, but one was called "Indian Anthropology." That might be interesting; it was a course on ancient American Indians. I read it aloud to Don.

"That's just right for you. Why don't you sign up for it?" He was enthusiastic.

"All right." I sulked as I filled out the form for the university. If he wanted a high school graduate for a wife, he should have married one!

In a week some books came in the mail and were soon followed by my first lesson. I was back in school again, the thing I hated most in my life. It was a correspondence course, but it was still connected with school.

I enjoyed reading the books, and the questions on the lessons weren't as hard as I had expected them to be. The books said that people started out as slimy cells in the ocean, and in a few million years they became apes. Then they lost their hair, turned different colors, and became men. The course was supposed to take a year, but I had a lot of spare time and I finished it in six months. When I received an "A" for the course, Don was beside himself with excitement.

"You did great! I knew you could do it! You could probably get some kind of degree if you worked on it. What do you think you'll take next?" He took a thumbtack and stuck my grade paper to the wall.

"Take next? You didn't tell me I had to take some more courses! I thought if I did good on this I could quit! I don't want to go to school! Why are these papers so important?" I reached up and jerked the grade paper off the wall, threw it on the floor, and ran into the bedroom, slamming the door behind me.

Don followed me in a few seconds later holding the paper in his hand.

"I'm sorry. I thought you would enjoy studying, since you read all the time anyway. I thought you would like to set a goal for yourself. I thought I was helping you. You don't ever have to take any school courses again," he said.

I stopped crying. "I like reading and learning things, but I don't need a piece of paper from somebody telling me what I've learned. That piece of paper doesn't make me any smarter."

I was angry with Don. Because of him I had a government

Social Security number and a driver's license. And now I had taken a course from some school to learn about Indians, and they thought Indians came from a cell in the ocean and weren't even created by God!

Like most white people, Don thought what was written on a piece of paper was important. Like most Indians, I didn't think anything written on a piece of paper was important.

Weeks went by. The conscious and unconscious hurts and slights made me depressed and weary. I decided I had had enough of this married life. I would divorce Don and return south, where the sun was warm and where I wouldn't be up to my neck in papers. Mr. Stafford could stay here with his papers and his snow! I'd show him.

I ran to the closet and took out all his clothes and laid them in a pile. Next I emptied his drawers and folded everything neatly. Then I pulled the blanket off our bed and cut it in half and wrapped his clothing in his half of the blanket. I carried it outside and set it in front of the door. Last I placed his shoes beside the blanket, with the toes pointing away from the door.

I stood back and looked at it. There! I would never see him again.

I sat down and began painting on some rabbit skins. At exactly five-thirty, the front door opened, and in walked Don holding his blanket and clothes under one arm and his shoes in his hand.

I stood up. "What are you doing here?" Didn't he know I had divorced him? When a man saw his belongings outside the door, with his shoes pointing away, he picked up his things and left. He didn't come barging back inside with his clothes bundled under his arm!

"Is this dry cleaning, or were you just cleaning out closets?" he asked and dropped everything onto the couch. He held up his half of the torn blanket. "What happened to this?" he asked.

I stood there with my hands on my hips. Didn't he know anything? I looked at him a minute, then decided I might as well let it drop for the time being. I walked over and grabbed the blanket out of his hands and headed toward the bedroom.

"What are you going to do?" he asked.

"I'm going to sew our blanket back together," I said, and wondered how he had survived this long when he didn't know anything. I would have to find another way to end this marriage; Don didn't know how to play by Indian rules.

Don told me every day that he loved me, but I had learned at a very early age never to trust anyone, so I didn't believe him. I was sure it was just something he said because he felt he was supposed to. After all, what did it cost him? They were only words; words are cheap. Still, I could never bring myself to say "I love you" to him.

I kept remembering what Flint had said the last time I had seen him. "What could he possibly see in you? Why would any man want to marry you?" I couldn't think of a single reason why Don should want me. He could have married prettier girls, girls who would say "I love you" and mean it. He must realize by now that he had made a terrible mistake, and soon he would leave me and never come back. What would become of me when he left? I didn't know anyone up here; I was far from my home. He would probably throw me out with only the clothes on my back, and I would freeze or starve.

I decided that since it was only a matter of time before he would walk out on me, I would walk out on him first. People had run out on me all my life; I was always ending up broke, scared and alone. But this time I would be smart—this time I would do the leaving!

I knew that I had made vows in church and before God to love, honor, and obey this man until I died, so I was very careful not to ask God's opinion of my idea. I knew He wouldn't approve. I would go ahead and leave, and when I got safely back home I would ask God to forgive me and hope he wouldn't strike me dead with a bolt of lightning.

I began to make plans. I saved the money I made from my paintings and planned to leave in a few weeks. I didn't mention it to Don; it was my secret. Don had been kind to me, and I was grateful for that, but I was sure things were near the end for us, and I was restless. I was very careful not to do anything that would cause Don to suspect what I was going to do. I was sure he didn't know a thing.

A week before I planned to leave, Don brought home a shoe box and handed it to me. When I opened it, I found a darling, black, fuzzy kitten inside.

"He's beautiful! Where did you get him?" I asked.

"There was an ad in the newspaper," he said and petted the kitten.

I held the ball of soft fur against my cheek. "What's its name?"

"Stay Awhile," he answered.

I looked up into Don's gray eyes, and they seemed to bore into my mind and read my thoughts.

"What?"

"His name is Stay Awhile," he said. "I'll go get him some milk." And he disappeared into the kitchen.

I held the cat on my lap. Did Don know? He couldn't! I had been too careful. It was a coincidence.

"Stay Awhile," I repeated, when Don came back. "That's no name for a cat."

"I thought it was a good name. Maybe it will keep him from running away and getting lost." Don scratched the kitten behind its ear and it purred loudly and lapped up some milk from the saucer.

The kitten soon took over our cabin and seemed to think he owned it and we were his pets. I was determined not to become attached to him because I knew he would be leaving soon. I had already packed my suitcase with a few clothes and had slid it under the bed to hide it from Don. I would only take what I had had before we were married, and that wasn't much; it easily fit into one suitcase.

The time came for me to leave. I had avoided looking into Don's eyes all day, afraid he would be able to see what I was thinking. I wasn't sure what he would do if he knew I was going to leave him that night. I kept myself busy cleaning the house and cooking. I had baked two apple pies so he would have something to eat after I left. I tried not to think about what I was doing, because if I did, I became confused and I knew it was really a very simple thing: I was just leaving Don before he left me.

When I was sure Don was asleep, I quietly slipped out of bed and tiptoed into the bathroom, where I quickly dressed and gathered up a few last-minute things to put into my suitcase. In an hour I would be on an airplane headed back home. Nothing could stop me from leaving now.

I carefully pulled the suitcase out from under the bed, praying I wouldn't wake up Don. I opened it to put the last of my things inside and found a piece of paper lying on top of my clothing. I picked up the scrap of paper, and in the dim light I read, "I Love You. Please Don't Go."

Don knew! He had known all along!

I stood there in the darkness, with tears streaming silently down my face. Stay Awhile stretched, rolled over in his box, and went back to sleep.

If I didn't leave soon I would miss my plane. If I stayed, what would happen to me? What if Don left me and I was all alone again?

Then I could hear God's voice in my heart. *Don isn't the one standing here with a suitcase and sneaking off in the middle of the night like a thief! Don is asleep in his bed, where he is supposed to be. He's not going anywhere! You asked me to give you a husband, and I did. Don't you think I knew who was the right one for you?*

I closed the suitcase quietly and slid it back under the bed. I slipped out of my clothes and climbed carefully into bed so I wouldn't wake up Don. Maybe I really could trust him; maybe he really did love me and wouldn't leave me.

"All right, God," I prayed, "I'll stay."

I fell asleep holding the note tightly in my hand—a note written in pencil on a scrap of paper; a note that said, "I Love You. Please Don't Go." ☀

CHAPTER EIGHTEEN

God Gave a Son

Neither of us ever mentioned the note in the suitcase. We both pretended nothing had ever happened. I decided that I didn't love Don, but I could pretend I did. And if I pretended well enough, he would never know the difference.

I began trying out recipes in the cookbook Don bought me, and I learned to sew his clothes on the sewing machine instead of stapling them. I tried to keep my fire-red temper under control and to keep our home peaceful and comfortable. I would ask myself, *What would I do for Don today if I really loved him?* and I would polish his boots or bake a pie. I knew I was doing a good job of fooling him, because he seemed much happier than he had before.

Summer came, and the sun made up for not shining all winter. I loved the long days and didn't go to bed until three o'clock in the morning because it was still light out. Don took me for long drives in the wild countryside, and we went camping and hiking and paddled a canoe up icy rivers. It felt good to be close to mother earth again and to feel the wind and sun and to walk through tall grass and giant trees.

One day we walked for miles through a dense forest where

ferns were taller than we were. We picked berries and dug up fossils. It was a beautiful day, and we were so far out in the wilderness I felt we were the only two people in the world.

When we stopped for a rest Don reached down and picked up a dandelion and handed it to me. "Have a sunshine flower," he said.

Suddenly the memories of the day he had "come courting" with penny suckers and dandelions flooded back. We had been married nearly a year now, and he had brought me more happiness than I had ever dreamed possible.

"I love you," I said. My words hung in the air like a bird in mid-flight. I couldn't believe I had said them. I didn't know which of us was more surprised.

"I love you," I repeated and found it easier to say the second time. "I really do!" And my heart burst with feelings I had kept buried all my life. I flung myself into Don's arms, overcome with the joy of falling in love with my husband.

Our love grew, and each day was an adventure. Two lonely people would never be lonely again. When he was away working in the oil fields, we wrote to each other every day, and when he was home it was a celebration.

As women have from the beginning of time, I began to pray I could give a child, the greatest gift of all, to the man I loved.

Countless times I would pray, "Lord, please give us a son, and I will raise him up to worship You."

When time passed and there was no child, I began to fear I would remain barren. I would became a dry, twisted, old oak that had never borne fruit. I sat in the darkness many nights and wept bitter tears. I had been cheated many times in life, but this time Don was being cheated too, and that made the emptiness hurt more.

I tried to pray "Thy will be done" and accept that there would always be just the two of us. We loved each other and had more happiness than most people. I should have been satisfied, but I wasn't.

I began to grow angry. I felt God had turned against me. Other women had children—why not me? Animals had offspring—why not me?

"No, God! I can't pray 'Thy will be done' if it's Your will for me to be childless! I won't give up. I'll beg You for a child a hundred times a day for the rest of my life! I want a child! Give me a son, and I promise I'll raise him to worship You." Hundreds of times my lips uttered that prayer, "Give me a son! Give me a son!

I searched the Bible, reading every passage that mentioned children, and I soon found out that in ancient times it was a disgrace for a woman to be childless.

Rachel was barren and then "she conceived, and bare a son; and said, 'God hath taken away my reproach,'" in the book of Genesis.

In the book of 1 Samuel, Hannah wept and prayed to the

Lord, "If thou . . . wilt give unto thy handmaid a man child, then I will give him unto the Lord."

"Children are a heritage of the Lord: and the fruit of the womb is his reward," wrote the psalmist. If children were a reward, then I would remain childless, because I had done nothing to deserve a reward from God.

But I clung to the Bible stories of women who had been barren and then later had children. They were my hope, and I suffered with Rachel and Hannah and rejoiced because their prayers were answered.

I bought infant clothes and blankets and rattles and hid them away where Don couldn't see them. He wouldn't understand; he would think I was losing my mind.

On days when I was depressed, I would get out the baby clothes and hold them against my heart and would close my eyes and again say, "Please, God, give me a son."

One September night, as the moon hung just above the treetops and the wind tore the leaves off the limbs, leaving them naked and cold, I stood at the window and for the thousandth time made my plea to God. "Give me a son, and I'll raise him to glorify You."

The scene before me disappeared, and instead of the moon I saw a huge eagle flying across the sky. Instead of trees I saw a high, rugged cliff with a nest tucked in a crevice. The eagle landed on her nest and folded her wings and settled herself on several eggs. An instant later, the eagle spread her wings and fled down the canyon. She was followed by baby eagles.

The vision disappeared. Once again the moon and the trees were before me. I rubbed my eyes and looked again. The night was the same. There had been no eagle, no cliff, no eggs; but I had seen them as clearly as anything I had ever seen in bright daylight.

"Thank You, God. I know that was Your answer. I know that at this very minute I carry my son beneath my heart." And I wept for joy.

I started to wake up Don to tell him, but I was afraid he wouldn't believe me. He would say I had imagined it or dreamed it. There was no way I could put the beauty of the vision into words. It was too special, too precious, a secret between God and myself.

I was like Rachel; God had taken away my reproach. He had answered my prayer.

I made a pair of tiny baby moccasins out of the softest leather I could find and sewed blue beads on them.

I stood before my husband and handed him my gift. "These are for your son," I said, trying hard not to show the great excitement and pride in my pounding heart.

"My son?" he smiled. He could see the light in my face,

and he knew God had blessed us. "Maybe it will be a girl," he said looking at the blue beads.

"No," I answered, "a man must have a son. I asked for a son. That's what it will be."

I counted the days with great happiness and spent my time making things for our baby and praying for his safe journey into our world. I made a wooden cradleboard to carry my baby, and more clothes than he could ever wear.

It was a happy time for me, and Don was even more thoughtful than he had been before.

I sometimes found myself wondering what I would have done if he had left me, as Flint had said he would. Would I have been so eager to have this child? What if I had had a child and been alone, as my mother had been? For the first time I had an inkling of her side of the story. She had been married too young to a man who didn't love her. When he had walked out on her, she must have been frightened and terribly hurt. It was easier now to understand why she had left me with Grandmother. I wished she knew she was going to be a grandmother now.

Don urged me to go to a doctor. But Grandmother had had eleven children at home—surely I could have one at home. The idea of going to a hospital terrified me. I had heard terrible stories about hospitals. I had heard they cut off all your hair and shave your head. They kept you there as long as they wanted to and you couldn't get out. And sometimes they made mistakes and operated on the wrong people. I didn't want to go to a hospital. I wasn't sick; I was only having a baby.

On a Monday morning I knew it was time for the baby to come. My heart beat fast as I realized that in a few hours I would be a mother. When Don came home from work that night I told him it wouldn't be long; the time for the baby to arrive was near.

Hours passed and the pains grew worse. Night passed and morning came. Don stayed beside my bed. Neither of us slept all night, and my strength was gone.

"It's taking too long," Don said. "I'm taking you to the hospital."

I began to cry, "No! Wait! He'll come when he's ready." And I begged him not to take me to the hospital.

A nurse at the hospital helped me into a bed. "How long has she been in labor?" she asked.

"About forty hours," Don said in a voice that didn't sound like his at all.

The nurse led Don out of the room, and I cried harder. I wanted to have my baby at home with my husband. Now they had taken him away, and I was alone.

A Kickapoo woman who died in childbirth was considered as having died in battle and was given full honors of a warrior's burial, but that was small comfort now.

Another nurse came in and gave me ice to hold in my mouth. "Don't be afraid," she said and held my hand.

I was sure God had sent an angel to comfort me.

Early Wednesday morning our son was born, a healthy, screaming baby.

"Thank you, God, for our son!" I laughed, "He looks like a baby antelope!" And that's how he was named—our firstborn son, Little Antelope.

Don was standing against the doors of the delivery room so that when the nurse flung the doors open to wheel out my bed, they hit him in the back.

"We've got a son!" I laughed, "We've got a son!"

Later, when I held Little Antelope for the first time, tears ran down my cheeks. How beautiful, how precious he was! My son! I was a mother; I had been blessed by God to bring life into the world. Never again would I feel useless or ugly. I had borne a son!

When it came time to fill out the birth certificate, Don insisted we give the baby a Christian name as well as Little Antelope, so our son became Aaron Little Antelope Stafford.

Back home again, I stood beside our baby's crib for hours, amazed at the miracle of life. At night I would creep into his room to make sure he was still there and still breathing. "Don and me and baby makes three," I would whisper.

When I heard the hymn "How Great Thou Art," it touched me in a new way. I had always loved hearing about wandering through the forest glades and about the thunder and the stars—these were things I understood. It was a beautiful song. Now when I heard the part that said, "God, His only Son not sparing," tears would rush to my eyes and I would look down at the baby wrapped in the soft blue blanket in my arms. My son! I would never sacrifice my son—no, not even to save every single person in the whole world! And yet God had sacrificed His only Son for people as unworthy as myself. How much more God loved His Son than I loved mine, and yet how much He loved us to let His Son die so that we could go to heaven! God's sacrifice took on a new and deeper meaning, and I knew I would never take it for granted again. I understood for the first time how much God loved me and what His love had cost Him.

When Little Antelope was seven days old I began reading the Bible to him. God had answered my prayer; now I would keep my promise. Not one day would pass without Little Antelope's hearing God's Word. I figured that if I read a little of the Bible to him each day, I could read it through ten times before he grew up and left home. I wanted him to have God's Word hidden in his heart before he became a man and went out into the world.

When Little Antelope was ten days old, I took him into the woods and removed his blanket and all his clothing and held him up to the sun. "Sun, warm this baby and shine on him always." Then I kneeled down and laid my naked baby on the ground. Little Antelope kicked his tiny feet but didn't cry.

Small baby, naked on the soft floor of the forest,
Grow, my son, and become strong.
Be a happy child; be happy as a man.
Grow my son, strong and wise,
Do not forget your God.
Do not forget your mother in her old age.
Grow, my son, but not too soon.

"Oh, God hear me and see the beautiful child You have given me! I dedicated him to You while he kicked beneath my heart. Every day he will hear of Your love and mercy and greatness! Let me keep him and raise him for You, and let him grow into a man and hold his own son in his arms someday. Amen."

I dressed him and wrapped him in his blanket and tied him back onto his cradleboard and returned to the cabin.

The whole world was beautiful. The future was full of promise. God answers prayer!

Little boy laughing in my arms,
Captures my heart with his little boy charms—
Little boy making my life worth living,
Little boy sharing and loving and giving,
Little boy showing me the world with bright, shiny eyes,
Putting the sun back into dark, stormy skies.

THE WORLD ON A SILVER PLATTER

I'll give you the world, my son, the world and even more;
I'll give you crime and pollution and poverty and war.

Just look at the beautiful cities, my son, the buildings are so high;
It's too bad the smog's so thick that you can't see the sky.

And see the superhighways, my son, going everywhere,
And see the powerful cars polluting our clean air.

Oh, the wonderful world of science, my son,
we've made it to the moon;
No, I don't think it's true that we'll all be blown up soon.

Isn't medicine amazing, my son? Now we can nearly cure cancer.
I wouldn't worry about famines; someone will find an answer.

Your father and I aren't rich, my son,
but we'll give you your heart's desire;
It's the American way to "charge it"
as the cost of living goes higher.

All the finest education, my son—learn to read and write.
Equal opportunity—it's too bad you're half red and half white.

You'll have a war of your own;
each generation must have one.
Don't use alcohol or drugs;
ignore those who say they're fun.

It's too bad there's no wilderness left, no wild animals around,
But we've killed all the animals and subdivided the ground.

Oh, it's a wonderful world, and I'll give it to you, my son,
And ask but one small thing in return—
forgive us for what we've done!

YOUR VERY FIRST CHRISTMAS

Sleep warm, my little baby boy;
Beside you is your favorite toy.
It's your first Christmas Eve tonight;
The gifts are wrapped and the tree shines bright.
Here are the gifts I give to you—
A heart full of hope all wrapped in blue.
I'd buy you peace if it could be sold,
And mark it "Fragile" and wrap it in gold.
And I'll tell you a story so you will know,
About a Baby born long ago;
It was the Son of God, who came from above,
And brought us all the Gift of Love.

CHAPTER NINETEEN

Sign of the Cross

Not one child. One is a lonely number. No, there must be at least two. Two to play games—one to chase and one to run.

I didn't know any games, because as a child I had never played. Only once had some children asked me to play hide and seek with them. I had hidden behind some bushes and waited and waited, pleased with myself because I had found such a good hiding place that no one could find me. Then it had slowly dawned on me that no one was looking for me— they had only wanted to get rid of me. "I will never play stupid games again!" I had cried, and I never did.

The "games" my uncles and I had played were not for children. Our games had been shooting tin cans off of each other's heads, shooting at each other's feet to see who would jump first. Savage games, deadly games; racing horses at killing speeds and taking hard falls and rolling in the dust but somehow surviving. No, these were not games for my children. I would buy books. I would learn how to play games, how to be a child again.

When Little Antelope was six months old I found I was going to have another baby.

"I'm sorry, Little Antelope," I whispered to him. "You won't get to be the baby very long."

Don announced he had just lost his job. The company had closed down, and it didn't look as if he could get another job very soon.

"I think we should leave Alaska. I've heard farms are cheap in Oklahoma. What do you think?" he asked.

"It's warm in Oklahoma! The children can play in the sun! We can have a garden. There are more Indians in Oklahoma than any other state!" I was ready to go.

Don bought a camper, and a week later we started a journey that would take six months. Don wanted to show me as much of the country as he could, so we didn't drive straight to Oklahoma but wandered leisurely through all of the western states. I was sure I would have our second child beside the road in the middle of the Arizona desert, but we finally arrived in Oklahoma, bought a forty-acre farm, and almost had our things unpacked before he was born.

Don took me to an Indian hospital, and our second son came into the world weighing ten pounds and measuring twenty-three inches. He was the largest baby ever born in that hospital. Just before we had left for the hospital, a doe had wandered through our front yard and had walked up to our porch, so we named our new son Lost Deer. Once again Don insisted on a Christian name, and he added Shane to the birth certificate.

Now I had two beautiful sons, and I learned to trust God in a way I never had before.

Six months later I was once again expecting a child. Don shook his head and said, "Don't you think you can stop praying for children now? God has just about blessed us into poverty!"

Now I had two tiny babies to care for, and a third was on the way.

Our farmhouse was old, and the walls had cracks big enough to let "creatures" inside. I killed tarantulas and scorpions and mice and a thousand bugs without names. One day I opened the knife-and-fork drawer and found a snake curled up inside! I slammed the drawer shut so fast it crushed and killed the snake, but for months I couldn't open a drawer without cringing. We covered the house with tar paper in the hopes of keeping the bugs out, but it wasn't long before the strong winds blew all the paper off.

I planted a garden and sang a little song, "Little pregnant mother seeds, will you deliver your children for us?" Most of them didn't deliver, because, unknown to me at the time, Lost Deer had followed along the rows behind me and picked up the seeds I had "spilled" and put them safely into his pocket.

Our only near neighbor was a Cherokee medicine woman. She treated twenty or thirty Indians a week for every sort of ailment, real or imagined. She kept a frog and a hawk in her house for "good medicine" and wore a necklace of eagle claws and one of human bones.

She was called Herb Woman of the Turtle Clan, and there wasn't a plant in the forest she couldn't use for some purpose.

She was wise enough to stay abreast of modern times while keeping one foot in the past. She not only used ancient chants and spells but she also studied astrology and made charts for people according to their stars and Zodiac sign.

One day she asked me what sign I was born under.

"The sign of the cross," I answered.

"There is no sign like that to be born under." She frowned.

"Yes, I was born under the sign of the cross of Calvary," I responded, smiling.

"You're an Indian girl. You best stick to things you know about!" And she went on to tell me stories and legends and the power of "white," or "good," witchcraft. Because she used witchcraft she was called Powacca, meaning "two hearted."

So began a friendly battle. She tried to win me back to the "Old Way" and I tried to win her for Christ.

As I was pulling weeds in my garden one day, I found a copperhead snake coiled around a corn stalk just inches from my hand. Cold fear sent me running to the house, and I came back with a gun and shot the head off the snake. Before I left the garden I had killed two more copperheads. As I walked back to the house on weak, trembling legs I praised God for letting me see the snakes before they saw me.

Later, when I told the medicine woman about the copperheads, she scolded me for killing snakes. "All creatures are your brothers. You should not kill except for food! I live here beside a rocky cliff. I see snakes all the time, but I say to them, 'Hello, my brother, let me go in peace!' and the snake god promised he would never harm me."

Walking home from her house I saw a black snake beside our chicken coop.

"Hello, my brother," I said. "Prepare to die!" And I shot him and then looked over my shoulder to see if Herb Woman had been watching.

We had many visits. When she spoke of astrology, I spoke of Jesus. Neither of us ever gave an inch, but we enjoyed each other's company. She was a very special person.

On a rainy day in spring, Herb Woman was found lying dead among astrology charts, packages of herbs, and ceremonial objects in her home. She had died from a snake bite that she'd tried to treat herself.

I hate it when ignorant people say, "The Indian religion is beautiful—let's leave them alone to worship their own gods!" How I wish they could have known and loved Herb Woman and known the terrible loss of her senseless, painful death.

The snake god had failed Herb Woman. ☀

CHAPTER TWENTY

Life is Sweet

Finally all the weariness caught up with me.

"Lord, I'm so tired," I whispered. "Give me strength to get through this day." I pushed up out of bed and stood on shaky legs.

"Lord, I can't make it. I'm too tired." I fell back across the bed. If I could only sleep a few more minutes—even one more minute. "Please, please let me rest!" I begged, but before I had finished my prayer I could hear "Mommy!" coming from the next room.

Tears trickled out of my eyes and slid down my cheeks. I was so tired my body felt like lead. I moved slowly and with great effort.

The night before I had been up sixteen times with the boys. They had earaches and had hardly slept because of the pain. Today they were better, but my head throbbed and my body ached.

Somehow I made it through the morning and praised God when it was time for the children's naps. Now I could lie down and catch up on the sleep I had lost the night before.

On my way to my bedroom the world went black! I rubbed my eyes, but I couldn't see. It was as if a blanket had been thrown over my head. I felt my way to my bed and lay down. I closed my eyes.

I'm only tired. I'm only tired. After I rest I'll be fine, I thought.

The children were as tired as I was, and we were all still asleep when Don came home from work. He woke me up, and when I opened my eyes he looked as if he were at the end of a far tunnel, with darkness all around him.

"My eyes are bothering me," I said and rubbed them again. "I can't see right today. I think if I could just sleep awhile I would be all right."

Don looked at my eyes. "I don't see anything wrong with them." He held my hand and noticed my wedding ring was gone. "Where's your ring?"

"It kept falling off, so I put it away," I said.

He dug in the closet until he found the scale and set it beside the bed. "Get on," he ordered.

I stood on the scale while he read the weight. "Ninety-two pounds! You only weigh ninety-two pounds! Where did the other fifteen pounds go? You're pregnant—you should be gaining weight, not losing weight! You lost fifteen ponds!"

I began to cry. Something was wrong! I had lost weight, I couldn't see, and I was so tired I wanted to die.

Early the next morning Don drove me to the doctor for tests. The results of the tests were not good. Four organs were not functioning properly, I had anemia, I was near exhaustion, and my blood cells were malformed and were not producing as they should. In spite of all this, however, the baby seemed to be all right.

The doctor didn't know what was wrong, and some of the tests seemed to contradict each other. All he knew for certain was that my body was not working as it should, and it was affecting my blood.

There were more tests, diets, and medication, but nothing helped. I was six-months pregnant and still weighed less than a hundred pounds. I looked like a skeleton and had deep, black circles under my eyes. I prayed constantly for my baby to be born normal and healthy.

One doctor suggested I "terminate" my pregnancy and, calling him a murderer, I ran out of his office and refused to go back to him.

Another doctor said I had some of the symptoms of leukemia, but the results of the tests didn't confirm it. I was going into the clinic for blood tests every five days. The doctor talked of starting blood transfusions, but I refused because I was afraid it would do something to my baby.

At home Don took over more and more of the cooking and cleaning. I did as much as I could for the boys, but many days all I could do was sit and hold them in my lap and tell them stories. My vision was so bad it was difficult to read anything. Some days I had double vision, and other days everything looked so dark I would turn on all the lights, hoping they would help me see.

I was so weak I was sure I was dying and couldn't hang on much longer. I had been to so many doctors I couldn't even remember their names, and all they could say was there was something wrong with my blood. They didn't know what it was or what was causing it, but they all agreed it was becoming serious.

I cried. I prayed. I went to more doctors and attended healing services at different churches, all to no avail. Nothing changed the downhill road I was traveling.

I went to a lawyer and made out a will so Don wouldn't have any legal problems after I died. I left instructions that my favorite hymns and Scripture verses be used at my funeral. I was putting my house in order the best way I knew how, and all the time I was asking God, *What will happen to my children?*

I wrote long letters to Little Antelope and Lost Deer and put them in their baby books. Above all else, they must know that I loved them with all my heart and that I didn't want to leave them. I told them to obey their father and to follow Jesus. It was hard to put a whole life of teaching into a few pages of a letter.

I told Don he should get married again as soon as he could find a Christian woman who would love him and the children. But I warned over and over that she must be a Christian.

I had worried so much about losing my children that it had never occurred to me that I might die before they did.

Now it looked as if my time was running out.

I grieved for all the times I wouldn't be beside their beds to tell them a story and hear their prayers and tuck them in. I felt sorry for all the times they would be sick and have no mother to comfort them. I thought of all the games we would never play, all the walks through an autumn forest we would never take, and all the Christmases we would never celebrate together. It was more than I could bear. I wasn't afraid to die, because I knew that as soon as I had accepted Christ as my Savior I had been given eternal life; when I died I would go to heaven and be with Jesus forever. But I ached for my children, my little orphans. And what about the baby I carried? Would I live long enough to give it life, or would it die with me?

God, let me live long enough to raise my children! Just let me stay here long enough to help them grow up! It was an impossible prayer. With such young children, I would have to live another twenty years to raise them and send them off from home. I was asking God for twenty years, and the doctors couldn't guarantee I would live long enough to have my baby.

Don moved through the house like an old man. He was quiet and he no longer stood tall and proud. His eyes were hollow and sad and he didn't smile anymore.

I tried to be brave, but many nights I cried myself to sleep in his arms.

I remembered the lonely days before I had met Don. I recalled how I had tried to kill myself because life hadn't been worth living. Now life was sweet and full. Now that I wanted to live, I was going to die.

I began keeping a diary so there would be something of me left behind for the children. They must remember that I loved them!

THE DIARY

I began this diary to tell you
All of my secrets and dreams,
So I could share a bit of my life—
Oh, how important that seems!

I promise I will write in it
Each day so faithfully;
Perhaps it will help to keep
My life slipping away from me.

I save pieces of my days
With just a word or two,
And page after page fills up so fast
As I try to say that I loved you.

I take the little book
And put it on the shelf;
I touch it gently and with pride;
The book is part of myself.

If this book is ever read,
Long after I have gone to rest,
Please read the words with love,
And understand I did my best.

Maybe by reading my secret thoughts
You'll know me as no other;
This is the "real me," the inside of the book;
The "me" people saw was only the cover.

So I leave you this book, my children,
Something for you to share,
To tell you how much I love you
And how sorry I am I can't be there.

The days go by as the pages turn,
And someday I know I will find
My name is written in God's book of Life,
And I'll go home and leave my diary behind.

Friends everywhere were praying for me. I continued to have blood tests every five days. I did everything the doctors suggested unless there was even the smallest chance of hurting the baby. I would not sacrifice my baby so that I could live.

In the ninth month I gained some weight, and there was more hope for the baby now. Then my right leg became paralyzed, and I had to use crutches to get around.

When at last the time came to go to the hospital, I was sure I would never see my family again. God had let me live long enough to see my baby born. Now my time was at hand.

Trinity Snow Cloud, our third son, was born on a Sunday in January. How we rejoiced that he was healthy and normal, even though he weighed only six pounds.

Within minutes after his birth I noticed there was feeling in my leg again and there was no more pain in my back. I was starving, and a half-hour after the baby was born I was eating supper. I ate continually during the next few days while I rested in the hospital. My vision was normal and I couldn't remember ever feeling so strong.

The doctor said I was better, but he wouldn't say I was well until he took tests.

After I left the hospital I couldn't get enough to eat. I ate as many as six meals a day during the next two weeks. A month later I returned to the doctor for a checkup. Snow Cloud was small but in perfect health. My last blood tests showed nothing wrong but low blood sugar. The strange, malformed blood cells that had shown up in every test for the past six months had disappeared.

The doctor smiled and said, "I don't know what's happened. You've been very ill. I never could find out what was wrong, and I don't know why you're well. I want you to have a blood test every six months, but as far as I can tell now, you'll live to see your grandchildren."

I had the follow-up blood tests, but the problem never showed up again. The doctor never did know what my illness had been, what had caused it; or why it had disappeared. I didn't know the answer to the first two questions, but I was sure that prayer was the answer to the third.

Life had a new sweetness now that I knew how fragile it was.

SNOW CLOUD

May life bring lovely things your way,
Golden sunsets at the end of day,
A quiet home among tall trees,
A restful soul, a heart at ease.

Let your life be filled with happy hours,
Good books, a hillside of flowers,
Trusted friends all the years through,
And may gentle Jesus richly bless you.

CHAPTER TWENTY-ONE

What Could Go Wrong!

I was so busy taking care of the three little boys I had isolated myself from the rest of the world. I went six months without seeing anyone but Don and the children.

"Don't you want to see other women? Don't you want to go visit some neighbors or something? Don't you need to gossip?" Don finally asked.

I shrugged. "I'm happy with my family and my home. I don't need outsiders."

"I think it would do you good to get out and go somewhere and see someone. Tomorrow I think you should take the car and the children and drive into town and buy groceries."

"But you always buy groceries, and anything I need I can order from a catalog. I don't want to go to town." I had the feeling I had already lost the argument and Don's mind had been made up before he had even mentioned the trip to town.

"It will do you good. You won't have any trouble. Just drive into town and take Cloud to the clinic for his checkup and buy some groceries and come home. What could possibly happen?"

That night I hardly slept. I worried about all the things I was sure would happen to me—flat tires, getting lost, and having a wreck were just a few of the milder problems I expected.

"Don't worry, you'll do just fine," my husband said the next morning as he slammed the car door and handed me the keys.

"I still wish you were going along. What if I have trouble?" I pleaded.

"You won't have any trouble. All you are going to do is buy groceries, stop at the doctor's and come home. What could possibly happen?"

"I guess you're right." I started the car and drove away. It was my first time out alone with the children since Cloud had been born, and I wasn't sure I could handle all three of them and still drive and do the shopping. But I smiled to myself. Don was right. What could possibly go wrong?

As I drove into town I saw a MAGIC WATER WAND CAR WASH and decided to wash the car to surprise Don. I had never washed the car before, but I had watched Don do it, and it had looked simple enough.

I pulled into the car wash and drove over the curb. As the car bumped the curb the horn let out a short honk. I got out of the car and picked up the water wand with one hand and put my quarter in the slot with the other. I began squirting water at the car, and the boys began squealing and jumping up and down in the back seat. It was then that I noticed the windows were still rolled down. Soap and water covered the back seat and children.

"Roll up the window!" I shouted and directed the stream of water onto the trunk of the car.

"I can't!" yelled Antelope, "The handle is covered with soap!"

As I reached for the door to help him, the magic washer wand slipped from my hand and suddenly turned into a wild monster trying to beat our car to death.

Bang! Bang! Bang! It flew through the air and hit the top of our car. I ran around the car trying to catch it, but it was swinging so wildly I couldn't even get close. I jumped into the car and sped out of the car wash before the water wand could smash our windshield. I left the monster thrashing around inside the car wash, banging against the walls and squirting soap and water in every direction. A block away I could still hear the banging. I wondered how long a quarter lasted in a car wash.

I wondered if Don would notice the car was half-washed and hoped the boys' clothes and my dress would dry out before we got to the store.

The trip through the grocery store was uneventful except for the fourteen heads of cabbage that rolled down the aisle after Antelope pulled one out of the bottom row.

Finally all I had to do was to take Cloud to the clinic for a checkup, and then I would be on my way home.

The waiting room was crowded, and every seat was taken. I stood against the wall and held Cloud while Antelope and Deer wandered around the room. They soon had the attention of everyone there and were busy making new friends.

One lady who had a white shawl draped across her lap started talking to Antelope. Suddenly, without warning, Antelope picked up the corner of her shawl, wiped his nose with it, and ran off down the hallway, with Deer close behind.

Praying she wouldn't faint, I hurried over to the horrified woman. I apologized and offered to pay for having her shawl cleaned. She refused and mumbled something about never again telling a child to use a handkerchief.

A shrill scream suddenly drew everyone's attention toward the emergency room. A nurse left the desk and headed that direction. A lady next to me said she thought they were treating a child who had been hit by a car.

The noise from the emergency room grew louder.

"It's terrible! Why don't they do something for that child's pain!" one lady said.

I looked around for my sons. They were nowhere in sight, so I headed down the hallway to search for them. As I passed the emergency room I saw the cause of all the noise and confusion. Deer and Antelope were racing around an examination table with a nurse and doctor close behind them.

I stepped inside and grabbed them and pushed them into a chair, where I held them by their shirt collars.

"Those are the fastest kids I've ever seen!" puffed the doctor. "There were two other patients ahead of you, but I think I'll see you now."

In a few minutes he assured me that Cloud was in perfect health and there was no need for us to come back for at least a year. I loaded the three boys into the car and headed home.

On the way home I noticed there was a large black car just

ahead of me. Suddenly the wheels of my car bounced through a deep puddle and the car came down with a thud. The horn blared. It was stuck! I hit it with my hand a couple of times, hoping to jar it loose and stop the noise, but it continued. When I looked up, I saw that the black car ahead of me was a hearse!

I started to drop back, but the driver of the truck in back of me waved for me to keep going. The road was too narrow and too muddy for me to pull over or to stop without getting stuck. There was nothing to do but follow the hearse with my horn sounding. Mile after mile we bounced down the road—the hearse, me and my horn, and the truck behind.

Finally the road widened enough so that I could pull over and let the hearse go on its way without the accompaniment of my horn. I got out to see if I could find a way to stop the noise.

The truck that had been following me pulled over too, and the driver came up to me. "Why are you honking your horn at that hearse?" he yelled above the noise.

"It's an old Indian custom to drive away evil spirits!" I shouted as I raised the hood. "Do you know how to stop this?"

In a few minutes I was quietly on my way home.

When I drove into the yard, Don came out of the house to meet me and help me with the grocery bags. "Did you have any trouble?" he asked as he grabbed some sacks.

"No. No trouble at all," I said and followed him into the house. "After all, what could possibly go wrong?"

I loved my three sons but Don and I would have liked a daughter. I prayed about having another child and felt that God would carry me through.

When Snow Cloud was six months old another child was on the way. This time my health was perfect. I was convinced from the start that a daughter was on her way, and everything I bought was pink.

THE NEW BABY

A new little baby to hold real tight,
A new little baby to keep Mama awake all night.
Daddy just smiled and said with a grin,
"Well, I guess here we go again!"
Two little boys running through the door,
A baby in the crib and one crawling on the floor,
Four little children, the oldest one is four,
We're rich in children so we'll never be poor.

Toys, blankets, and diapers all over the place;
We might be tired but there's a smile on my face.
"Go forth and multiply," was the first command in the Good Book—
It might have said more, but I've been too busy to look.

CHAPTER TWENTY-TWO

Rich Rewards

D on't tell me you are expecting another baby!" My friend looked at me and shook her head. "Four children in four years? Haven't you heard of family planning?"

"Yes, I've heard of family planning. I planned to have a family, and I'm having one," I said.

She laughed. "You must be crazy!"

I was so angry I was on the verge of tears. With that one thoughtless remark she had spoiled my day and taken the sparkle out of the announcement of our coming baby.

Why do some people consider it a mistake to have a baby? What is wrong with a world where a baby is considered a burden instead of a blessing? Why do mothers think they have to apologize for having babies and loving their families? Why is there so much pressure to work outside the home and "be somebody" and have a career? Why can't motherhood be a career?

I was still biting my tongue as I was hanging out my laundry an hour later. "I don't understand it! I don't understand any of it!" I muttered to myself. I knew it was wrong to be angry, but I felt like a bear protecting her cubs.

My friend had been looking for a job. In my mind I wrote an imaginary newspaper ad. I knew it was not the kind of ad she would ever answer!

WANTED: *An attractive, well-kept woman with a good education and pleasant personality. She must be friendly, cheerful and willing to work twenty-four hours a day with no pay, no vacations, and no sick leave. She must scrub floors, cook meals, clean house, do laundry and ironing and heavy cleaning. She must be able to stretch a dollar six ways, and wear the same dress five years and still look nice. She must have spare time to read bedtime stories, dry a tear, kiss a skinned elbow, make cookies and play with small children. She must be a companion to her husband, friend, lover, bookkeeper, nurse, cleaning woman, and gardener. WANTED: A MOTHER.*

My anger was gone now. I was truly sorry for my friend who didn't know or understand the rich rewards of being a mother. As I went back to the house I called to my sons, "Come inside for milk and cookies."

They answered with squeals of delight and came running to the house and tumbled through the door. Their chubby, dirty arms wrapped around my neck and pulled me off balance, and the four of us tumbled to the floor with shrieks of laughter.

"We love you, Mommy!" they said and scrambled to the table.

My children. Always a blessing, never a burden.

The baby I carried beneath my heart stirred. Thank You, God, for my children.

There had been tornado warnings out for three hours. It was near midnight when the storm hit. The wind howled with fury and blew the bedroom windowpanes out and rain soaked the bed. I stuffed a pillow in the window and sat on the edge of the bed. My fourth baby was on the way. Don would not be home for hours, and I knew I couldn't wait that long.

We didn't have a telephone, and I didn't have a car. Our nearest neighbor was a mile away. I woke up my three sons, put shoes on them, and put their coats over their pajamas. They were sleepy, and Snow Cloud was as limp as a dishrag. I picked up Cloud in my arms and handed the flashlight to Antelope. I grabbed Deer's hand, and we started out across the fields to get help. Antelope aimed the flashlight everywhere except onto the muddy path in front of us. Lightning flashed and lit our way more than the wandering flashlight. The four of us were soaked to the skin by the time we had reached the neighbor's house.

I banged on the door and shouted, and in a few minutes a sleepy-eyed man answered the door.

"Can I borrow your phone? I need to call my husband," I said, pushing the three boys inside out of the rain.

I called the plant where Don worked, and the night watchman promised he would give the message to Don.

"I'd like to help, but my pickup don't run," the man said and yawned.

"I'm all right. Thanks for letting me use the phone," I said and led the boys back out into the dark, rainy night. It took longer to walk the mile back home because I had to carry Cloud in my arms and Deer rode piggyback. The fourth child reminded me constantly that it would soon join us.

When we arrived home again I put dry clothing on all the boys and changed my own clothing. Then I gathered up some blankets and pillows to make a bed in the car for the children. It was a seventy-mile drive to the hospital, and the children could sleep in the back seat.

It usually took my husband an hour to drive home from work, but that night, in spite of the rain, he made it in twenty minutes. As we bundled the children into the car he said, "A tornado touched down two miles from here, and the bridge is out at Twin Oaks. We'll have to ford Spring Creek and go through the hills."

"I won't make it," I said through clenched teeth.

"Yes you will," he said, and the tires spun as we pulled out of the yard.

For the next seventy miles we drove through puddles of water up to the front bumper, we slid through mud, and we sped along winding roads. We crossed the state line and skidded up to a stop in front of the hospital in Siloam Springs, Arkansas.

As my husband left me in the delivery room to go back and take care of the boys, who were bedded down in the waiting room, I waited for words that would help me. I expected him to say, "I love you," or "I'll be praying for you." Instead he looked at me biting my lips and clenching my fists with pain, and said, "Well, have fun, honey."

A short time later our only daughter was born, and her name had already been decided. She was Spring Storm.

The plump nurse handed me my beautiful new baby girl. She was only a few hours old, and I hugged her tightly against me with my heart ready to burst with happiness.

I looked up and saw the nurse watching me as I fed my baby.

"Do you have children?" I asked.

"Yes, I had a daughter but I lost her," she answered.

"I'm sorry," I said.

"I don't mean she died. I mean that somehow I just lost her. I was so happy when she was born, but I felt we were too far in debt. So when she was six months old I took a part-time job—just for a couple of months to pay off some bills. The part-time job turned into a full-time job, and the couple of months turned into years. She's eighteen years old, and this week she's getting married, and I don't know her at all. We are strangers, and now she's gone. When she was little she'd beg me to read bedtime stories to her, but I was too tired or too busy and I never seemed to get around to it. I'd always promise her, 'Tomorrow,' but it never came. You know, I can't show you one thing I ever bought with the money I earned working. I didn't really need to work. We could have managed without my small income. I cheated myself and my daughter, and nothing can ever give me back my little baby." She wiped her eyes.

My baby was asleep and the nurse gently picked her up to take her back to the nursery.

"You have a beautiful baby. Don't lose her," she said.

"I won't," I said, and my heart ached for her. As I lay back down I promised myself I would read lots of extra bedtime stories to my baby to make up for that little girl whose mother had always been too busy to read to her.

As we brought Spring Storm home from the hospital Don said, "You've had four babies in four years in four different states. I don't mind if you want to have a souvenir from places you've been, but can't you collect plates or salt and pepper shakers like other women?"

FOR SPRING STORM

Jesus, my shepherd, bless my little bed,
Put an angel on my pillow, where I lay my sleepy head.
Brothers and Mommy and Daddy bless.
And tonight give us all sweet dreams and rest.
Keep us safe and with us be,
Until we wake up in Heaven's eternity. Amen.

Robins and blue skies and butterflies too—
These are the things I wish for you.
With each sunrise, a day special and new,
Love and laughter and dreams come true.
May sunshine always light your way
And life have all the beautiful surprises of Christmas Day.

Life suddenly became very busy. There didn't seem to be enough hours in the day to do half the things I needed to get done.

I had just finished setting supper on the table one evening when I happened to glance out the window and see the ducks heading for the pond. I groaned. How did those ducks get out of the chicken coop? I must not have hooked the door after I fed them. I would have to go chase them back into the coop. It was nearly dark, and if I left them outside all night a fox would kill them before morning.

Little Antelope and Deer were busy playing with blocks, and the two babies were in their cribs, so I slipped quietly out the kitchen door and ran toward the pond. As soon as the ducks saw me coming they each went a different direction, quacking and flapping their wings. I chased them around the pond twice and finally cornered them in tall grass and grabbed two of them. I carried them back to the chicken coop and shoved them inside and locked the door. As I was chasing the other two ducks, I noticed how dark it was getting. I hoped the boys weren't getting into trouble. Catching the ducks was taking longer than I expected. I finally caught the last two and locked them in the chicken coop and returned to the house.

An unexpected stillness greeted me when I walked into the kitchen. It wasn't like the boys to be so quiet. My steps quickened on the way to the living room.

The gory sight before me made my eyes blur. My knees buckled, and I sank paralyzed to the floor.

Antelope stood on the couch, his eyes wide. Clutched in his tiny hand was a kitchen knife. Around his mouth was blood and the front of his shirt was soaked with blood as if his stomach had been ripped open. Blood formed a pool at his feet. On the floor sat Deer, splashed with blood.

"Oh, God! Don't let them die!" I tried to get back on my feet, but I couldn't move. My heart had stopped beating. My sons had been playing with knives while I was chasing stupid ducks, and now they were both badly hurt. I knew that with the blood Antelope had already lost, he couldn't live!

I began screaming, "Don! Don! Don! Don!"

I had seen him feeding the rabbits down the hills. He would never hear me so far away. But I had underestimated the shrillness of my screaming. In seconds he burst through the door. He was out of breath from running up the hill.

I pointed across the room to Antelope. I still hadn't stopped screaming. "He's ripped his stomach open! He's dying!"

Don ran to him, "If I can pinch off the artery that's cut, maybe I can get the bleeding stopped until we can get him to the hospital!" He shoved his fingers into the red gore on Antelope's chest and asked, "Why isn't he crying?"

"He's in shock!" I said, struggling at last to my feet but still unable to walk. "He's dying!" I sobbed.

Don pulled his hand away and looked at his fingers and rubbed them together. He reached over and touched Antelope's shirt again and sniffed the red stuff on his hand.

"This isn't blood!" he said, and looked around. Then he bent over and picked up something from beside the couch and held it up for me to see.

"It isn't blood. Antelope just helped himself to a quart jar of strawberry jam!" Don took the knife out of Antelope's hand and dropped it with a clink into the empty jar.

Tears of relief streamed down my face as I rushed over and saw that the blood and gore were just red jam. While I had been chasing ducks, Antelope had crawled up on the table and taken a knife and "fed" himself and his brother supper.

Don and I both sank weakly onto the couch. We didn't care that we, too, were now covered with strawberry jam. We burst into laughter and continued laughing for joy over the knowledge that the son we thought we had lost was alive and well.

Antelope and Deer sat on the floor and watched with wonder as their parents laughed until their sides ached.

I remembered the joke Flint and Kansas had played on me years earlier, and I laughed even harder. I had fallen for the same trick twice!

I began mopping up the mess, and as I put the boys' clothing into the washing machine I looked at them again. We were lucky. It could have been blood. The knife had been real enough, and I had been out of the house too long. The nightmare could have been real, but praise God, instead of a terrible tragedy it had turned into a joke, a story we would tell the children when they were older. They would ask to hear it again and again: "Mama, tell us again about the night you thought we'd killed ourselves!"

"Thank You, God" I prayed as I poured bleach into the washer. "Thank you for protecting my children while I was trying to protect a bunch of dumb ducks!" ☀

CHAPTER TWENTY-THREE

Maybe I Could Write

Anything interesting in the mail?" Don asked as he looked through the pile of bills.

"Reverend McPherson wrote a card today. He asked when I was going to write my book," I laughed.

Don looked up from reading the light bill. "What book?"

"It's a joke between us. He always used to tell me I should write a book about what it's like to be an Indian," I said.

"That's a good idea. Why don't you do it?" he asked.

"I don't know how to write a book," I replied, shrugging.

"How do you know? You've read thousands of books. You know what sounds good and what doesn't. I think you should do it. It might help a lot of Indians—maybe white people too."

"Do you really think I could do it?" I asked. "I wish I could help people know the truth about what it's like to be an Indian."

"You could do it if you really wanted to. Ask God to help you write it," he said and went back to reading the mail.

Maybe it wasn't really a joke. Maybe I really could write a book. Maybe I would start tomorrow.

Reverend McPherson's words came back to me the next morning. "When are you going to start your book?"

I looked out the window. A restless wind was blowing, and it was cold outside.

"Today!" I said out loud. "Today I start my book!"

I hurried to the closet and began searching for an ancient typewriter that a friend had thrown out years ago. I had dug it out of her trash and had carried it off with her blessings. I searched through old snow boots, Christmas decorations, and Halloween masks until I found it. The typewriter was covered with dust, and the ribbon was missing, but I wasn't discouraged. I carried my treasure into the kitchen and placed it lovingly on the table.

Fired up with enthusiasm, I drove to town and bought a new typewriter ribbon, a package of carbon paper, and a package of two thousand sheets of typing paper.

I carefully arranged everything on the table and glanced at the clock. It was noon. I still had four hours to write a novel before my husband came home from work.

It took a little while to figure out just how to thread the ribbon, and that the *L* key didn't work. But that didn't matter; I would use the number *7* key until I could get it repaired. I would just have to remember that a *7* is an upside down, backward *L*.

I typed my first sentence.

"Don pu77ed me to him and his 7ips gent7y touched mine."

I leaned back in my chair and read my work. So far, so

good. It would be a beautiful love story. All I needed now was a plot and characters and some filling in between the beginning and the climax. I liked the word *climax*; it was a good writer's word. An ordinary person would have said "beginning and end," but a writer like myself would say "climax."

I looked at the clock. I decided to get the roast in the oven so it could be cooking while I created.

Back to work. *Let's see; where was I?*

"Don pu77ed me to him and his 7ips gent7y touched mine." Who knows, maybe this was the start of a best-seller.

Maybe it could sound better. I rewrote. All us famous authors rewrite our manuscripts. That was another good writer's word, *manuscripts*. I'd remember that.

"Don's man7y arms pu77ed me to him and his gent7e kiss sea7ed our 7ove."

That's what I call writing!

That's what I call smoke!

The roast had burned. It had taken all afternoon to polish up that sentence. Oh well, *Gone with the Wind* wasn't written in a day, and once I got the hang of it I could write faster.

I heard Don's car pull up in front.

Well, I had written enough for that day, anyway. I pulled my "manuscript" out of the typewriter, folded it up, and put it away in my apron pocket. I put the typewriter back in the hall closet.

The roast was burned and nothing else was thawed out. I

could make pancakes for dinner. I hadn't washed dishes all day because with all that creating I hadn't had time. We could use paper plates for dinner. I hoped the syrup wouldn't soak through paper plates. Maybe if we ate fast—

I smiled and patted my apron pocket, where my manuscript rested. The next time Reverend McPherson asked when I was going to write a book, I could tell him I had already started!

I would need a pen name. No one would ever read a book written by someone called Crying Wind. I would use a typical white woman's name. I would call myself Gwendolyn Lovequist.

I had to spend the next day digging a peanut butter and jelly sandwich out of the keys after Lost Deer tried to run his sandwich through the roller to "smash it more flat."

Late that night, while the family slept, I began writing a book called *Crying Wind*.

"Moccasined feet moved quietly down the dry arroyo. . . "

As the pages piled up I found myself weeping as I relived the past. The glory of my horse, Thunder Hooves; the death of my grandmother; the long search for the true God. As I struggled to get my thoughts on paper, I wondered if anyone would ever read the words of an uneducated half-breed.

I had underestimated God's plan for my life. ※

CHAPTER TWENTY-FOUR

Looking for My Mother

Suddenly my eyes flew open and I was filled with dread as I rolled over and looked at the alarm clock. It was nearly time to get up. I groaned slightly and shut my eyes tightly, wishing I could shut out the day. Today was my birthday. I hated birthdays. I hated becoming a year older.

I sighed, climbed out of bed, pulled on my faded pink housecoat, and staggered down the hall. The children were still asleep, so maybe Don and I could have a nice quiet breakfast together for a change. I put on the coffee and scrambled some eggs. The toast had just popped up when he walked into the kitchen.

"Morning," he said, and he reached for a cup of coffee.

He hadn't even looked up at me. I didn't know whether I was glad or mad that he had forgotten my birthday.

Don gulped down his breakfast and grabbed his lunchbox. Kissing me on the cheek, he dashed out the kitchen door and let it slam behind him.

The door slamming sounded like a rifle shot, and I heard a cry from the boys' bedroom. The day had officially begun.

I dropped the sugar bowl on the floor, scattering sugar to the far corners of the kitchen. The angel food cake I baked fell so flat that it looked like a tortilla with a hole in the middle. A sudden shower splashed mud and leaves on my laundry before I could get it off the clothesline, and my son pulled the tablecloth off, taking dishes, food, and all onto the floor with him. Tears rolled down my cheeks as I mopped the floor for the third time. I growled, "I hate birthdays!"

Lost Deer pulled on my skirt and said, "Don't cry, Mommy, Jesus loves you."

How many times had I said those very words to him? Now he was handing them back to me.

Of course Jesus loved me; I knew that was true. Then why did I become so upset over such small things?

I reviewed the morning. I had gotten up in a bad mood. It had been my own carelessness that had broken the sugar bowl. Had I really followed the recipe for the cake, or had I just guessed at the measurements? I had seen those clouds blowing in from the north; if I had paid attention, I would have had time to get the clothes in off the line before the rain came. All my troubles could have been avoided if I had begun the day in a better mood and had been more careful.

My son's words reminded me that even when I'm out of sorts, God isn't. Jesus loves me even when I'm grouchy, even when I'm having a bad day, and even when I'm unlovable.

My mind went back to my fifteenth birthday. It was the day of the accident that cost grandmother her life. A few days later my wonderful horse had died, and then I had been abandoned by my favorite uncle. It had been a dark time in my life and had spoiled all the birthdays afterward.

I went to my bedroom and lifted the heavy lid of the old cedar chest. I searched around the bottom until my fingers touched a small box.

I lifted it out and opened the lid. Inside was a small, china horse. The legs were broken off, but it was the horse's head that I cared about. I had seen this figurine in a shop years ago, and my heart leaped when I saw it. It was the image of Thunder Hooves. How I loved this figurine! It had stood proudly on a shelf, with its little glass mane flowing out from an invisible wind. It had made me feel good to look at it. Then one day one of the children had knocked it off, and its legs had broken. I had thrown the broken pieces into the trash, and then later I had dug them out again and wrapped them in a handkerchief. Now I kept the broken pieces in this box. On days when I was restless, I would take out the little figurine and look at the face that reminded me so much of Thunder Hooves. It was a secret link with the past.

I thought of my mother and wondered if she remembered it was my birthday. Today memories of my past haunted me, troubling my mind.

When Don came home I was still in a bad mood.

"You forgot my birthday!" I sniffed. "And I'm the only wife you have!"

He laughed. "Have I ever forgotten your birthday?" He

opened his lunch box and took out a small package and gave it to me.

I eagerly tore off the paper and found a beautiful turquoise ring. I felt ashamed for scolding him about my birthday.

We spent a rowdy evening wrestling with the children and playing every game we could think of. We were all exhausted by bedtime, and a gentle rain outside made a soft, warm bed a welcome sight even to the children.

The raindrops became larger and fell faster. Lightning tore jagged streaks across the sky, and the thunder crashed so loud-ly it rattled the windows. The thunder woke up the baby and she cried. I carried her into the next room and rocked her until she fell asleep in my arms.

I looked out the bedroom window. The storm was blow-ing away. The thunder was only a distant rumble, and the lightning lit up clouds far away.

I put an extra blanket on the baby and tucked her in. "Daddy and me and baby makes three," I whispered, but now there were four babies. "Thank You, God, for my wonderful family." We had come a long way together. How I wished we could go back and do it all again! How sweet life could be.

I drew the curtains and went to bed. The storm was past, and I was grateful my birthday was over and wouldn't return for another year.

I fell asleep quickly, but it was a troubled sleep. I dreamed of a voice calling me over and over, a familiar voice but one I couldn't identify. Suddenly in the darkness she appeared! My mother, Little Bird, stood before me, calling my name. I started to run to her, but someone caught my arm and stopped me, saying, "It's too late, she's dead!"

I began to cry, "It's not too late! It can't be too late!"

The grip on my arm became stronger and began shaking me.

"Honey, wake up!" It was Don's voice, and he was shaking me. "You're having another nightmare."

My pillow was wet from tears, and my throat ached. "I saw my mother! She was calling me!" I cried.

He pulled me closer to him and tucked in the blankets. "It was only a dream. Go back to sleep."

"No! I saw her! She was here in this room!"

"It was a dream," he said and went back to sleep.

I got out of bed and turned on the lights. There was no one here but Don and myself. It had only been a dream, but it had seemed so real!

I went back over every word in the dream. What if she really were calling me from somewhere? What if she were dying and the dream had been a warning?

I wiped away my tears and went to my desk for a pen and some paper.

I was going to find my mother. I wasn't going to wait until it was too late, as it had been in the dream.

I had been out of touch with my family since my marriage, partly because I had become a Christian and partly because I had married a non-Indian. It wouldn't be easy to go to them now and ask help in finding my mother. It was possible that none of them knew where she was. She had disappeared a long time ago.

I decided to write to my Aunt Fawn. I was sure she had always known more than she had told.

My letter was short. "Dear Aunt Fawn, Can you help me find my Mother? Love, Crying Wind."

I sealed the envelope and addressed it and slipped into my coat. Holding a flashlight to find my way, I waded through the rain to the mailbox. I knew if I waited until morning I probably wouldn't send the letter, and after all these years I was afraid to wait any longer.

I was shivering as I dropped it into the mailbox. "Please don't let it be too late," I prayed and hurried back inside and snuggled up to Don for warmth.

My mind was at peace. I had taken the first step; now it was out of my hands. The next move was up to Aunt Fawn, and to God.

It was nearly a month before I received an answer from Aunt Fawn. I had nearly given up hope of ever hearing from her and had decided that my search had ended before it had begun.

Dear Crying Wind,

I have not heard from your mother in several years. I think she worked with this lady, she might know where she is. Here is her address,

Aunt Fawn
P.S. I heard you got religion.

I smiled as I read, "I heard you got religion." Everyone in the family had probably heard about Flint and Cloud and me becoming Christians. I bet tongues really wagged and heads shook when they spoke of us. I would write to her and try to explain what God had done for me, but right now I wanted to write to the woman who had been a friend of my mother.

Her reply came quickly.

Dear Little Crying Wind,

Your mother spoke of you often when we were together but I lost track of her when she moved to Kansas. I'll enclose the last address I had for her.

Good luck.
Mrs. Murphy

I felt I was getting close to finding my mother now. The next letter I wrote was to her. I wrote a dozen letters before I decided on a simple, short note.

Dear Little Bird,

I am Crying Wind, your daughter. I am married now and have four children. I would like to hear from you.

Crying Wind

I sent it to the address in Mrs. Murphy's letter, and on the outside of the envelope I wrote "Please Forward," in case she had moved.

Now the hard part began. Days passed with no answer, and I expected my letter to come back marked "Address Unknown."

A week later it came.

My Daughter,

Thank you for writing to us. I ask you to forgive me for all the years I wasted. I made many mistakes, my heart breaks because of them. I'm getting old, I wasted most of my life.

Your father and I are together after all those years apart. We both came to know our Savior and are Christians now.

I wanted to find you but I thought it was too late. You never answered any of the letters I sent to you after I left you with Shima Sani. I thought you hated me too much.

Please, my daughter, write to us again. Do you have a picture I could have?

Do you need help? Please write.

Love,
Mother and Father

I sat down on the floor and wept and read the letter ten times.

"We are Christians," she had said, "Your father and I are together." I couldn't believe it! My parents, who had hated each other enough to kill each other, were now together and knew the Lord! It was a miracle!

I puzzled over the line, "You never answered any of the letters." I had never received any letters from my mother. Was it possible that Shima Sani had hidden them from me? She had done many sneaky things in her life; this could have been one of them.

When Don came home I showed him the letter.

"So, you've found your mother," he said and handed the letter back to me. "How do you feel about her?"

"I don't know. I'm glad I found her. I'm happy she and my father are Christians, but it has been such a long time—I really don't know yet how I feel, but I want to know her better."

Don's face looked worried. "Be careful and go slow," he warned.

I nodded. "I'll be careful. I won't expect too much."

I answered her letter and sent her pictures of all of us.

Her next letter held a picture of herself and my father. I looked at it a hundred times. My mother had Grandmother's eyes, black, hooded eyes like an eagle. In twenty years she would look as old and wrinkled as Grandmother had been. I wondered if I would look like my mother in twenty years.

She looked like a gentle, shy creature, like a timid rabbit about to run away and hide. It hurt to see my father looking so old and tired. I hadn't thought about my parents aging; in my mind they had stayed young.

They had married too young, and they had both run away from the unhappy marriage. She had left me with Grandmother because she had thought it was the best thing for me.

Letters traveled back and forth. Sometimes awkward, sometimes funny, often sad, our letters began pulling us together.

New knowledge came to light. My mother said she had tried to return to me, but Grandmother had forbidden her to come back home. She said she had written to me many times, but her letters had come back unopened.

She repeated often that she had lived to regret her mistakes, and from her letters it was plain that she and my father were really Christians. They had found God just a year earlier, both on the same night, at a revival meeting in their small town.

It would take time to unravel all the knots in our relationship. It's not easy to overcome the hurt and loneliness of so many years.

"Do you want to see your parents?" Don asked.

"Not yet. I think we all feel like we want to take things slow. We need time to get used to each other. No one wants to make a mistake that would spoil things. I think this is our last chance to be—to be friends. When we all feel the time is right, then we'll get together. Right now the letters are enough. They are more than I ever expected to have."

"You know," Don said after he read the last letter, "they sound like the kind of people I'd like to have for friends."

It was a strange feeling to have parents after so many years. It seemed that for so long I had been all alone in the world. Then God had given me friends, a husband, children, and now my parents.

It never fails to amaze me how God can work the impossible. ☀

CHAPTER TWENTY-FIVE

Speaking for the Indians

My book is going to be published!" I shouted. "I knew it! I knew it!" Don swung me around the room.

"I told you so!"

I praised God for this great blessing, because I knew that I had no talent of my own and He was responsible.

When I told Reverend McPherson my book *Crying Wing* was going to be published, he smiled and said, "I knew it."

I laughed, "That's what Don said."

"Don and I had faith in you. We've come a long, hard way together." He took my hand and prayed that the book would be a success and that it would touch lives and save souls. "I wish Audrey could have shared this day," he said.

"I want to read the dedication to you," I said, and began reading in a shaky voice.

"For Rev. Glenn O. McPherson
Because he believed in me, I learned to believe in myself."

He shook his head, and his eyes filled with tears.

"I can't speak. I can't tell you—Thanks."

Many kind and encouraging letters came. When the

publisher asked if I could go on some tours with the book, I said I couldn't go. "I don't have anything to say. Besides, I can't leave my family," I explained.

"We could arrange very short tours so you wouldn't be away from your family more than a few days at a time. We know the family comes first. Say what is in your heart, Crying Wind. Tell the people the truth about the Indians. Tell them the Indian religion is not beautiful—that no religion is beautiful unless it has the living God as the center."

"I can't talk in front of people. I get afraid," I said.

"You don't have to be afraid. You will be speaking for God, and He will help you. Someone needs to speak for the Indians, why not you?"

I looked to Don for direction.

"It's the chance of a lifetime. I can take care of the children. You have to go. I want you to," he said.

"I'll go," I said.

I prayed for God's help for the months ahead. I would be in a strange new world of airplanes, travel, and skyscrapers. Wherever I would go, whether to a reservation in New Mexico or to a hotel in New York, my message would be the same: the Indian needs God, and so does everyone else.

I couldn't believe God had taken such an unimportant nobody as myself and given me the opportunity to share my story with thousands of people across the country. You never know what God can do until you let go of your life and let Him take over. 🔆

CHAPTER TWENTY-SIX

Home Again

Our farm was a beautiful place, but the tornadoes and flash floods frightened me. I watched for snakes constantly and lost count of how many I killed. Each day I prayed, "God, protect my children from snakes while they play outside." The tarantulas made me nearly faint when I saw them, and the scorpions sent me running.

I missed the mountains and the forests of pine and aspen. I missed my church and my friends. I was homesick. I spent most of my time thinking about old friends and old times.

While I was hanging out the laundry one morning, homesickness engulfed me like a tidal wave, and I fell to my knees and cried out, "I want to go home! I want to go home!" Over and over I said it until it was no longer a wish or a desire but a desperate prayer.

Don wasn't as happy with the farm as he had been, and when I told him how much I wanted to go back home he decided to sell the farm.

It was harder to leave the farm than I thought it would be. I had never been satisfied with it; it was as if something had always been missing, something I couldn't put into words. It had never really seemed like home to me. But now, as we packed to leave, I felt the grief I would have felt if a friend had died. I was losing something. We had made memories here. Our children had been babies here. What if we could never find another home, and we wandered around forever? I was afraid, terribly afraid, and wondered if my homesickness was going to make my family pay a terrible price. It would mean a new start. Don would have to find new work, the children would leave friends behind.

"God, help us," I prayed as we drove away, leaving our farm behind.

PRAYER FOR A NEW HOME

God, give us a little home
From which we'll never roam,
A fireplace and soft chairs,
Four cozy, little beds upstairs,
Just a few acres of ground,
With tall trees standing all around,
Mountains and rocks and blue sky above,
Lots of laughter, lots of love,
Soft winds to blow, soft rains to fall,
God, bless our home and family and all,
Kittens, toys, books and balls,
Games and teddy bears and dolls,
A garden with some pretty flowers,

Children playing and laughing for hours.
Give us a home, and we'll do our best,
To make You the honored Guest.

When we arrived in Colorado, we found a small place to rent while Don hunted for work and I searched for a home. Flint and Cloud now had small ranches up in the high mountains. Flint and his wife had two sons; Cloud and his wife had two daughters. They all led quiet, Christian lives.

Cloud came to visit and handed Little Antelope the small bow and arrows he had made with his own hands. "Here, little warrior, go kill a bear," he laughed.

"I will shoot a hundred bears!" Little Antelope boasted and ran off with his new toy.

"That was a beautiful gift, Cloud. It took you a lot of time to make it, and he will remember it after he is grown." I thanked him.

Cloud shrugged. "It's nothing." But I could see he was proud of his work.

"Cloud, I've written a book," I said timidly.

"What about?" he asked.

I swallowed hard. "About us."

He looked up.

"I wrote about us, the family, about everything," I said weakly.

"Everything?" he asked.

"Yes."

He was silent for a moment. Then he smiled. "Good for you!" he said, and he slapped my back so hard I staggered under the blow. "It's about time somebody in this family did something. I'm proud of you!"

A big weight slid from my shoulders and I stood taller.

He looked back at Little Antelope, who was trying out his new bow.

"You know, Cry, there will be those who will be against you. Some in the family won't like you telling about Indian ways. They will be angry with you. It could even be dangerous. You will be called some bad names. They will say you are a liar, to make themselves look better. It is going to be hard for you."

"I've thought about that. But I felt in my heart I was doing the right thing. Our people have lived in darkness too long—too many secrets, too much fear. It's time to throw open the windows and let some light into our lives and sweep out the ancient dust of the old ways," I said.

"I'm with you, Cry, but those who walk on the old trails will fight you," he warned.

"If you're behind me, Cloud, I can face the others," I said.

I soon found that a clear line was drawn through the family. Those who had become Christians liked the book; those who followed the old religion hated the book and hated me for writing it.

If my book did nothing else, I hoped it would tell people the truth so they would stop saying, "The Indian religion is beautiful. Let's leave them alone."

Leave them alone, so they can live without hope? Leave them alone, so they will never know the forgiveness of sin or the love of God? Leave them alone, so they can die in darkness and go to a Godless grave? What is beautiful about that?

Don and I looked at dozens of houses. Most of the ones with acreage were too expensive for us, but we knew we wouldn't be happy living in the city because we needed "breathing room."

A friend sent a real estate agent over to meet us. "I'm T.J. Calhoun, and I'm going to find you a home!" he smiled.

T.J. showed us several places in our price range, but nothing was quite right.

I was becoming discouraged and Don was growing impatient to be settled. He had found a job as a truck driver making local deliveries, and although the hours were long and the pay was low, we were grateful he had found work so quickly when so many people were unemployed. Now all we needed was a home, a real home.

I was feeling guilty for uprooting my family and bringing them here and now having us homeless and unsettled. It seemed impossible that we would ever find the kind of home we wanted for the small amount of money we had.

T.J. came by late one afternoon. "I have one place I haven't shown you." He hesitated. "It's my own place. I guess I didn't want to let it go yet, but I know I have to. Your life changes; you have to let go of the past and make a new start."

He drove us slowly over the dusty, twisting, mountain roads.

"It was an old homestead surrounded by national forest, and I sold all but eleven acres and the house and barns. Now I guess it's time to let go of the last piece." He left the main road and drove half a mile through thick forest.

The sun was setting as T.J. drove up to the old wooden gate. "We'll have to walk in from here," he said.

We climbed out of the truck and walked up the twin ruts that led through the rocks in the road.

As we walked around a bend, I saw the ranch for the first time, and tears filled my eyes. The log cabin and log barns were nearly a hundred years old. Tall pines and huge rocks surrounded the ranch and kept it hidden from view in a safe little valley.

When we stepped inside the cabin we found a huge fireplace, beamed ceilings, and lamps mounted on wagon wheels.

"We'll take it!" I said.

Don broke into a fit of coughing, and T.J.'s face went pale.

That night Don gave me several lectures on how not to buy a house and how we couldn't possibly afford T.J.'s old ranch.

"Offer him less than he's asking," I begged. "I have to have that place! It's my home!"

"He won't take less now that he knows you want it. You should have kept quiet, kept him guessing." He changed the subject. "That little goat farm near here isn't so bad, and we can afford it."

"It's awful. The goats have killed most of the trees. There's no heating system. No! No! I want my home!" I cried. "God wouldn't have shown me that ranch to tease me. He meant for me to have it!"

The next day Don went to T.J. and offered him thousands of dollars less than he was asking for the ranch. Much to his amazement, T.J. accepted.

We had our home! It didn't take us long to move into Thundering Hills, our own hidden valley, our own refuge from the outside world.

Home again. Each Sunday we sat in our church, where dear Reverend McPherson was still pastor, and our hearts were lifted with his messages of God's love.

I looked around the church. Sally was still there, but many faces were gone. Audrey, Edythe, and many others had been called to glory. Where I had once sat alone, I now sat with my family, and we filled an entire pew.

Reverend McPherson stood in the pulpit. The years had made him a little grayer, a little more humble, and a little more precious to us. ☀

CHAPTER TWENTY-SEVEN

Winning the First Battle

How I loved autumn! God touching the trees and turning them to gold, and the leaves falling down on me like blessings from heaven! I loved catching the leaves in my hands and swishing through piles of them with my feet. What a pleasure to watch the children tumble and roll in the crispy, crunchy leaves until they had leaves covering them and clinging to their clothing and hair. Autumn was special. Nature seemed to work extra hard making the mountains beautiful so we would have pretty pictures to hold onto in our memories through the hard, cold winter.

It had always been my favorite season, but this year I dreaded the end of summer because I knew the sweet days of innocence and freedom would be snatched away from my eldest son, who was now old enough to enter school.

The very word *September* sent a cold shadow over my heart. The end of summer and the beginning of trouble.

"I won't send my son to school!" I said too loudly. "School is a terrible place! The teachers are cruel, hateful people who enjoy embarrassing and humiliating children!" My mind flooded with painful memories of my own schooldays. It was a nightmare I had relived often. I wouldn't let my children be laughed at. My children would not be chased home by gangs of children taunting them. No! My children would not go to school!

"The law says we have to send our children to school," my husband said firmly.

"The law has no right to take my children from me!" I said through tears. "It is legalized kidnapping!"

"They aren't taking your children away from you. They want every child to have an education. He will only be gone a few hours each day," Don said. "Why are you so angry?"

"I'm more than angry! I'm mad and sick! I want to fight, but there is no fight. The government says they need an education, but they don't teach them what they need to know. Does the school teach them about God? No! Does the school teach them how to cook or hunt or how to survive in the wilderness? No! Does it teach them how to be good people or how to care for a family? No! They teach Johnny ate six apples and how many are left. They say a white man named Columbus discovered America, but the Indians had discovered America thousands of years earlier. They teach Custer was massacred by the Indians, but Custer was a cowardly glory-hunter who butchered women and babies! They teach lies!" I shouted. "I can teach them at home. I'll buy books. The government has no right to take my children! I will fight them!"

My husband smiled. "An Indian, more than anyone else, should know you cannot fight the government."

I wilted. I knew he was right. You cannot fight the government and win. My son would have to go to school. I was sending my lamb to the slaughter.

I ran from the room and sought refuge in the forest. I sat under a dead tree and wept bitterly as I saw my children suffering the same agony I had suffered.

It wasn't fair! My heart was on fire. I would take my children and run away. We would go back to the reservation, where people would not care whether or not my children went to school. They had been through the same treatment at the white man's school, and they would understand.

I remembered my uncles speaking of the "education" the government had given them. A bus had come to the reservation, and children were dragged screaming out of their homes and put on the bus. They were driven away to Indian boarding schools, where they were kept in dormitories. They didn't see their families again until the end of the school year, because the school was far from their homes and their families didn't have money for transportation. They couldn't even communicate by mail, because many of the parents could not read or write. Often neither parent nor child knew if the other was even alive.

Many of the teenagers would jump out the emergency doors of the buses and run across country and hide to escape. Then the buses began showing up with leg chains, and the runaways were shackled into the bus seats until they were "safe" at school. It wasn't until recently that schools were built on the reservations so the children could return to their homes each night instead of being kidnapped for months at a time.

My own tribe, the Kickapoo, had fought education more than any other tribe, burning down six different schools that the government had built to force change on the young people. No tribe has held onto its old ways more than the Southern Kickapoo. They are nearly all illiterate, not because they are stupid but because they refuse to learn the "white man's way" of doing things. They choose *not* to be educated.

I ran out of tears. I took several deep breaths. The evening air would clear my thoughts. There was a way to win; there is always a way to win if you can just think of it.

Little Antelope would have to go to school. The law said so. If I didn't take advantage of the "free education," I would be put into prison. The law said—but if a child is sick, even the law cannot force him to go! I smiled. Yes, Little Antelope would miss much school. I would just say he was sick and keep him home most of the time. It would be easy. I stood up and brushed the dirt off my clothes. I felt better now. I would send him to school a few days and keep him home a few days. It was settled.

The next day my heart was heavy as I drove my small five-year-old son to school. He was dressed in his new blue jeans and a new shirt. His eyes were shining with eagerness. I watched him as I drove him to school. He was excited. He didn't understand he would soon find out that school was not fun, teachers were not your friends, and the other children did not play with half-breeds. The lessons he would learn this day would hurt for many years to come.

I drove as slowly as I could, but too soon we arrived at the school. I tried to ignore the knot in my stomach as I took his small hand in mine and led him inside the building.

A frightened child was pushed into the room by his mother. She said a few quick words, looked at her watch, and hurried away, leaving the child alone and terrified in a strange new world. The child began to sob and covered his eyes with chubby little hands.

A thin woman with shiny blue stuff on her eyelids was sitting behind a desk.

"Hello," I said, "This is my son—"

"Fill out these forms, go to room 2A, and Mrs. Jones will take care of you." She shoved a handful of papers across her desk and went on checking her list without even looking at us.

I picked up the papers and sat down at a table to fill them out. Little Antelope clung to my hand as if he were drowning.

I read the forms. *Name of pupil—*

"Little Antelope Stafford," I wrote. Then I looked around. All the children were white. I erased the name. "Aaron Stafford," I wrote. It would be easier for him to be called Aaron here. I felt guilty for letting them push me into their little niche.

Address—

"Wagon Tongue Gulch."

Age—

"Five."

"Race—"

What difference did it make? I was not ashamed to be an Indian, but I didn't think I should have to declare it as if it were a handicap. *I am Chinese, I am from the moon, I am purple!* I debated a moment. If I wrote "Indian," I would deny his father. If I wrote "White," I would deny myself as his mother. If I wrote "Indian/Caucasian," I would label him a half-breed. I was tempted to write "Peppermint" (red and white). I considered leaving the space blank. No, that would make me look as if I didn't know what my son was. I wrote, "American."

I erased my son's name again, and in bold letters I wrote, "AARON LITTLE ANTELOPE STAFFORD." We were who we were. The school would not bully me or my children into being someone else. I picked up the papers in my right hand, and with my left hand led my small son to room 2A.

A woman in a brown suit glanced at my papers. "You're in the wrong place. Go to room 1B."

We walked down the hall to another room. A short woman in a pantsuit took the papers and looked them over.

"Little Antelope?" She raised her eyebrows.

I looked her straight in the eye without speaking.

"Yes, well—" She read some more and flashed her teeth, but it was not a smile.

A few minutes later I left Little Antelope in the school and drove away trying not to think of the terrified look on his face as I left him with strangers for the first time in his life.

Strangers who thought him of less value than themselves because he was different. Strangers who didn't care about him, who thought of him as the boy in desk number four.

Anger raged in my heart. School had not changed; it was still the same, impersonal, spirit-breaking system. I dreaded the days ahead when my son would come home from school crying because of names he had been called. I knew that "half-breed" was probably the kindest he would hear. I knew he would be the target of cruel jokes about Indians, knew he would be bullied into fights he didn't want and would probably lose because he was small for his age and illness had kept him thin.

All I could do was try hard to make his home happier. His home would become a hiding place for him. We were a family, and as long as we stuck together and closed our ranks against "them," we could survive. I hated school for keeping my child a prisoner so many hours each day. It was as if a huge bear were chewing my son into little pieces, grinding him into nothing in its powerful jaws, and sending him home stripped of his identity. The school would spend hours each day stealing his personality, and I would spend hours each night trying to put him back together again.

I watched the clock all day. The hands moved so slowly I thought the day would never end. I cooked Antelope's favorite food for dinner and made cookies, trying to make his first day of school special. Maybe he would come home happy. Maybe everything would be all right. Maybe school had changed.

At last it was four o'clock! I drove the truck down the road and waited for the big, yellow school bus to come bumping along in a cloud of dust.

Antelope climbed off the bus and ran to the truck like a bird set free from its cage. His face was streaked from tears. The pocket was torn off his shirt. My heart sank, because without asking, I knew what had happened.

"I'm happy you are home again." I tried to sound cheerful. "I made cookies for you today." And finally the question, "How was school?"

"A big boy shoved me down on the playground," he said and then silently looked out the window.

When we drove into the yard, and when he saw his brother Deer waiting for him he smiled. "I have friends at home. I don't need friends at school," he said, and he ran to his brother.

I picked up his coat and his lunch box to carry them into the house, and I noticed the lunch box was heavy. I opened it and found his lunch untouched. He had been too nervous to eat a single bit of food.

Don came in to wash up for supper. "How did school go today?" he asked and slung a wet towel back on the rack.

I gave him a stormy look. "Well, how do you think it went!" Somehow I blamed him. He was the man of the family—he should have protected his son, he should have done something.

After dinner I began packing Antelope's lunch for the

next day and he came into the kitchen for another cookie.

"What are you doing?"

"Getting things ready for school tomorrow," I answered.

"But I already went! I don't have to go back again, do I?"

"Yes, you have to go back many times," I said.

"But I don't want to go back! Don't make me go back!" he begged and grabbed me around the legs. "Please, Mommy!"

I picked him up and hugged him. "The first day is always hard. Tomorrow will be easier. Maybe tomorrow you'll find a friend."

He wiped his eyes. "Do you think so?"

"Sure. You won't be afraid tomorrow. You'll do better. You won't be too nervous to eat your lunch."

"I don't want lunch," he said.

"You'll get hungry," I said.

"I can't eat when I'm alone," he answered.

"But you eat with the other children, you aren't alone," I said.

"Yes, I am. I have to eat in a room all alone."

"What do you mean?" I asked.

"All the children eat in the lunchroom, but the teacher makes me eat in a room by myself."

"There must be someone else in the room with you." He just couldn't be right, he couldn't be eating alone.

"No, the teacher said there wasn't room for me in the lunchroom and I have to eat in another room. I can't eat when I'm alone. My throat closes up and I can't swallow," he said.

"Were you in trouble? Were you being punished?" I asked.

"No, I didn't do anything. I wasn't bad. She doesn't like me."

"I'm sure she likes you. There is a misunderstanding. I will send a note with you tomorrow. I will tell her you must eat with the other children in the lunchroom."

He smiled. "Then I can eat with the other children?"

"Yes, tomorrow will be a better day." I watched him grab a cookie and run off to find his brother.

I wrote a note and put it inside his lunch box.

Dear Mrs. Matthews,

Antelope is very unhappy about eating alone. Please let him eat with the other children.

It would be all right. We had got off to a bad start, but it would get easier.

The next day when he came home from school I was relieved to see his shirt wasn't torn and his face wasn't streaked with tears.

"Today was better, wasn't it?" I asked.

"Yes, nobody shoved me down. I found a piece of green glass on the playground." He dug it out of his pocket and showed it to me. "I found some other treasures, too." He took a bent nail, a broken pencil, and a gum wrapper out of his pocket.

"Those are nice," I said.

"I look for treasures while the other kids play games."

He shoved them back into his pockets.

"Don't you play games?"

"They won't let me. When I try to play, they just push me away. I don't care. I'll just hunt treasures."

I wanted to scream. The other children played games while my son went off by himself and hunted pieces of broken glass and bent nails!

"Isn't there a teacher on the playground with you?" Maybe she didn't know how the children were treating Antelope.

"Yes, Mrs. Matthews was there."

"What did she say?" I asked.

"She told me to stay off the swings."

I was too angry to speak.

The next morning I drove Antelope to school and went into his room. There sat Mrs. Matthews. She showed me her teeth but it was still not a smile.

I hoped my voice wouldn't sound too angry when I spoke.

"My son says he has to eat his lunch in a room alone."

"Yes," she said, "there is no room for him at the table. It is a very small lunchroom."

"Then there is room for all the children except one?" I asked.

"Yes, that's right."

"Then the children could take turns. My son could eat alone one day, and then another child could eat alone the next day," I suggested.

"No, that wouldn't work. The other children all know each other and are used to eating together," she said.

"But my son will never know the other children if he is in a room by himself," I argued.

"He will adjust. After all, that's what school is about—adjusting," she said, as if I were five years old.

"He can't eat when he is alone," I repeated.

"He will learn. Perhaps he hasn't any discipline at home," she said, and her blue eyes looked like ice.

"He is very good at home," I said. "He seldom needs discipline."

"Mothers don't always see things from a teacher's point of view," she responded.

"Maybe not. I am not perfect. My son is not perfect." I wanted to add, "Teachers are not perfect," but thought better of it. "I do not want my son punished by making him eat alone. Find another way to punish him if he is in trouble."

"He is not being punished. There just isn't any room for him at the table."

I thought to myself, *He is being punished for having an Indian mother.*

"I think you could find room for him at the table," I said.

"I'll see what I can do." She showed me teeth again and I left.

"Please, God," I prayed, "let this be the end of it. Let Little Antelope eat with the other children."

Days passed. Nothing changed. Each day Little Antelope

brought his lunch home untouched. Each day he had been sent to a room to eat by himself.

I sent more notes to school asking that he be allowed to sit with the other children. None of my notes were answered.

Two weeks passed. My patience was gone.

"Why isn't Antelope in school?" Don asked one morning. "He's missed three days."

When I said I had stopped sending him, the dam burst.

"What do you mean you stopped sending him to school?" he shouted.

"The teacher makes him eat in a room alone. I talked to her. I wrote notes. She won't listen. She just says 'There is no room for your son at the table,'" I explained. "I won't send him to school unless he eats with the other children."

Don stood in silence a minute. Then he stomped across the floor so hard that the house shook, and the windows rattled when he slammed the door behind him.

I looked out the kitchen window and watched as he threw boards and a hammer and a bag of nails into the back of the pickup truck. His tires spun as he sped out of the yard.

In an hour he returned and came into the house. His boots were no longer stomping, and he looked pleased with himself.

"Where were you?"

"I was visiting school. I told Mrs. Matthews that if there wasn't room for my son at the table I would build him a table of his own to eat at, and to show me where to put it. Before I took the second board off the truck she said there would be room at the table for Antelope from now on. Send him back to school tomorrow."

The next day when Antelope returned from school my first question was, "Where did you eat lunch today?"

He smiled broadly. "I ate in the lunchroom with the other children!"

We had won the first round, but it was only the beginning. There would be many battles ahead. We would win a few, but we would lose most of them. We had to fight for the rights that other people take for granted.

Each night I would pray for God to protect my children at school—to protect them from the children who were cruel and especially to protect them from the teachers who could do so much harm. I prayed that someday it would be possible to send them to a Christian school, where they would be cared for, and loved and understood, and where they wouldn't have to fight for the right to eat at a table because there would always be room for them.

In my mind I pictured the perfect teacher and named her Mrs. Baker. She would be kind and understanding. She would love children. *Please, Lord, send me a Mrs. Baker someday to teach my children.*

THE PERFECT TEACHER

Mrs. Baker, thank you.
Thank you for greeting my son with a smile
to start his day off right,
For protecting him against bigger boys who try to pick a fight.
Thank you for helping him unbutton his coat
and take off his hat,
And for making sure he's bundled up warm when
you send him home. I appreciate that.
Thank you for your patience and loving concern,
For being firm but not too stern.
Thank you for caring enough to tell him when he's wrong,
And for teaching him some prayers and songs,
Thanks for teaching him to say "May I?" and "Please,"
And for showing him his ABC's.
If I have to share my son with another woman who's new,
I'm glad that "Other Woman" is you.
You're setting the cornerstone for his future by what you teach;
It's up to you how far he'll reach.
So please tell my son to reach for a star.
And thanks again for being the kind of teacher you are!

Sticks and stones may break my bones but names can never hurt me. No, not true. Names do hurt, names are important. God knew names were important when he told Adam to name all the animals, and later God changed people's names when the direction of their lives changed.

My son was playing outside with a neighbor boy when I heard "Half-breed!"

I opened the back door and invited them inside for refreshments.

"Yes," I said, "Little Antelope, Lost Deer, Snow Cloud, and Spring Storm are half-breeds. That only means they are half Indian and half white. You know what it means to be white. Do you know what it means to be an Indian?" I asked,

The bully and his two friends shrugged and followed Antelope inside.

I handed each child a blanket to wrap himself in and seated them in a circle on the floor.

"Would you like some Indian food?" I asked, and they eagerly nodded.

I passed around popcorn, peanuts, potato chips, hot chocolate, and molasses cookies.

"This isn't Indian food," the bully snorted.

"Yes, it is. Indians grew these foods hundreds of years before the white man ever came to our country. We also had maple syrup, potatoes, gum, and a hundred other foods."

"I didn't know that," the bully said, and he stuffed more popcorn into his face.

I told them the legend of the Thunderbird and sang a song about Geronimo, and suddenly they were full of a dozen questions about Indians.

Just as they started out the door I took a rubber ball out of one boy's hands. "We invented the rubber ball a thousand years ago," I said and handed it back.

"Wow!" He whistled and ran after my son.

"Hey, Little Antelope! Do you think you could give me an Indian name too? Can I be your blood brother? Have you ever lived in a real teepee?" His voice faded away as they ran across the yard.

I shut the door and picked up the blankets off the floor.

The bully probably wouldn't call Little Antelope half-breed again. Right now he was too busy wishing he were part Indian. Today's problem was taken care of with a few cookies and some legends.

Someday he again would be called half-breed, and it would keep him from marrying the girl he loved or from getting the job he wanted. Then a handful of cookies wouldn't make the hurt go away.

Please, God, be near him on the days people call him half-breed and worse names. Son, be proud of what you are. You can have the best of both worlds. You have a choice—when you grow up you can live like an Indian and walk a forest path, or you can live like a white man and follow the paved highway. Choose the one that makes you happy. Be proud, always be proud of having two bloods in your veins! ☀

CHAPTER TWENTY-EIGHT

Pet Potato

Because of my children I was able to catch glimpses of the kindness and tenderness of God that couldn't be preached in a thousand sermons. Children seem to know more about God than anyone, and by listening to them, I could hear God speaking to me.

Little Antelope came running into the house with the pieces of a broken truck clutched in his little hands.

"Fix it, Mommy," he cried.

The wheels had slipped out of their grooves. It would be simple to fix it—just snap them back into the slots.

"It's all right, I can fix it," I said, but as soon as I reached for the toy, my son's fingers tightened around it."

"Fix it, Mommy!" he sobbed.

He handed me the truck but kept the wheels.

"Son, you have to give me all the pieces, or I can't fix it."

Suddenly I knew that I had been asking God to "fix" my problem, but I hadn't turned over all the pieces. Now I knew I had to turn the whole thing over to God.

"Casting all your care upon Him; for He careth for you" (1 Peter 5:7). Don't cast some of your cares, or a few cares, cast *all* your cares.

My son handed the wheels to me, and in a second I snapped them into place. The toy was as good as new, and he went back to his play.

I couldn't help him until he had trusted me enough to give me all the pieces. I hadn't been trusting God with all the pieces of my life. I was going to do better.

When I hung up our new picture of Jesus standing at the door and knocking, Deer was greatly impressed.

Later that day there was a heavy rainstorm, and a loud crash of thunder shook the house and rattled the windows. My son's eyes grew big and round, and he looked at me and asked, "Is that Jesus knocking at our door?"

I explained to him that it was only thunder, but he wouldn't believe me until I opened the door and showed him there was no one there.

How real Jesus is to a child! How sure my son was that Jesus would be standing on our porch. Somehow, even at his early age, he sensed that the knock of Jesus on the door would sound different than an ordinary knock. Somehow his knock would contain power and strength, and perhaps even sound like thunder.

Would I know when Jesus knocked on my heart, or was I too busy? Was I close enough to hear His whispered messages, or did He have to beat my door down to get my attention?

Now when I feel a tug on my heart or conscience I ask myself, "Is that Jesus knocking?" "Behold, I stand at the door, and knock: if any man hear My voice, and open the door, I will come in to him, and will sup with him, and he with Me" (Revelation 3:20).

Antelope spilled his bowl of cereal on the floor. Lost Deer took a crayon and scribbled all over the mirror. Cloud climbed up the drapes, and the nails pulled out of the wall, and drapes, curtain rods, son, and all came crashing to the floor. While I was trying to rehang the curtains, the boys went into the kitchen.

Knowing they were being far too quiet, I called, "What are you doing?"

Antelope was quick to answer. "Nothing, Mama. We are just trying to put the eggs back together."

I dropped the drapes and hurried into the kitchen. They had broken a dozen eggs on the floor to see if they were all alike inside, and now they were trying to scoop the runny, raw eggs back into the shells before I found out what they had done.

Although I was upset over the waste of good food and awful mess, still I laughed at their efforts to hide their crime. There is just no way in the world to put an egg back together again!

Sometimes I get into trouble and try to put things back together again, hoping God won't notice what I've done wrong. My efforts to hide my sins from Him are just as useless as my sons' efforts to hide broken eggs from me.

"For there is nothing covered, that shall not be revealed; neither hid, that shall not be known" (Luke 12:2).

How proud I was of my new rosebush! On each branch, huge, pink buds were swelling, just waiting to burst into full, beautiful roses.

Each day the children and I would walk out and look at the bush and look forward to when it would finally be covered with blooms.

One morning Antelope reached the rosebush ahead of me, and I could see he was carefully peeling back the protecting green leaves and patiently prying open each petal.

"What are you doing?" I asked, trying not to sound too worried about my flowers.

"I'm trying to help the roses bloom without bruising the petals," he said seriously.

I told him nature couldn't be hurried, and the rose would bloom in its own good time.

As I tucked him into bed that night and saw how tiny and fragile he was, I breathed a silent prayer, *Please, Lord, teach me to help my children bloom without bruising their petals.*

"Train up a child in the way he should go: and when he is old, he will not depart from it" (Proverbs 22:6).

Today Little Antelope picked some dandelions for me. He held them so tightly the stems were nearly crushed, and there were beads of sweat on his forehead from running in the hot summer sun.

"I love you, Mama. I picked these sunshine flowers for you," he said as he handed them to me.

"Like father, like son." I smiled as I remembered the day many years ago when his father had handed me "sunshine flowers." I gave him a kiss. It takes a special kind of person to see beauty everywhere. Even a common weed becomes beautiful when love touches it.

Lost Deer had been asking for a puppy for over a month, but his Daddy kept saying, "No dogs! A dog will dig up our garden, chase our ducks and kill our rabbits. No dog, and that's final!"

Each night Lost Deer prayed for a puppy, and each morning he was disappointed not to find one waiting outside.

I was peeling potatoes for dinner, and he was sitting on the floor at my feet asking for the thousandth time, "Why won't Daddy let me have a puppy?"

"Because they are a lot of trouble. Don't cry. Maybe he will change his mind someday," I encouraged him.

"No, he won't, and I'll never have a puppy in a million years!" he wailed.

I looked into his dirty, tear-streaked face and couldn't deny his one wish, so I said the words that were first spoken by Eve.

"I know a way to make Daddy change his mind."

"Really?" Lost Deer wiped away his tears and sniffed.

I handed him a potato. "Take this and carry it with you until it turns into a puppy," I whispered so no one else would hear. "Never let it out of your sight for one minute. Keep it with you all the time, and on the third day, tie a string around it and drag it around the yard and see what happens!"

Lost Deer grabbed the potato with both hands. "Mama, how do you make a potato into a puppy?" He turned it over and over.

"Sh! It's a secret!" I whispered and sent him on his way.

Lord, you know what a woman must do to keep peace in her home! I prayed.

Lost Deer faithfully carried his potato around for two days.

On the third day I said to Don, "We must get a pet for Lost Deer."

"What makes you think he needs a pet?" Don leaned against the doorway.

"I'm afraid he's getting an emotional problem," I said. "He's been carrying a potato around with him for days. He calls it Skipper and says it's his pet. He takes it to bed with him, he gives it baths, and right now he has a string tied to it and he's dragging it around the yard."

"A potato?" Don looked out the window at Deer taking his potato for a walk.

"It will break his heart when the potato gets mushy and rots." I put away the last of the dishes. "Besides, every time I try to peel potatoes for dinner, Deer cries because he says I'm killing his pet's family."

"A potato?" Don queried. "My son has a pet potato?"

"You said he couldn't have a puppy, and I think it was such a terrible disappointment that something snapped in his little mind, and he's probably having a nervous breakdown," I said.

"He's only three years old!" Don said. "Three-year-old kids don't have nervous breakdowns!"

"Then why is he dragging a potato around the yard on a string?" I asked.

"I'll bring home a puppy tomorrow," he said and walked outside to look for Deer. As the door slammed I heard him say once more, "A pet potato?"

The next day Don brought home a wiggling puppy and two pregnant cats that soon blessed us with fourteen kittens.

Everyone was happy. Don thought he had saved his son from a nervous breakdown. Lost Deer had his puppy (and sixteen cats), and he believed his Mother could change a potato into a puppy. And I was happy because I got back my potato and cooked it for our dinner.

Blessed are the peacemakers!

In the back of my mind, though, there was a small voice that kept reminding me that I had played a trick on my husband and hadn't been honest with him. True, I had convinced him to get Lost Deer his puppy, but I wished I had found another way to do it. What had begun as a simple thing had grown, and it made my heart feel heavy. I wondered if I should confess my deception to Don and tell him I was sorry.

At dinner one evening Little Antelope said, "Daddy, I saw a little black pony at the Oak's Farm today. He was sure pretty. Daddy, can I have a pony?

The room grew quiet as all eyes were on Don. He laid down his fork and put his hand on Little Antelope's shoulder.

In an exaggerated whisper he said, "Son, if you want a pony, this is how you get it. First, take a large watermelon, tie a string around it and drag it around the house—"

I knocked over my glass of iced tea and began choking. "How did you know?" I gasped.

Don laughed, "When I gave the puppy to Lost Deer he told me that you had said you could turn a potato into a puppy. That's when I figured out what had happened."

"Are you mad?" I asked. "I knew it was wrong to trick you. I didn't realize it until later, and then it was too late."

"If I hadn't been so hard-nosed and stubborn, you wouldn't have had to use tricks. When I saw the look on Lost Deer's face when he hugged his puppy, I knew I'd been wrong. If I'd been more open and willing to listen to you, and not so sure I was always right and everyone else was always wrong, we could have worked it out." He laughed again. "I'll forgive you, if you'll forgive me."

I smiled as I felt that small bit of guilt slip out of my heart. "A watermelon change into a pony?" I asked, and we all laughed together.

LOST DEER

I think that there are two of me,
Myself and another,
But he looks exactly like me,
So it can't be my brother.

Sometimes when I wake up,
I feel like being bad;
I stomp and throw my toys,
And get so doggone mad!

I am a terrible grouch,
When nothing goes right;
I want to jump right back in bed
And pretend that it's still night.

My shoes are on the wrong feet,
My shirt is backward side out,
I throw myself on the floor
And kick and scream and pout.

I wish I was a grown-up man
And very, very old—
I would never wear any clothes,
Except when it was cold.

I get so mad I want to cry,
And then I want to shout,
But then my Mom would want to know,
"What's it all about?"

I sit on my bed with my chin in my hand,
And wish that I was a grown-up man,
And then my Mom tiptoes in,
And looks at me with a cheerful grin.

She asks if she can help me dress,
But I can dress myself, I guess!
I grin at her, and I'm so glad,
That she doesn't know that I was mad.

I grab my pants and I
Pull on my clothes,
And my T-shirt doesn't even
Catch on my nose.

Mom hugs me and fixes my breakfast,
And I'm as cheerful as I can be,
Because I don't want her to know
About the "other" me!

CHAPTER TWENTY-NINE

God Filled the Emptiness

The summer sun was setting red and wild behind the mountains as Don and I stood hand in hand on the rocky hill overlooking our home.

The children were busy running between the tall pines and hiding from each other.

Little Antelope had grown tall. He was quiet and thoughtful and sensitive, and I knew our firstborn would always make us proud.

Lost Deer was all laughter and jokes, and he teased his little brother until he was in tears. Lost Deer could always make anyone laugh, even on his worst days. Life would be easier for him than for most.

Snow Cloud was small for his age and sometimes difficult to understand, but he had the face of an angel and would grow up to do great things.

And Spring Storm, our chubby bundle of love! How precious you are, my daughter; what joy you bring!

Spring Storm toddled over to me and handed me a dandelion she had crushed in her chubby hand.

I took it and held it to my lips and kissed it. Sunshine flowers! What memories you hold!

I looked at Don, my wonderful, strong, patient husband. My anchor, my rock, my great love.

He turned and caught me watching him and smiled.

"I think next spring we can get you a horse," he said.

"A horse! I'll have a horse!" I was thrilled. "With a horse I will be an Indian again!"

"Crying Wind, you have never stopped being an Indian! You will always belong in the sunset past of a hundred years ago. The rest of the world is living in the twentieth century and talking of rockets to Mars. You live in the eighteenth century and talk of horses running across the open desert. You have always been an Indian; you will always be. Your wildness was born into our children. I can see it in their eyes. The mountains, the wind, call to them and make them restless. Look at them now, running through the trees—they aren't just children playing, they are more like wild horses thundering through the valley." My husband said sadly, "They are your children, Crying Wind. How little of my blood they have."

"But they look like you." I wanted to take the sadness out of his voice.

"Yes, their skin is fair and their hair is yellow, but in their black eyes is the look of wildness I once saw on the face of a Kickapoo maid in a forest long ago," he smiled.

For so long life had seemed like a handful of dust, but when I had surrendered my life to God, He had filled my emptiness, taken away my fear, and put peace in my heart.

"I have everything, everything in the world!" I smiled.

Don's hand folded around mine and we began to walk toward the cabin.

Our three strong sons ran far ahead of us, laughing and shouting for us to hurry. Spring Storm toddled at our side.

The sun was going down, and the sky and earth looked golden.

Crying Wind had come home at last.

The End

Do you know the Creator's Son?

After reading *Crying Wind/My Searching Heart,* do you feel that Jesus truly is the Creator God's Son? Is He speaking to you? Would you like to respond to what you have just read?

Here are five things you need to know to believe in Jesus as your Savior.

You need to:

REPENT—Be sorry for the wrong things you have done—sorry enough to quit doing them. "God did not remember these times when people did not know better. But now He tells all men everywhere to be sorry for their sins and to turn from them" Acts 17:30

CONFESS—Tell God you have sinned. "If you say with your mouth that Jesus is Lord, and believe in your heart that God raised Him from the dead, you will be saved from the punishment of sin" Romans 10:9.

BELIEVE—Jesus died for you. "Put your trust in the Lord Jesus Christ and you…will be saved from the punishment of sin" Acts 16:31

ASK—God to forgive you. "If we tell Him our sins, He is faithful and we can depend on Him to forgive us our sins. He will make our lives clean from all sin" 1 John 1:9.

RECEIVE—Jesus as your Savior. "He gave the right and the power to become children of God, to those who receive Him...to those who put their trust in His Name" John 1:12.

If you want to ask Jesus Christ into your life, pray the following prayer or pray in your own words:

Dear Jesus, I realize I am a sinner. I long for peace in my heart. I believe You are the Holy Son of God, that You came down and died on the cross for my sins. Thank You for doing this for me. I am sorry for my sins. Please forgive me. With Your help, I will turn my back on them. By faith, I receive You into my life as my personal Savior and Lord. From now on, I want to please You.
In Your name, Amen.

If you have followed these steps and asked Christ to take control of your life, get a copy of God's Word, the Bible, and begin reading it. Also start talking to God in prayer. Go to church regularly. Choose a church where God's message of salvation is taught.

If you have prayed the above prayer, the publishers of *Crying Wind/My Searching Heart* would like to hear from you. Please write your name on the coupon to the right, or if you don't want to cut up this book just write on another sheet of paper and mail it to:

In Canada:
Indian Life Books
P.O. Box 3765, RPO Redwood Centre
Winnipeg, MB R2W 3R6

In the U.S:
Indian Life Books
P.O. Box 32
Pembina ND 58271

I prayed the prayer suggested in *Crying Wind/My Searching Heart* and now I would like more information on how to live as a Christian. Please write to me and tell me the name of someone who can give me personal help.

NAME _____

ADDRESS _____

TOWN/CITY _____

STATE/PROVINCE _____

ZIP/POSTAL _____

Check out the latest titles from Indian Life Books!

When the Stars Danced

If you enjoyed *Crying Wind/My Searching Heart*, you most certainly will want to read Crying Wind's latest and catch up on where things left off. In her new memoir, *When the Stars Danced*, Crying Wind picks up where *My Searching Heart* ends. You'll laugh and cry, and find your faith strengthened. From a story circled with colorful marbles to the triumph of daughters-in-law in the laundry war; from unexpected loss to God's gain, Crying Wind shares her own family journey.

Well-known author Jane Kirkpatrick had this to say about *When the Stars Danced*: "Through her honesty and simplicity, we dance along with the stars celebrating God's faithfulness and provision and His everlasting love." This is one book you'll read and want to share with others.

Keepers of the Faith, Five Native Women Share Their Stories

Native North Americans are well aware of the strength, perseverance, courage and encouragement women are in our culture. These five stories weave together the journeys of five courageous women—all examples of the power of change in a person's life when they allow God to move. Read these stories and think of your mother, grandmother, aunt or another friend who made an impression on your life.

More Good Reading from Indian Life Books

God's Warrior

This life story of Ray Prince, tells us about a World War II veteran and a veteran of many personal battles including residential school life, abuse and alcoholism. He found hope and healing in Jesus Christ and then committed himself to spreading the good news.

The Council Speaks

A collection of answers to over 60 questions on life, tradition, culture and practical issues. These may have been questions you have had, but were afraid to ask. Join the circle and listen to the answers. They may change your life!

The Lonely Search

Albert Tait is an Oji-Cree man whose life God completely changed around. He went from being an unwanted orphan and an alcoholic, to a man of faith and a leader and teacher for Native believers. Discover how he found freedom from a curse and the source of all blessing.

The Conquering Indian

An amazing collection of 70 stories showing that Jesus Christ can heal the deepest hurt of Native people. This book tells the stories of how these people, young and old, reached out to Jesus and how He answered their pleas and helped them to have victory over the problems they faced. You, too, can face up to your problems and conquer them. This book can be used to guide you to the One who can help you win that victory.

The Grieving Indian

Every Native person needs to read this book for the help and hope it offers. With over 70,000 books in print, find out why it has attracted so much attention.

Read one man's story of pain and hopelessness. Learn how his wife took a desperate step to turn his life around. This is a powerful book of hope and healing. Used by treatment centers and addictions counselors.

Whiteman's Gospel

"This is one book that should be read by every man and woman in North America," says Bill McCartney, founder of Promise Keepers. The author, Craig Stephen Smith, a Chippewa from the Leech Lake Reservation in northern Minnesota, examines Christianity and how it has affected Native North Americans. His experience led him to believe that change is desperately needed in both native and church communities.

Indian Life Newspaper

The most widely read Native publication in North America. In its pages you will find positive news of Indian people and events, first-person stories, photo features, family life articles, and much more. Published six times a year. Write for a free sample copy. Find out why over 100,000 people read this newspaper.

Video: *Learning to Fly—The Path of Biblical Discipleship*

A true-to-life story illustrates the challenges facing a new believer. This video will change your life and the life of your church by giving you a perspective on what discipleship is all about. It will show you why making disciples is so important. The Great Commission is more than making converts—it's making disciples. That's done through relationships.